THE ROLLOUT

THE ROLLOUT

A Novel about Leadership and Building a Lean-Agile Enterprise with SAFe®

ALEX YAKYMA

ISBN: 978-0-9981629-0-4

Contents

About the Author

Alex Yakyma brings unique, extensive, and field-based experience to the topic of implementing Lean and Agile at scale. Throughout his career he has served as an engineering and program manager in multi-cultural, highly distributed environments. As a methodologist, trainer and consultant at Scaled Agile, Inc., he has led numerous rollouts of Scaled Agile Framework® (SAFe®) involving teams in North America, Europe and Asia, and has trained over a thousand SAFe Program Consultants (SPCs) - change agents whose key role is to help their organizations achieve higher productivity and quality through the adoption of scalable, agile methods.

Alex is one of the key contributors to the Scaled Agile Framework® as well as multiple associated training courses and workshops.

Preface

You may be asking yourself: "How is this book going to help me?"

With your permission, I will assume that since you managed to stumble upon this book, you are in some way concerned with implementing Lean and Agile at scale. Whether you are an executive, program or portfolio manager, development or QA manager, system or enterprise architect, team leader or facilitator, change agent, consultant or coach - this book is for *you*.

This book can help you in a couple of ways:

First, it will introduce you to the world of Lean and Agile at scale and more specifically–Scaled Agile Framework® (SAFe®)–a set of integrated Lean-Agile practices for enterprises that depend on software and systems development for their success.

Secondly, apart from familiarizing you with the method, this book will guide you through the implementation journey of Lean and Agile with all its challenges and unexpected solutions. You will witness a story of transformation; an enterprise that appears to be on the edge of disaster, desperately fighting for survival.

While writing the book, I encountered an interesting paradox: the more I tried to make the book about implementing Lean-Agile at scale, the clearer it became to me that the primary theme of the book is actually *mindset*. But this should come as no big surprise. As you and I know perfectly well, no implementation can be successful unless *the enterprise's thinking* undergoes a significant change. Only then can we expect a breakthrough in process improvement and the subsequent attainment of better business results. Therefore the topic of *leadership* appears first on the subtitle of the book. *The organization's leaders must lead in the transformation!* If they don't, it's doomed from the very beginning. It is very discouraging to watch companies fall into this trap over and over again: they set out on the adoption path of Lean and Agile, yet fail to bring their leadership into the heart of the transformation process. Of course it is often hard to change the mentality of leadership, but regardless of the difficulty, that change is absolutely necessary for the successful rollout of a new method. This book will provide you with a variety of tools to help you solve this problem.

But why write a novel? Why not just write a conventional book on the subject – there are certainly plenty of good books like that out there. Why not simply follow a well-known pattern and do the same thing?

Well, here's why. There's something mysteriously powerful about parables, tales, sagas, epics and legends. We don't know the exact mechanics of how they work, but we know the effect they produce: a narrative that is capable of fully immersing you in the subject. A narrative, by setting you in the middle of action, rewires your brain in a way that can never be achieved through formal knowledge acquisition. When you become part of the story, the learning is similar in quality to that gained through actual experience. This helps solve a serious problem: knowledge transfer alone does not guarantee *understanding*. The fully immersive format of the novel promotes understanding – it creates traction at a deeper level of comprehension.

However, the "business novel" is not an entirely new genre. There are outstanding examples that you may be familiar with. Two that stand out for me are "The Goal" by Eliyahu M. Goldratt and Jeff Cox, and of course, "The Phoenix Project" by Gene Kim, Kevin Behr and George Spafford.

So, is "The Rollout" a real or a fictional story?

The answer is: neither. It is a novel, created from hundreds of real bits and pieces that occurred across different organizations and with various people. All of the method-related experiences were real, but the names, titles and places have been changed to preserve anonymity. More importantly, the problems highlighted in the book are real and so are the solutions. My job was just to arrange them into a consistent story.

Even though the book has an obvious protagonist, the story does not revolve entirely around our hero, Ethan. Most of his personal achievements as a change agent, in fact, are possible *only* because of the people around him. One such person is Adi – a consultant and trainer who Ethan meets at a conference and goes on to help his organization get started on the SAFe® implementation journey. Her vast experience in implementing Lean and Agile, and her exceptional coaching skills, are instrumental in helping Ethan and his company navigate the challenges of the rollout.

The book does not only make you a part of the exciting story, but is designed to allow you to easily lookup a topic at a later date. To enable this, two helpful tools were created. First, the ending of each chapter (except for the last one) contains "Ethan's diary" – a refined set of bullet points summarizing the method and the implementation strategy. Secondly, the index at the end of the book shows where various notions, processes or other aspects of Lean and Agile at scale appear in the book.

This book wouldn't be possible without help from many people. First and foremost, I would like to acknowledge the thousands of men and women in the industry whom I have had the chance to meet and work with throughout my career. I've had the opportunity to work with many great change agents, trainers and coaches, and leaders and engineers who continue to inspire me to do what I do. For what I learned as a consultant, coach and methodologist, I express my deep appreciation for Dean Leffingwell – my mentor and friend. We began working together a long time ago and have been on quite a journey, both building systems and helping others to do it. I also appreciate my family for their incredible moral support. And finally, I would like to thank my proofreader and friend, Greg Ward. His patience while working with me is beyond my understanding.

At this point, dear reader, you and I will have to part. You are about to be introduced to the people whose actions and feelings will tell the story of a SAFe® rollout. I hope you'll enjoy their company while navigating your way through the Lean-Agile transformation of VeraComm, an enterprise at risk of imminent collapse....

CHAPTER 1

Catching the Firebird

"How much value can there be in locally optimizing team behavior while the entire program remains completely misaligned?"

–ADI

MY FATHER USED TO SAY that our best comes to the surface when we dare to face our deepest fears. Lately this thought of his has possessed my mind entirely. I wish I had his strength and his ability to plunge into uncertainty where the 'real' begins. Or maybe I do have it, but there's just no way of knowing. My father is a decorated war veteran–a war that was likely preventable–but he would never say that out loud. In the haste of the retreat, his platoon left him behind enemy lines. He crossed the front line multiple times without even knowing it, fighting for his life; and as he used to say with a serious expression on his face – for his own country. So he speaks from experience when he talks about fear and facing the unknown.

The battles of my generation, however, are fought behind the closed doors of modern enterprises. Nobody is taking a bullet in the head or having a limb blown off by a land mine, but the fears of this modern age are in a way much worse. We are not dealing with fight or flight imperative. We are dealing with the nagging tenants of our unprotected minds that restlessly whisper the fear-spells of job security, workplace competition and financial uncertainty. The fears of our times cannot be easily evaded or fought, for they are like ghosts – always around and yet never substantial enough to land a blow on them.

I need to grab a cup of coffee. They must have plenty of coffee at big conferences like this. There is no time for breakfast; and who needs food after a sleepless night anyway.

The huge hotel lobby is packed to the brim with people who are probably just enjoying their business trip. For most of them this is a fun, entertaining event that diverts them from the boring reality of their comfortable corporate lives. But that's them. For me, it is a matter of survival. I think both my company and I are looking at a sad finale, even though there are still a few people like myself unwilling to fully accept such an ending.

There it is, by the window: a big container of coffee. All I need is one sip. While I'm filling up my cup, my exhausted brain turns its attention to the fascinating dance unfolding on the opposite side of the window. The rain is teasing and poking, trying to awaken the majestic river from its lethargic sleep. But despite all of the rain's effort, the old Potomac remains still and unresponsive to the myriad of minuscule drops that eventually join the grave calmness of the water giant, never to return.

The talk that I'm supposed to attend starts in four minutes. I still have to find the room and I had better hurry. I need to find the app on my phone that shows the conference agenda. But the second I pull out my phone it desperately signals that I have just gotten a whole bunch of new emails, most of them being from my boss, his bosses and the bosses of their bosses. As of late this does not surprise me: it's nothing more than the annoying evidence of an approaching disaster that may consume us all.

I love my company a lot, I have dedicated eight years of my life being part of it, but things started to change drastically even before this latest cataclysmic slide. I used to like this company because it had a clear mission – making conference calling truly simple, reliable and accessible for modern enterprises. That resonated a lot with me because the incumbents in this niche market had become really sloppy with overly ambitious, bloated applications. These apps could potentially do a lot except for allowing the busiest people on the planet to quickly and easily initiate a call, have good audio and video quality, share a screen and just focus on the topic of their discussion rather than troubleshooting the system. Their sloppiness and lack of focus opened a great opportunity for us to jump in and make a difference. I remember the sense of pride we felt when using our own products and realizing that we had managed to get out in front of the competition and truly build something better. I also remember we became editor's choice in multiple nominations on multiple platforms, as recognized by the world's most prominent technology sources. But those times are long gone, drowned in the deep waters of reality that began having its way with the ship, driving us full-speed toward the reefs.

It's not that we betrayed our company's mission. No, that's not it at all. We didn't violate a single bit in of our mission – it all remained unchanged. We simply couldn't fulfill that mission anymore. These days we are known in the market as a company that develops bloated, not particularly reliable products, that can't keep up with the defect logs. Customers wait for patches and other updates for way too long. We are a big company and that, I think, is the reason why we are still afloat – it just takes a while to spiral down to the ground for an enterprise like us. But it looks like, in light of these latest events, this process is rapidly accelerating and our gentle descent is turning into a violent tailspin.

Eight years back, when I joined VeraComm as a development manager, we had a little over 100 people in software engineering. Last year I think we hit the 2,200 mark. And that is not counting our hardware and firmware people. These days getting something done and released is nearly impossible. I knew that problem had been cooking for a while but then someone big and important came up with a solution: strengthen our PMO capability and increase its influence across the organization. At that time, I was offered a position as head of the software branch of the Project Management Office, an offer which just seemed too attractive to turn down. But as attractive as it appeared, here's a little caveat: we are neck-deep in all sorts of trouble with our development process and the PMO did not help.

Two years ago I launched a new initiative - all of the teams were to adopt Agile development. We trained all of our teams in Scrum and some basic XP practices. The adoption–even though it wasn't entirely smooth–went quite quickly and I was patted on the back. But the truth is, it didn't actually change anything. It seemed like we should have been more productive, but there was no evidence of that. Brian, my boss and the one who was patting me on the back, eventually changed his attitude and soon made it clear to me that he was completely unhappy with the way the software PMO group was leading this organization's process improvement.

At that time, things were bad, but stable. We knew we had multiple problems, but we were able to contain it within company boundaries. Recently it all went to hell after an employee, unjustly terminated according to him, leaked information to the public. According to him, the real reason why VeraComm was unable to provide a much anticipated integration with cloud identity providers, had nothing to do with a covert strategic plan by VeraComm to provide its own much more powerful identity management solution (which had been speculated on earlier and discussed in the press.) The integration with third parties was already in the works. The problem, as he pointed out, was that the company couldn't finish the functionality. And that resonated with the market like a nuclear blast. Nobody likes to feel betrayed, especially people that buy ink by the barrel. I remember that the week the news came out, our shares dropped by nearly 70% in value.

So what am I doing here at this conference? Well, as much as my boss Brian may come to hate Agile, he's got no choice. He can't fire me at this point because that would only make things worse for him. And, since he has no particularly productive ideas of his own, I think I have some flexibility, even though the evidence suggests I may not have it for long. And I think the real reason that I'm at this conference is because I hate quitting. I hate when people give up; when they 'mentally resign' and let a problem chew them up and spit them out. But all my aspirations aside, if I don't find an answer here, it probably won't matter whether I give up or not.

I finally found the room, which was already full, so I had to stand. I didn't care as long as they had something useful to say. The presenter, a casually dressed lady in her early forties, took the stage.

"Good morning everyone!" she said with a very slight accent that I couldn't quite place.

The room responded with a cascade of 'good mornings.' The first talk of the day is always invigorating, at least initially.

"My name is Adi and I will be your host for the next 45 minutes. Today we're going to talk about building really big systems. I am, to be honest, surprised to see so many people in the room," she continued. "You guys either ended up in the wrong room or we as an industry are in deep trouble..."

The audience laughed.

"How many of you already apply Agile at the team level?" she asked the audience. "Please raise your hands and keep them up a minute."

Most of the people raised their hands. Well, good to know. I don't really care about all the criticism from my bosses about our Agile initiative, but it's good to know that I chose the right course... Or maybe she's correct with her latter statement and we all are, as an industry, in deep trouble.

"Please keep your hand up if you know what your enterprise's velocity is," she said, looking around the room.

People began lowering their hands and the few that still had them up looked very puzzled. Seconds later, those hands went down too and the audience became still like I've never seen before.

"Agile has long been a de facto industry standard for teams, but how did it really improve our enterprises? Did this adoption process make our *programs* Agile? Did our large programs become truly responsive to change?"

She paused for a second to let the audience digest what she had just said. People began to chatter. I sensed that these questions resonated with many in the room. They certainly resonated with me. I couldn't agree more with her sentiment: at VeraComm we have no idea what our enterprise velocity is. But let's forget the enterprise level for a minute; in our case it's impossible to say at what velocity our programs operate. And responding to change? – give me a break... We are unable to execute even those things that are known, much less the things we haven't anticipated yet.

"Most of you raised your hands when I asked about team Agility," she continued. "Agile promotes iterative and incremental development. So let me ask you, given that your teams are iterating, how about the system they develop? Is the system itself iterating too?"

No, it's not. There's no such thing for us. I noticed that the other attendees stopped their chatter and were listening very carefully. I think everybody in the room realized that they can chat all they want later, but that now they need to listen.

Adi continued: "Isn't it true that in most cases when adopting team Agility, we have just created a bunch of little 'islands', each living by its own set of rules and not paying much attention to the rest of the program? They often iterate on their own rhythm, applying story points that only their team understands, and not aligning very well on what is going to be built next and how it will be done.

"How many of you have Agile teams, but apply some flavor of traditional program and portfolio management methods?"

I automatically raised my hand, as did most of the people in the room.

"It turns out there is a fix to this problem, but it takes different type of thinking."

She moved to the next slide.

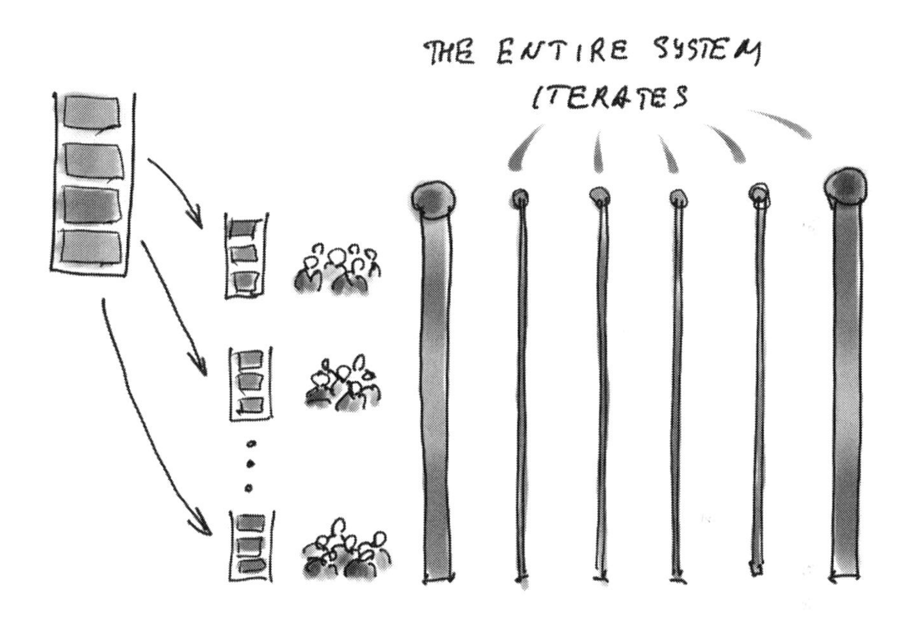

"The answer is simple: we need to apply Agile to the entire program, not just to individual teams. If it was up to a single team of six to nine people to develop the entire solution, we would be legitimately happy with the state of the industry. But that's not even nearly the case with modern solutions: it takes tens or even hundreds of such teams to develop those systems. And if we, for just a quick moment, abstract from how many people are working on the system and only focus on the system itself, the picture on the slide appears to be undeniably obvious. We are looking for a way to make our *entire system* iterate. For that to happen, the entire program has to execute iterations synchronously, producing integrated system increments every two weeks. Let me ask you… what does Agile tell us is the best measure of progress?"

"Working software," replied someone in the back.

"Yes, you're right. Working software is a true measure of progress. Some might say that's a trivial question," confirmed Adi. "But somehow it turns out not to be so trivial in reality. Our customers don't buy components or even features; they buy systems. That's why an iteration can be successful only if it produces an increment of the entire system, end-to-end."

This is just bizarre. Not what she said, no; what she said makes perfect sense. It's just weird and unspeakable that something as simple as that had never crossed my mind.

I think I'm beginning to understand why our programs are so hopeless. None of them is truly operating as an Agile program. Each one is just a bunch of disjointed Agile teams. All of the benefit that we get from Agile at the team level, is effectively diluted by the lack of synchronization of the program as a whole.

"We call such a construct an Agile Release Train," continued Adi. "Or an ART, for short. If you think about it, ART is a self-organized team of teams that takes the core notions of Agile and scales them up one level. In that sense, every train–which is typically anywhere from 50 to 125 people–behaves a lot like a small Agile team. As we said, they produce integrated system increments every two weeks and rely upon *that* as the ultimate measure of progress. But with the ART construct, we go far beyond that. How many of you think there is an alignment issue in terms of what to build and how to do so across multiple teams in a program?"

A large number of hands were slowly raised this time, including mine.

"So why is it," she proceeded in her naturally passionate manner, "that we acknowledge face-to-face communication as the best way of conveying information at the team level, but at the program level this simple, yet absolutely fundamental tenet of Agile is demonstrably ignored? How much value can there be in locally optimizing team behavior while the entire program remains completely misaligned? What are we optimizing?"

Thank goodness she took a little pause and sip of water. That little pause was quite helpful, as my mind had already begun racing through everything she had said and trying to contrast those thoughts with how we do things at VeraComm. The takeaway was not highly encouraging: all the deficiencies she had mentioned accurately line up with our organization, without a single exception. My wife would say that I've got the best hindsight in the world, maybe even 20/20. I wish I had come up with that metaphor. But all joking aside, this presentation explained a lot in terms of why we haven't been successful in our endeavors.

Her water bottle had either some sort of poetry or some quote written on it—I couldn't say precisely from my vantage point. Adi put the bottle on the table and said: "Everything I've just said was intended to demonstrate that as an industry, we have a fundamental flaw—we have failed to apply systems thinking to the adoption of Agile in large enterprises. Somehow we have not found enough courage to mandate that the systems we develop are frequently integrated and demonstrated, end-to-end. We haven't realized the importance of gathering a program of eighty or a hundred people together at least once per quarter to understand the bigger picture, and to discuss those critical dependencies and implementation risks face-to-face. Neither have we truly applied the Inspect and Adapt process to the entire team-of-teams. Instead, we keep playing Agile games in our little team sandboxes, and that unfortunately has not done much for us..."

The rest of the presentation passed very quickly, at least for me. The ten-minute Q&A section ran even faster, leaving a host of people swarming around Adi, who didn't seem unaccustomed to such attention. I really need to talk to her. But it's not a quick question that I can ask in a setup like this. I'll try to get a few minutes of her time once she's done with these guys.

I've decided that I will just wait in the lobby. My coffee has gone cold–I completely forgot about it during her presentation. The rain has stopped and the wind is sweeping the remaining drops from the window. The clouds have begun to retreat to the north, giving up more and more room to the unmatched blue of the skies. A minute later, a miniscule fraction of sunlight welds its way through the ionized lining of a slowly departing cloud, and the whole river suddenly explodes, celebrating the victory with billions of tiny fragments of light shattering across the vast surface of the water.

Finally, Adi walked out of the room.

"Adi," I said, approaching her, "my name is Ethan, I'm with VeraComm."

"Hi Ethan," she said, smiling. "You were in the room, right?"

"Yes I was. I wanted to ask you a couple of questions, but something tells me that it may involve more than just a quick answer, which is why I didn't approach you during the Q&A. I wonder if you have a couple of minutes for me?"

"Sure. I have a couple of minutes."

We walked downstairs to the first floor where they had half a dozen different cafés and restaurants in this unusually large hotel.

"So, how can I help?" she asked.

"Well, before we start, I wanted to tell you that the presentation was really something. I think you hit on pretty much every problem we have with adopting Agile development in our organization. We just stopped at the team level and it never even occurred to us that it's the whole program that needs to iterate and increment value in a synchronized manner. It looks so obvious now that you have pointed it out..."

"Thank you. It's my pleasure to be of help."

"Yeah. Now, I'm here because we are kind of... desperate. We are consistently failing to release anything new and significant to our users. And frankly, even small and less significant things represent a huge struggle. I hope we can talk confidentially about all this?"

"Yes, sure."

"Nobody is even trying to pretend that we are doing fine anymore - bad signals are coming from all segments of our market. The data consistently suggests that our customers are unhappy. They are unhappy with the quality of our core product offerings and they are unhappy with the fact that we don't want to build features that have been requested many times and are already implemented by our smaller, but much more responsive competitors. It just takes us forever to do anything these days. Teams working on new features always seem to acquire good momentum in the beginning, but quickly bog down and in many cases completely grind to a halt."

"I understand."

"I think I'm at the point right now where I'm ready to build the real Agile capability in our programs, which is what I want to ask you about. If I wanted to do a rollout of something like this, what should I pay the most attention to in the beginning?"

"Sure. Before we get started, what role in the company do you have?"

"Oh, yeah - sorry, I didn't fully introduce myself. I'm the head of the PMO organization for our software solutions. There is another branch of PMO that oversees hardware products, but that part of the business is not relevant to a conversation like this."

"Oh, I would be more than happy to argue that," she said, as a little sparkle ignited in her eyes. "Lean-Agile development is even more important to the world of cyber-physical systems. But, please proceed."

"My organization is basically responsible for two things: processes and coordination of the actual programs in-flight. I have 42 people in the PMO group with different roles, but most everything we do pertains to one of the two things I just mentioned."

"Understood. As to your question, Ethan, there are multiple aspects of Lean-Agile transformation, of course. Many pertain to the question of preparation prior to, as we call it, launching Agile Release Trains and then supporting their execution over time. I will be more than happy to provide you with references for implementing ARTs. But a much bigger issue is addressing leadership."

"Leadership? What about it?"

"You see, what we discussed today is just the model itself; the model that allows us to apply Agile development to the entire program. Describing it was the goal of this presentation. What I didn't have time to talk about in this format was how *to implement the model*, which is a whole separate discussion. There's something that I learned a long time ago when I was an Agile team coach and was invited to help an organization adopt Agile for all of their teams - about five hundred people in software development. That rollout largely failed, and the reason was actually quite interesting: if a company's leadership doesn't lead in the rollout, it is not going to be successful."

"I'm not sure I follow. Isn't it *my* job to do the rollout?"

"Ethan, you are the change agent, the transformation champion, yes. But you cannot do it yourself: there are things you cannot do for your company's leadership - they must do it themselves."

"Like what?"

"Just getting your teams to operate in a synchronized manner won't really solve much. Yes, if you are lucky, they will be able to move as a whole and that is good, but even if you succeed with that, you will be facing many issues in other areas. If the leadership does not clearly understand the new operating model, they will act in their old ways which will eventually suppress the entire initiative... The new process deployed on top of a traditional management mindset is like an old ship: patched everywhere you can imagine. She seems watertight in calm seas, but as soon as the slightest turn in the weather hits the sails, she will wreck on the reef of organizational impediments. And when all patches suddenly come off–one after another–nothing can save her. She goes down."

Okay, I have to admit I don't get why she brought that up. Either way, that's not my primary focus at this point. I need to stay on target here. I need to learn more about how to help the whole 'team-of-teams,' as she calls it, to be Agile and iterate over the entire system.

"I don't see a big problem with our leadership, Adi. In fact, they are in search of better answers. First things first. We need to launch Agile Release Trains. And if it becomes necessary later on, I will address the leadership question, but right now that is not our biggest impediment, I'm afraid."

Adi smiled in a knowing way and then, after a short pause, proceeded in a very serious tone: "Just so we're clear, Ethan," she said, "that would be a mistake I caution every enterprise to avoid at any cost. I recommend that every rollout involve a leadership training session first. And only when they have acquired the gist of Lean, Agile and systems thinking, when they speak the same language as the teams, only then should you start launching trains."

Well, I think we are slightly misaligned here. Consultants need to teach training courses for a living, while I need to focus and be selective about where we apply our efforts next. I do have a shot at this, but it might be my only shot, which only leaves me room for pragmatic steps.

"Adi, I truly appreciate the advice, but I will have to move forward with the implementation of trains. Please send me those links and I will look into all of that carefully with my guys. They are really smart dudes and girls. Also, they never give up. We will make it happen. Quite frankly, I am truly excited about this."

Adi said nothing in response.

"Oh, Adi, I almost forgot to ask you something. What is written on your water bottle?"

"I like your attention to detail, Ethan. Those are the governing principles of Lean and Agile at scale. I have an extra one here in my backpack if you want it."

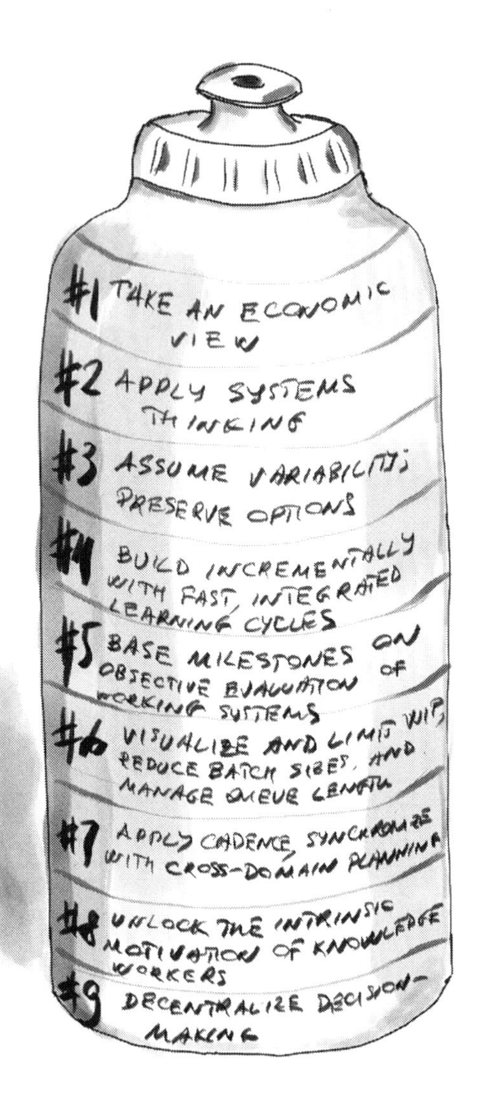

"I do, thank you. I like principles. And I really appreciate you helping me understand more about the process."

"You are welcome. Use it. Not just for hydration, but to fuel your rollout," she said, smiling. "May I ask you a question as well?"

"Go ahead."

"What is that red notebook you hold in your hands all the time, as if your life depends on it?"

"Oh, this?" I asked, twisting it in my hands. "This is my diary. I left it at the coffee station this morning and when I realized that I didn't have it with me, I freaked out and had to return to pick it up. But luckily it was where I had left it, waiting for its master."

"You mean you are maintaining a real diary? I thought diaries where the craze of 19th century, no?"

"There's quite a story behind it. My wife once told me about Carl Jung's Red Book and I told her, as a joke, that I could make much better use of a red notebook than Jung did, and that it would be less psychotic. As a continuation of the joke, I actually started keeping a diary bit by bit. Very soon I was surprised to find that it is actually very handy. It's been over five years now that I've been doing it."

"Very interesting. Is your wife a therapist?"

"Yes and no. She's a PhD in clinical phycology. She's a university professor and spends much more time at conferences and with students than she does with her patients these days. And as you can see from this example, she's my real inspiration, too..."

• • •

For Adi, the conference was over. She had to pack her bags and head out to the airport. Before she left, she told me she was helping one of her customers that was in the middle of a big Agile rollout. For me the conference was over, too, even though I had initially planned to stay here all week. But I had found what I wanted and staying longer would be just wasting precious time. My updated itinerary was slowly coming out of the hotel printer. It was time to finally face the real issues and make things work at VeraComm.

ETHAN'S DIARY

- *I think I understand our problem: we're Agile at the team level, but our programs are not so. Unlike individual teams, our programs are not iterating as a whole.*
- *"Systems thinking" is the answer I was looking for. Not that this is a new term or anything, but I had never thought of it in the context of adopting Agile development.*
- *I need to talk to my guys ASAP. We are going to turn our programs into what Adi calls an Agile Release Train, a self-organized team of Agile teams. I have come to like that concept a lot.*
- *Overall, Adi's talk was super helpful even though she suddenly shifted the discussion towards leadership training.*
- *I wonder what it takes to become a speaker at a conference like that? Well, I will ask Rachel about it on my return home. I'm proud of my wife for being an author and a speaker, even though she picked a field of study so removed from what I do. But that can actually be a good thing, as it helps sustain the authentic sense of mystery we have for each other...*

CHAPTER 2

A Beautiful Mindset

"Dig a little deeper and under the thick layers of logic, you will discover a belief system."

-RACHEL

I'M FINALLY IN MY HOMETOWN airport. The landing was nearly perfect - or maybe I just forgot to pay attention. I don't travel too much, but when I do, I enjoy returning to where I belong: to the fresh morning air, and to the mountains that are ready to embrace me in their cold arms. The mountains seem to enjoy donning dazzling garments to match their unsteady moods. But today they look perplexed: the wind blows masses of air away from them, gradually suffocating them and when their patience is exhausted, they avenge with a dramatic breakdown in the weather. Then the warm, tender air suddenly soars. The wind, gasping heavily, summons thick white clouds under the cover of night, and in the morning a thick layer of snow will cover the grass in heavy, white dreams. But the infantile weather of the Front Range can do exactly the opposite as well: the temperature can climb thirty degrees in the twinkling of an eye, making the snow sizzle in pain before eventually evaporating into other worlds, leaving only pathetic remnants of its erstwhile might on the shoulders of the road.

It's only 1 PM and I'm going to go straight to the office and talk to my guys about my findings. I haven't even had a chance to email anybody, even though the idea of doing so briefly crossed my mind after the conversation with Adi, but was graciously drowned in the oblivious multitude of other things. This whole deal with VeraComm has turned me into an insomniac lately and I'm not sure I can remember things so well anymore. I should probably talk to a doctor before Rachel notices that something is wrong. She really cares about me and I need to respect that. She's shown concern for me in that way ever since we first met. And even in moments of utter disagreement, we've managed to survive with dignity because at some point we just can't confront each other anymore. We used to call it a *threshold* beyond which conflicts make no sense. Over the last couple of years, we've developed a bunch of jokes about what's allowed before reaching the threshold, how the threshold is automatically raised on holidays and vacations, and what the relationship is between our threshold and the world economy, and so forth.

I'm starving. I should have gotten something to eat at the airport but now it is too late. I'll grab something in the kitchen at work to keep my brain cells running.

"Oh hey, look who's here. The Savior of Rome," said a man sitting in the corner near the fridge, as I entered our kitchen.

His name is Raymond. I could never figure out this guy and his superpowers; it just doesn't compute. He always reminded me of the Frenchman from the 'Matrix' who knew everything that was happening in their world, and who used to turn the matter of causality into a deep philosophical subject, along the lines with Aristotle and Descartes. Raymond is the director of our infrastructure support group. I often see him in the kitchen and we converse every once in a while.

"Rome may not need a savior after all, have you thought about that?" I asked. I was hoping to find out whether he knows something I don't, or if he's just enjoying his usual verbal workout.

"Oh, no, friend of friends, Rome *does* need a savior. Without a savior," he paused, looking around, "it will collapse faster than you can imagine. You're obviously clueless, I'm sensing..."

"Clueless about what?" I asked as I finished texting one of my guys about a meeting in 15 minutes, with as much of the PMO team as they can find. I hate multitasking, but sometimes it just happens involuntarily.

Raymond leaned forward and whispered: "Lay-offs are coming..."

"What? Lay-offs? What the–"

"Hey!... hey!" Raymond said, looking around again. "Keep it down! Most people don't have a clue yet. You didn't either, by the way."

"What departments are affected?"

"All departments – no exceptions. The percentages will vary across the board, but don't ask me what the target number is for your beloved

PMO, because I don't know. I don't even know what to expect for my own infrastructure and IT services group. All I know is that it's going to happen and happen pretty soon."

"Whose idea was it?"

Raymond gave me a surprised look. "Our CEO. I thought you could figure out that much. Most of the executives are in favor of it and the board has approved as well." He grabbed his mug and said, "Look man, I have to run. Sucks to be us; what can I say."

As he left, I walked up to the next floor to meet with my group. The guys were obviously clueless about the lay-offs, which is actually for the best, given the current circumstances. I hate to even think about losing anybody on my team. Or maybe I am the one to join the gang of those who will be made an offer they cannot refuse. But if there is a chance to help these guys, and the entire organization, it is by focusing on the solution to the problem, rather than on self-pity. So, off we go into a new way of working and I'm not going to second-guess myself, not for a minute. My dad used to say that he learned one important thing in the military: making a decision is critical. Your judgement may be wrong at times – that happens with everybody – but to survive, you must make explicit decisions and stick to them.

I described the whole idea of the Agile Release Train to my team and gave them the links that Adi had sent me. And here's the good news: most people in the room accepted it as a course of action without much distress and took on specific aspects to be explored in more detail, as part of the preparation to launch. We decided which program would be the best candidate for the first Agile Release Train, and determined what aspects of the preparation we could start with almost immediately. The only thing remaining to be done was to get the approval for the rollout from the CTO's office (which in reality just means we need to convince his direct reports). Everything else would just be a matter of formality.

It feels like my head is a big girder of iron. I did manage to send out an invitation for the next day's meeting and three people immediately accepted it. But that's all I can do. I need a hot tub or a run or a bike ride–or all of the above–to clear my brain so that maybe I'll be able to sleep tonight.

• • •

The prep to launching the Agile Release Train did not look too hard, and it appeared that we were on the right track. We were able to fully concentrate on priorities, like: balancing the team composition, deciding on the common iteration schedule, etc. It frankly surprised me how smoothly the meeting with the CTO's direct reports went. Everybody agreed to take on what we proposed and then they all ran off in their own direction. People are busy these days, which should not be very surprising. What matters the most is that we got the transformation initiative approved, and now we just need to execute. There were a few remaining tasks requiring program stakeholders, so my guys scheduled a meeting for the next day. Attending will be product managers and their bosses, as well as engineering management - consensus on what and how we will build once we launch the train will be our goal.

First, we need to decide what duration of the Program Increment, or PI, we should pick. As we found out in the links that Adi provided, PI is a higher-level planning and alignment horizon. A 'wrapper', if you will, for a number of iterations–usually 4 to 6–that creates the right context and reasonable levels of predictability for the program outcomes. Once we pick a specific PI timeframe, we will have to stick to it, as it will become our regular cadence.

Secondly, we need to set the start date for the first PI. And finally, we must align on the top priorities for the first PI, so that we can plan it in a bit more detail. If everything goes as smoothly and as quickly as the initial meeting that we had, it will be super awesome. My guys spent quite a bit of time preparing the presentation materials for this, and we have reviewed them together at least twice so far. We are going to make this work, for everyone's sake.

It's good to plan a little bit ahead of time and to apply a little bit of discipline to an important thing like the launch of an Agile Release Train.

• • •

The sky is still too dark to be able to see anything except the vague silhouettes of hills far to the north. In moments like this, it seems, time should pass much faster; but it doesn't. Instead, everything remains still; no motion or sound coming from anywhere. The entire earth is lost in the deep maze of sleep and there seems to be no power in the world to awaken it. There is no force to shake off its random dreams; no force to shift the veil off of the overshadowed land.

But the calm of the quiet, empty night was beginning to change. Light began to appear in the trees – a myriad of little dots that moved in a weird choreography, suggesting no particular order or intelligent goal. I began to sense some noise and as my hearing adjusted to the distant action in the dark, the noise became recognizable. Those were human voices, the speech of which I still couldn't parse, but there was something going on there for sure. I stared for a little longer but didn't know if I should join them. As I approached closer, the flickering in the trees turned out to be just lights in the hands of runners. Maybe out of curiosity or maybe out of some tribal instinct, as ancient as this world, I decided that I would run with them. They were in pursuit: not something you would see every day. They ran toward the barely visible lining of dawn. The next thing I knew; I was completely consumed by the action. I picked up a flashlight from the ground that somebody had carelessly left behind and became part of the run. We couldn't see in the dark, but we knew we were close. We heard a sharp rustling sound ahead and saw a light cloud of breath that quickly dissolved in the morning air ahead of us. The dark silhouette of the prey, it seemed, appeared for a split second and hid again behind the wall of trees and bushes. We weren't going to wait till the dawn exploded; we needed to get there faster, so every second mattered. The chase was about to end and everybody knew the outcome. I ran with the light in my hand, prepared to deliver the final blow when the opportunity presented itself. But suddenly I realized I had lost my flashlight. Or maybe I had never had it.

A sharp electric shock runs through my brain as I realize that the rustling and the breathing in the dark are mine. I'm not the hunter... I'm the prey. I can't breathe. I can't run anymore. I turn back to face those that hunt me. I summon the remainder of strength in my muscles and burning joints. I'm ready for the fray that will put an end to this.

"Are you okay? Ethan?" Rachel whispered in the dark, reaching out for the switch on the lamp. I can't answer her. I have to take a couple of deep breaths. It's hard to believe that I'm not being chased anymore. The dream seemed way too real. Now that I've eliminated any doubt that I'm actually awake, I think I can stop gasping for air and talk to my wife.

"Sorry honey. Bad dreams."

"There's nothing to be sorry about," she says, wiping cold sweat from my forehead. "But these are getting more frequent, Ethan. You can't keep ignoring this."

I know I can't. I look at the alarm clock. It's only 4:45 am, and the boldest bird in the park that is right next to our house is already rehearsing its song for the day. I had never paid attention to this before, but the song is astonishingly beautiful. I'm not going back to bed – I think I just started my day. I will use the extra time to tune up some slides and go through the entire slide deck again to make sure that our presentation today is flawless. It needs to be flawless. Once this conversation with engineering and product management is taken care of, there will be nothing to stop us from executing the plan.

The time before work passed quite quickly. It seemed that the coffee really kicked in only as I was approaching the parking lot of building 18, the place where the meeting was going to happen. My brain was still a little foggy, but fresh air and sun did their job of setting me up for my normal daily rhythm.

"I like the idea of a six-iteration PI," said Ed, one of the engineering vice presidents, and a direct report to the CTO. Ed is kind of a big dude at VeraComm, so we had better listen carefully to what he has to say. My boss Brian, seems to be in a good mood as well, which, truth be told, is in stark contrast to his mood of the last couple of weeks. He eagerly nodded in support of Ed's suggestion.

Ed looked around the room and pointed towards the product managers: "How do you guys feel about quarterly PIs?"

"Uh, we're fine with whatever works for you, Ed. We're good," said the product line manager, shrugging.

"Fine then. Six two-week iterations it is," I concluded for the record. "Now let's decide when the first one starts, which will also set the date of the PI planning for us. We need to make sure that you guys will be able to attend."

"We are busy all the time," said the product line manager, smiling, "But at least I know that we're not traveling the week after next, so we'll be able to move our other stuff around in the calendar if necessary. How much time do you need?"

"Two days."

"Okay..." It wasn't a 'sure-thing okay', but rather a 'fine-I'll-do-it okay'. "How long are you going to need us during those two days?" he asked.

"I meant to say that we need you guys for the full duration of the two-day PI planning."

He gave Ed a surprised look and shook his head. Then turned back to me and said: "I can't imagine what you could need from us that would take two days. I just can't guarantee you that I will have that much time. I will promise you to do my best. But expect that my guys and I will be in-and-out."

"How about you guys?" I asked of Ed and the other engineering leaders.

"Do you need us for the full two days as well?" asked one of the engineering directors.

"I do."

"To do what? You need both product and engineering management for two full days? Really? Can't we do it in a shorter timeframe? Seriously..."

"Well, actually that would be problematic because in that case, the teams would not be able to find answers to their questions and would end up with the wrong plan for the PI."

"Wait, wait, wait," said the director, waving his hands as if trying to impose some kind of spell on me. "We are not talking about team planning here. We are talking about program planning. Let's not confuse the two. As for the team planning – we will give their Product Owners the scope of work as we've done before, and they will perform their team planning then, based on that. What I'm talking about is two days of *program* planning, as you just mentioned."

"Yes, I'm talking about the same two days. We need to make sure that the teams will be able to plan productively during that period," I explained.

The room went quiet.

"Hold on, Ethan," said the director, "What exactly do the teams have to do with these two days?"

"They are going to plan the PI."

"For two days?"

"Yes, that's why I'm suggesting that we clear our calendars, because for those two days we, and the teams, will be planning together in the same place, at same time..."

For a couple of seconds nobody dared to say a word. But the expressions on people's faces began to change quite visibly.

"That is insane," said the director, looking at Ed.

"I couldn't agree more," said Ed. He turned to my boss and added: "Brian, looks like you guys are having a lot of fun there in PMO."

I noticed that Brian's face was gradually turning red, but he chose not to say anything in response. The product guys were just listening quietly, but the sour looks on their faces suggested anything but good.

"Ethan, are you serious?" asked the director. "I mean, if this is a joke, now would be the right time to let us in on it."

"Look, guys, I'm not joking. The method emphasizes the importance of a collaborative two-day planning event–"

"Then we don't need such a method," said Brian, sharply. "This is staggering."

The director was not ready to give up the argument so easily either. "Two days for the entire ninety-people program? All developers and testers... and various others? Do you understand how much money are you suggesting that we waste?" He was starting to lose patience.

Well, I could certainly calculate the amount, but the question was clearly rhetorical. Gosh, I was not expecting such a reaction from everyone.

"These two days provide critical alignment in terms of what and how the teams should be building in the PI. You're right: PI planning is an investment, but so is the PI itself. We have significant problems building new functionality, as we all know perfectly well. That's because the teams don't have the ability to consistently manage dependencies and risks."

The director stood up and said: "How do you know it's because of that? You guys have offered plenty of different remedies for us over the course of the last three or four years, but I don't think that any of us here feel like those recommendations actually improved the organization's ability to deliver."

Well, he might be right that we weren't very successful with our previous undertakings, but this is different.

"Guys, I understand what you're saying, but I would ask you to consider the following for a quick second. I am convinced that in just a single PI, we will see tangible improvement. I believe that in a PI, executed iteratively and incrementally, we will be able to deliver a couple of long-desired features, end-to-end. Currently, being able to reliably deliver anything would be quite an improvement. I'm sure we can make it happen. Besides, you will have much better visibility into the progress."

"Ethan, I don't see why wasting lots of time as an entire program will take us to higher levels of performance. Guys, I'm sorry, but I'm out; I have other things to attend to," said the director on his way out. Two more people stood up and followed him.

"Yeah guys, I think this is just too raw right now. It looks like you will have to figure it out between PMO and engineering first and then invite us back," said the product line manager, also leaving the room, followed by his team.

Ed just shook his head and smiled, saying: "Surprise, surprise. What can I say?" He gave me a meaningful look which I was not quite able to interpret. Maybe I'm just not too good at reading people's minds from their facial expressions. Ed exited the room, which left the PMO members only. It may be hard to read Ed, but Brian, my boss, had an expression that clearly suggested a tough conversation was coming. "Karina, Sunil, Jill, I think we're good for now," I said to my guys, letting them go before the real hell began...

• • •

"...Ethan!"

"Yeah?"

Rachel looked at me bewildered. "Are you alright? I called your name about three or four times. It's like breaking through a brick wall. Is it your work that's keeping you fully possessed?"

I am incredibly grateful that I have Rachel in my life. And yet I've hated moments like this ever since we got together. I really care about her, and I think that's why I find it inappropriate to throw my problems at her like that. She's got a stressful job, too. Academic life only seems fun. The truth is that there are far more politics in academia than in modern commercial enterprises.

"Ethan, please don't be like that. You may not realize this, but by keeping stuff close to your vest and sticking to your 'old silent type', you are only hurting yourself. It also hurts me to see you this way. Tell me honestly, when did you last have a really good night's sleep? The ones with nightmares don't count..."

"Well..."

Well, it's a really good question. I don't know the answer. I know I'm standing in front of the one person that really cares and loves me, and I can't do any better than just awkwardly smile.

"Ethan, this is not funny. This may lead to health issues." She took my hand and pulled me to the sofa. "Sit, please," she said, sitting next to me. "I'm going to break all of the normal rules by doing this, but hey, I'm not the only person in our family who's known for breaking rules, am I?"

"But I'm not a patient–"

"Shhh... relax." She let go of my hand. "This has been a tough couple of weeks for you. But let's not start with you this time. Instead let's talk about something you clearly care about more than your personal health and welfare. How is VeraComm doing?"

"Well, the company is doing... fine."

Rachel looked at me as if she were a five-year-old and I had just taken away her best doll.

"...I mean there are certain challenges with VeraComm. Some serious challenges."

Rachel gestured with her hands, inviting me to continue.

"Things are actually really bad, and unfortunately I have to say that much of it is my fault."

"What exactly makes you think that it is your fault?"

"Well, for over three years I've been trying to find a solution to a big problem that only keeps getting worse and nothing I've introduced so far has helped."

"Okay," said Rachel, "But something must have changed recently because you haven't seemed this exhausted for the last couple of years. Am I right?"

I nodded automatically. "I thought I had recently found a solution. I stumbled upon it at a conference last week. It all made sense. I even talked to our guys about it - most of the directors and VPs - and they all seemed to like the idea. Or maybe everyone was just so busy that they didn't have time to really think about it. One way or the other, when the time came for real action, the initiative suddenly turned into a real mess. I had about ten people in the room, all violently opposing it."

Rachel said nothing. She was a great listener. I would probably have noticed that before, if I had ever bothered to share what's bugging me, beyond benign things, of course. Well, this is truly weird: we have lived together for almost six years and I finally have an opportunity to learn something important about my wife. I should have created such opportunities myself that would allow us to get to know each other better.

"What's weird is that these people are not willing to try a new method, even in the light of the upcoming lay-offs..."

Rachel nodded without comment.

"And I... I'm not going to give up. I'm going to make this happen. But, I think I'm at the point where I don't know exactly what I need to do in order to move this thing forward."

Those last words were incredibly difficult to get out. It felt like a fuse between my brain and my lungs was about to burn out.

"Why do you think they didn't accept the idea? Did they explain their reasoning?" asked Rachel.

"Yeah... Just like with everything, there's a payoff with the new method, but there's also an investment. And they got really hung up on the time investment that has to be continuously made. And... I'm not sure whether they understand the ultimate benefit at all."

Rachel looked at me very seriously. "Ethan, what kind of relationship do you have with those people?"

"Well, Brian–my boss–hates me. He clearly hated me before this, but after the meeting he hates me even more. The others? Pretty neutral overall, I would say. But today almost everyone used the opportunity to bash me."

Rachel smiled and kept going. "Do you think these people might have a fundamental reason for not accepting the idea?"

"Yeah, as I said, they are afraid of the investment..."

"No, I don't mean why they *said* they didn't like it. I mean, why is it so difficult for them to accept the investment in the first place? Why are they failing to see the value in it?"

"I don't know. It seems to me they just didn't want to listen to any arguments or explanations of how it works. They seemed to be pretty positive up until I pressed the wrong button–the planning event that requires everyone's participation for two days every quarter–that's where the 'ice cream' hit the fan. I tried to reason with them, but they just wouldn't listen. Now I'm back at square one, Rachel. No, it's actually much worse than that now, because my biggest problem is how can I get them back in the room to try to deliver the message again. As a change agent, I have to keep working at this, until–"

Rachel shook her head. "That is you... You will never give up, will you? My change agent in satin armor." She kissed me between the eyes, stood up to leave the room. "Hold that thought," she said, walking gracefully out.

Is all therapy like that? Where they kiss you between the eyes? Or is it just Rachel's way of confusing me? Because if so, it's working perfectly. She came back in a few moments with a cup of tea that she must have brewed while I was absorbed in my thoughts.

"Sleepytime?" I asked, looking at the tag on the tea bag.

"Well, it won't knock you out or anything. But let's get back to our topic. I asked you a specific question about their fundamental reasons for rejecting your ideas, because the behavior of your friends is a classic example of a mindset issue."

"Mindset issue?" That's a weird description, but not as weird as the fact that she called those ass-hats my 'friends'.

"See, there's a plethora of empirical evidence demonstrating that the acceptance of new ideas which are designed to change people's behavior, often happens very superficially at first. An individual or a group of people that are introduced to a new model of behavior may very eagerly accept it and live with it. And everything seems fine, until the time comes when the new way of operating suddenly bumps up against one of the fundamental beliefs that constitute their standard mindset. People often have no way of recognizing any of that upfront, which is why your first meeting went well, but when push came to shove, all hell suddenly broke loose."

"So... what are you saying?"

"I'm saying that we often live under the false assumption that our position on a particular matter is a question of pure rationalism. Dig a little deeper and under the thick layers of logic, you will discover a belief system; a space where the rational is tightly intertwined with the emotional, a space that constitutes our mindset."

"Are you saying that my 'friends' cannot be convinced?"

"No, Ethan, no. That's not at all what I'm trying to say. All I'm saying is that when you all believe you are discussing the same topic, you are actually speculating about completely different things. And that's because a topic will be interpreted completely differently in different belief systems. That's why you can't win an argument like that one directly. In fact, if you're in the middle of a violent argument, you've already lost."

Yeah, that sounds just great. The problem is, I think she's right. No wonder our initial conversation with those guys went so well. We were speaking two completely different languages.

"A mindset is the very nucleus of every person, and is indeed the underlying cause of conflicts like the one you just encountered," Rachel continued. "You have to address the cause itself. But it is also important to do so very gently because you are about to shake the most precious asset of absolutely every human being - their belief system. The task becomes even harder when you are addressing the common mindset of a group of people, rather than just a single person. For different communities, teams, tribes, and squads, the mindset basically becomes the embodiment of the group identity. It hardens over a long period of time under the pressure of different external factors, and the more those adverse factors threaten the mindset, the bigger the pushback."

"Okay, this actually sounds super encouraging, Rachel. Any specific ideas about how to shift someone's mindset? Gently, of course..."

Rachel smiled. "To be entirely honest, in certain situations it can prove to be impossible. And yet in many cases you just need to know what you're doing and then you can move the needle."

"Yes?"

"Think about the acquisition of a new mindset coming as a direct result of a learning process. Learning happens in a multitude of different ways, but as obvious as this may sound, learning is often facilitated tremendously by teaching."

That last phrase struck me like a lightning bolt. It was so real that I could almost smell the ozone in the room. That's why Adi was so insistent about the leadership training. I'm pretty sure she was using the right words; I simply wasn't willing to listen. I think I might just have had the same mindset issue and resistance as my 'friends' who had thrown a fit earlier in the day. Now I can totally understand where their reaction was coming from.

There's one thing I can tell for certain: by now all the fuzziness in my head has entirely vanished. Maybe it's because of our weird little home therapy, or maybe it was the 'Sleepytime'. Do tell.

"Honey, I think I need to make a call...."

ETHAN'S DIARY

- *In adopting a new operating paradigm, the ways of working are only the tip of the iceberg. The real target of a change agent—the mass of ice below the surface—is the mindset of those who lead the organization.*
- *People can accept new practices without even understanding that it may violently contradict with their core beliefs. The contraction will become apparent later, and when it does, things may turn less than adorable.*
- *The bad news: I shouldn't have rejected Adi's idea of leadership training. The good news: now I know what to do next.*
- *Rachel, Rachel. She unearthed a precious stone for me, that I had been prancing over the top of without even knowing it. Lady Galadriel in the flesh. What can I say?*

CHAPTER 3
Inspect, Adapt, Live!

"... This skill does not come naturally to individuals and teams."

–MIKE

THERE'S SOME MAGIC IN THE takeoff of an airplane. I like observing it from inside the terminal; watching plane's nose suddenly pull up and within seconds haul the rest of the noisy machine into the air. But even more than observing it, I enjoy being part of a takeoff. At takeoff I find peace of mind, which is not something I have experienced much of lately. The intense acceleration does some magic to my mind; I rejoice every time I hear the war cry of the turbines as they prepare to ram through the crust of the clouds.

We are in the air. I'm full of anticipation of the mission that I have to accomplish this week, and the big event that I'm going to attend. After the long talk with Rachel, I called Adi and she agreed to help. I really appreciate that she didn't play the smartass and didn't give me any of that 'didn't I tell you...' or 'how come you suddenly changed your mind...' crap. I'm sure I'm not the only person she has had to deal with in her career who didn't initially see the value in leadership training as part of a rollout. In fact, Adi invited me to visit one of her customers that has been utilizing the method for quite some time now. I am incredibly excited about this visit. I want to simply watch and learn. I may have screwed things up with the training, but I'd like to think that I have not become entirely un-teachable.

We're finally at cruising altitude and I can get Wi-Fi now. I used it for the first time back in 2012 on a long flight and that made the overall flying experience a lot more entertaining. I use Wi-Fi every time I fly now. Here you are, sitting in a chair in the middle of the sky while browsing the Internet–it's quite amazing actually. Even though you don't have much bandwidth, just the fact that you can check your email and browse the web is terrific. Sometimes we get used to good things too quickly.

A few new messages have hit my mailbox since I left the airport. Here's an interesting one from Raymond. He just finished experimenting with Kanban boards within the IT support organization and the results, as he describes them, are really promising. He attached four pictures of ad-hoc boards. Some of those boards, as he described them, are used for incident management; some are used to track infrastructure improvement. I think he used the word 'visibility' at least ten times in his email. Well, good for him; I'm happy he's experimenting with new stuff. He and I had a chance to talk before my departure, in the kitchen, as usual. He started by telling me that he had heard about my unsuccessful endeavor with management and felt sorry that it had worked the way it had. But then he said that the only reason that I'm still employed is because I have a supporter who isn't going to let me get fired. I don't know whether I should believe this stuff or not. And who is this mystery person anyway? It cannot be my boss. I'm sure he would love to see my bacon fry, without any remorse. But I don't see who else it could be either. Nobody else in that meeting seemed supportive at all. Is it someone who wasn't in the room that day? Someone I had invited but that did not attend? While I have every reason to trust Raymond, it may just be that he's relaying inaccurate information in this case. I think the reason that Brian still keeps me around is because, although he hates my guts, he hates taking any unnecessary risks even more. At this point, getting rid of me would introduce a serious risk and that's something he can't afford. Brian is a huge fan of all the various forms of status quo. Unfortunately for him, this means that I can keep testing his limits for a little longer.

Another interesting email came from Rachel. She's guest-speaking at one of those events that are titled in long acronyms; real tongue twisters. She sent me a photo of a large auditorium filled with serious-looking dudes and girls. I would like to know how it went, but the photo is a good start...

Next is an email from my guys relaying the fact that Brian was looking for me today, and seemed very unhappy with me for having left for a personal trip 'while my company is going through such a struggle'. Well, for starters, this is not a personal trip. And secondly, I will do whatever is needed to save my company; and I believe that I can, despite all the odds. The whole idea of addressing our leadership's mindset makes a lot of sense to me at this point. I certainly have no idea how to get those people back in the room again, but if I'm somehow able to lure them into the training facility, I think I will have a great chance at succeeding – with Adi's help, of course. If I can only manage to get them in... But I'll worry about that when the time comes.

The rest of the flight passed very quickly. I had a book on my Kindle and that's the surest way to make the time suddenly shift its normal rhythm and appear to run faster while turning pages in pursuit of the inevitable denouement. The next thing I remembered was a fairly rough touchdown – something I enjoyed much less than the takeoff.

"Hi Ethan," said Adi, who wore much more formal attire this time. I pulled my bag out of the trunk of the cab and followed her to the reception. "They are gathering in 'Tundra'."

"Who is?"

"The train. Everybody: developers, testers, facilitators, POs, Product Management - everybody. Today we're going to observe an Inspect & Adapt session."

We walked into 'Tundra', a big room where most of the tables were already occupied. Two people were tuning up the projector, while the rest of the room participated in what appeared to be a big humming attempt to prove to the entire world that it is possible to have a thousand topics discussed in the same place at the same time - all being of equal importance.

Adi explained: "Inspect & Adapt, as I'm sure you've read from the links that I sent you, happens on the Program Increment boundary, usually a day before the PI Planning. It consists of three main parts. The first part is the PI System Demo - a consolidated demo of everything this train has built in the last ten weeks. That's the duration of their PI here. In the second part, business owners will provide quantitative feedback to the teams on the train. And finally, we'll have the problem-solving workshop. Today's I&A session is special, though. They have their investors attending. This will be an interesting thing for you to observe."

"Who are the business owners?"

"Business owners," said Adi, "is what we call the key stakeholders of a train. The people that essentially decide its overall course of action and provide feedback on value delivered."

"Are you running this event?"

"Nope," said Adi. I'm visiting with a different mission - to observe and make suggestions. This is their fifth PI. If at this point they still need my facilitation of this essential event, then something is really wrong with their process. That guy right there," she pointed towards the table with projector computers, "his named is Mike. He will be facilitating."

"So, he's the Release Train Engineer then?"

"Yup, that's right. You took the prep seriously, I see. That's really cool. Now I'm sure you'll enjoy the action even more as all those things start coming together in your mind. Theory is great, but observing a practical implementation is a completely different thing."

In the meantime, Mike tested the microphone. As soon as he made sure that everything was working, he announced the event as officially open. He introduced the participants, starting with the train itself: a little over one hundred people that call themselves 'Silver Arrow.' As Mike called out the name of the train, the whole group cheered something I didn't quite catch except for the 'Silver Arrow' part of it. It took another thirty seconds for the whole group to calm down. They were all pointing to something in the middle of each table, and I finally noticed what it was. Every table had a paper tent with the team name on it, but it had something else on it too. The tent next to our table read: Juggernauts@SilverArrow. The next one was SonsOfAnarchy@SilverArrow. I couldn't see any of the other names. Meanwhile, Mike introduced the business owners that included a couple of product managers, a director of development, and some folks from the portfolio management team. Lastly, he asked the group to give a special welcome to their investors, Erika and Vijay, who looked a little puzzled by the event. Once the introductions were over, Mike quickly moved to what he called 'the only real thing there is' – the demo of the entire PI.

"Mike is smart as hell," said Adi. She pointed at the table in the front. "You see those two guys there? Usually there would be a representative from each team showing their team's stuff at a demo like this. So you would have thirteen people, demonstrating one after another, taking about four to five minutes for a summary demo and two to three minutes for Q&A. That usually works fine. But sometimes it makes the demo a little... fragmented. Mike decided to experiment with a different approach this time, and called yesterday to run a new idea by me. What he wants is a consistent demo of end-to-end scenarios, so that the investors can acquire a good understanding of where the system is at this point. But he still wanted to have a clear acknowledgement of the teams' effort. So, let's watch how he is going to make it work."

Mike began the presentation by showing a slide with six bullets on it, and then inviting Ioana from product management to take over.

"These are our program objectives for the PI that just ended," she began. "In this PI, 'Silver Arrow' was busily working on user-generated traffic status, time-sensitive smart routing, integration with reminders for iOS users, full NDS support for all maps, real time route prioritization, and road bike routing. We are super excited about these features because some of them have no analogs on the market at the moment. And even though we are expecting our competition to implement some of this sooner or later, this is the third PI in a row that we have managed to finish while delivering awesome features that nobody else has. I don't want to throw out any spoilers, but how about 'road bike routing'? Has anybody here downloaded the new maps that support this feature on their phones yet?"

Over a dozen people raised their hands.

"I propose that we start the demo by showing this function first. Guys, it's all yours," she said to the two guys that were driving the demo environment at the front table.

"We will be demonstrating road bike routing on the Android phone," said one of them, while his demo-buddy was connecting the phone to the computer so they could project the phone display to the big screen in the center of the room. "So, let's say my friend Rob would like to go from our office to REI at Lincoln and 57th street to buy himself... a new cycling helmet, because he just got promoted and of course needs a bigger cycling helmet now..."

The room exploded in laughter. Rob was listening very seriously, though.

"Since our office is practically in the woods," he said, hitting 'route' button, "there are multiple paths from us to REI, and quite a few of the routes, as we can see, are offering dirt roads as options. That's what happens when we use 'cycling' mode. But Rob, my friend, what kind of bicycle have you got?"

"A Trek Madone," said Rob, with the same serious expression.

"Which is...?" his friend asked, with an obviously curious face.

"...a road bike," confirmed Rob.

"So, you don't want to kill your fancy five-grand bicycle on the Red Fox Trail, do you?"

Rob shook his head disapprovingly.

"Which is why," proceeded his companion, "Rob has no choice but to use our 'road bike' feature."

The group laughed, and as soon as they selected the 'road bike' tab, three of the five routes disappeared from the map.

The room went crazy. Mike, the RTE of 'Silver Arrow', stood up in the front and asked, "What teams where involved in developing this functionality?"

People from three different tables raised their hands. "Okay, that's great, guys. Let's ask our product people what they think. Ioana?"

"That's definitely a successful feature completion," said Ioana. "We had some known risks in the beginning of the PI, especially in terms of our ability to build a reliable path recognition algorithm for trails that don't have any terrain data associated with them. But you guys totally rocked it."

After that they moved to real time route prioritization, and then on to another feature, and then to the next one. Lastly, when demonstrating the 'end-user generated traffic status', they did something truly amazing. One of the team members was outside, on a campus road, about 500 yards from the office building. He was purposely moving at a speed of 5 miles per hour while his phone transmitted his speed data to the production-equivalent staging environment, which interpreted his low speed as a traffic problem on that section of the road. That data then showed up on Rob's device as a little red segment. The real-time nature of the demo created an unbelievable effect.

At the end of the demo, Vijay and Erika addressed the group. This was their first visit of this kind. They obviously had not been expecting such a showdown and were clearly stoked. The train succeeded with all major objectives, except for 'time-sensitive routing'. The algorithms turned out to be too raw and at that point unusable. The whole thread will require additional exploration, both in terms of feasibility and potential next steps.

"Now, Ethan, that was the part where external guests like Vijay and Erika are welcome," explained Adi. "I have another client that is a government contractor. They invite guests from the government agency they work with at least every other PI. This kind of demo is the best possible way to build trust with your customer or high-profile business stakeholder. But as you can see, Erika and Vijay are leaving at this point – the PI System Demo is officially over."

As the investors left, Mike invited all of the business owners to the front of the room. Then something interesting happened: every team had a large sheet of paper with their Team PI Objectives listed. Each sheet contained five to nine items. They started with the 'Juggernauts' team first.

TEAM JUGGERNAUTS
PI OBJECTIVES

- ROAD BIKE ROUTING ALGORYTHM SUPPORT 10
- ROAD BIKE ROUTING DATA VALIDATION 6
- REGION SUPPORT IN MAP UPDATES (NDS) 8
- BIKE LANE CONNEC-TIVITY ALGORYTHMS 10

----- STRETCH -----

- ROAD BIKE ROUTING RREFERENCES 7

"Teams create these objectives during the PI planning session, as I'm sure you read," Adi whispered, so as not to distract the group from the process. "Every team has two types of objectives: committed and stretch objectives. They plan for both types, but stretch objectives may or may not be delivered, and both the team and business owners know it. It's a touch of reality in a world where we used to pretend that we knew everything upfront and to a high degree of detail."

"What are those numbers?" I asked of Adi.

"Those numbers represent business value that Ioana and the other business owners assigned to every objective. It's just a relative expression showing how much value different objectives have, compared to each other, on a given team's sheet. We use numbers from 1 to 10 for that."

"And what are they doing now?" I asked, pointing to the same sheet on the wall where Ioana was adding a second column of numbers, starting at the top.

"They are closing the loop, so to speak. See, based on that demo that just happened, Ioana and the others are trying to figure out how much of that planned business value had been really achieved by this team."

The process continued until they had gone through every objective on the team's sheet.

TEAM JUGGERNAUTS
PI OBJECTIVES

- ROAD BIKE ROUTING ALGORYTHM SUPPORT 10 10
- ROAD BIKE ROUTING DATA VALIDATION 6 4
- REGION SUPPORT IN MAP UPDATES (NDS) 8 7
- BIKE LANE CONNECTIVITY ALGORYTHMS 10 10

------ STRETCH ------

- ROAD BIKE ROUTING RREFERENCES 7 5

Then Mike and one of the 'Juggernauts' team members did some magic and came up with a percentage, which Mike called the 'Predictability Measure' for the team. I looked at Adi hoping to get an idea of what Mike and the team had just done, but instead of explaining it to me, she did something much better. "Mike, I'm sorry to interrupt the process, but could you please do us a favor here? Could you maybe draw a line around the numbers that you use in your calculations so Ethan and I can clearly see what numbers you are aggregating?"

"Sure," said Mike, quickly drawing the lines and turning back to his initial conversation.

TEAM JUGGERNAUTS
PI OBJECTIVES

• ROAD BIKE ROUTING ALGORYTHM SUPPORT	10	10
• ROAD BIKE ROUTING DATA VALIDATION	6	4
• REGION SUPPORT IN MAP UPDATES (NDS)	8	7
• BIKE LANE CONNECTIVITY ALGORYTHMS	10	10
----STRETCH----		
• ROAD BIKE ROUTING RREFERENCES	7	5
	34	36

106%

"He adds up all of the *actual* business value across *all* objectives and divides that number by the sum of all the *planned* business value of the *committed* objectives," explained Adi.

"Why is that?"

"Well, that allows the team to hit over 100% of their goal for the PI, which kind of makes sense. Basically, every team tries to get at least 80% of value achieved, but this way, if they build something from their stretch objectives, they get additional credit."

That was quite logical. In fact, the 'Juggernauts' hit 106%. In the meantime, Mike and the business owners moved to another team, and then on to another, until they had addressed the whole train.

After a little bit more magic with numbers, Mike announced to everyone that the program predictability measure for this PI turned out to be 87%, which is a totally good result.

"Is that the average across all teams?" I asked Adi.

"Yep. But it's not just the math that matters here. See, Ethan, these guys learned one fundamental thing about measures and metrics. They have a saying: 'no demo, no numbers', which I think is worth remembering. 'Silver Arrow' had a pretty rough first PI, failing to demonstrate any meaningful outcome, other than a bunch of disjointed pieces of functionality in different branches of code. I had to honestly call them out on that and make sure that no one was using numbers as a way of reassuring themselves, when there was actually nothing to show. Inability to demonstrate PI outcomes is a significant dysfunction for an Agile Release Train, and must be addressed immediately and thoroughly without any concessions or tradeoffs. This attitude is purely a cultural matter; and a very important one. They learned their lesson: they invested significantly in engineering practices, established a strict discipline of fully integrated system demos every two weeks, and there you go – you see the result of it. And now that the basic prerequisite is fulfilled and they have stuff to show, numbers start to make sense as an additional aspect of the feedback."

"So what's next?"

"Well, Mike will stick to the agenda, I'm sure, and will start the final part of the I&A, which is the problem-solving workshop."

"How are you guys doing there?" asked Mike, who had just finished his conversation with Ioana and then sat down next to us.

"We're fine. It is really helpful to observe you guys in action," I responded.

"Glad you are enjoying it, Ethan," he said, turning to Adi. "I need to run something by you. I asked the teams to spend ten minutes trying to come up with the top three impediments they have encountered during this PI. Those will be our input to the problem-solving workshop."

Adi nodded. "Isn't that what you usually do though?"

"Well, that's exactly what I wanted to talk to you about. In previous PIs, we did exactly the same thing. But once we collected all of the input from the teams, did the dot voting, and started working on the top problems, Ioana and some engineering managers came to me and said that we are solving the wrong problems. Even though management had a chance to post their issues on the same board, they simply got voted out by the majority of the participants, that being the teams. Do you see what I'm saying?"

"I do see, Mike," said Adi. "Did you stop the workshop at that point?"

"No. The teams were pretty far into it. Plus, the problems they were picking still mattered. It's just that those weren't *exactly* the top problems, in everyone's opinion. And I can totally see how teams can get a bit of bias simply because they look at things from a slightly different perspective than the management. So, here's what I want to do this time around; please let me know what you think about it. This time, I want to split the board into two 'swim lanes': one for problems that originated from the teams, and the other one for those problems from the management. People will vote the way they want. In the end, however, we will pick, let's say, the top three problems from each swim lane. That way nobody is going to feel that their input was ignored. What do you think?"

"I think, that's a pretty good idea, Mike," said Adi. "My only suggestion would be that you mix up the working groups that are going to work on those problems."

"How do you mean?"

"Well, I mean that we shouldn't let teams and management split into isolated groups. I would suggest the following: for every issue that received enough votes, ask who from the teams would like to do the problem-solving. Encourage people from different teams to join, because that way you will get multiple perspectives on the issue, which is always helpful." She stood up and started drawing circles on the flip-chart. "But then, once you have groups of anywhere from four to eight people, ask at least one person from management to join every working group."

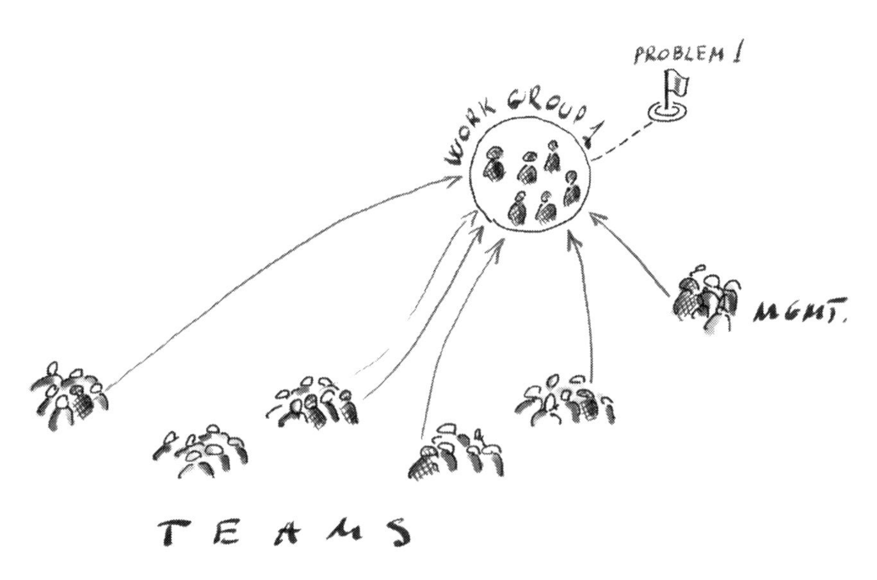

"I see. That makes sense. I'm going to run now. I'm sure the guys are ready with their lists."

Mike took the stage and helped the train to organize the voting on top impediments, while I continued thinking about that conversation. I realized what a luxury problem these guys were solving here! I can't think of any bait I could use to even get my management into the *same room* with developers and testers. These guys are light years ahead of us. But there is good news in this however: *we* can get there, too. And we will. It may even get me fired–I think I'm closer to that now than ever. But either way, I will give my company a chance to feel what is it like to have a real demo of complete features, fully integrated into the mainline. I will help our teams learn what it's like to take pride in belonging to something bigger than just a team of seven or so people; something that can deliver end-to-end value. I will help our management to embrace a new way of thinking about the problem of software engineering at scale. No matter what it takes, I will do it. I swear.

Meanwhile, 'Silver Arrow' managed to select the list of top problems. They split into seven groups – one for each problem, just as Adi suggested, and started working on it. Mike waved us over.

"Let's go, Ethan. He probably needs me there," said Adi, and we walked over to the other side of the room.

"I just wanted you guys to observe what this group is working on," said Mike. "It's quite an interesting problem, so you might enjoy spending some time around these guys. And hey, maybe you can even help," he said, smiling. "I need to attend all the groups within the next five to ten minutes and make sure they have everything they need for problem-solving."

In the meantime, our group drew a rectangle around their problem – 'Time-sensitive routing wasn't finished despite significant effort' – and started to build the rest of what they called a fishbone diagram to the left of the rectangle. They started with the 'spine' and the five main 'bones': People, Program, Process, Tools and Environment. Then they started playing a game of questions. It began with the first simple question from the facilitator of the working group: "So, why do we think this happened?"

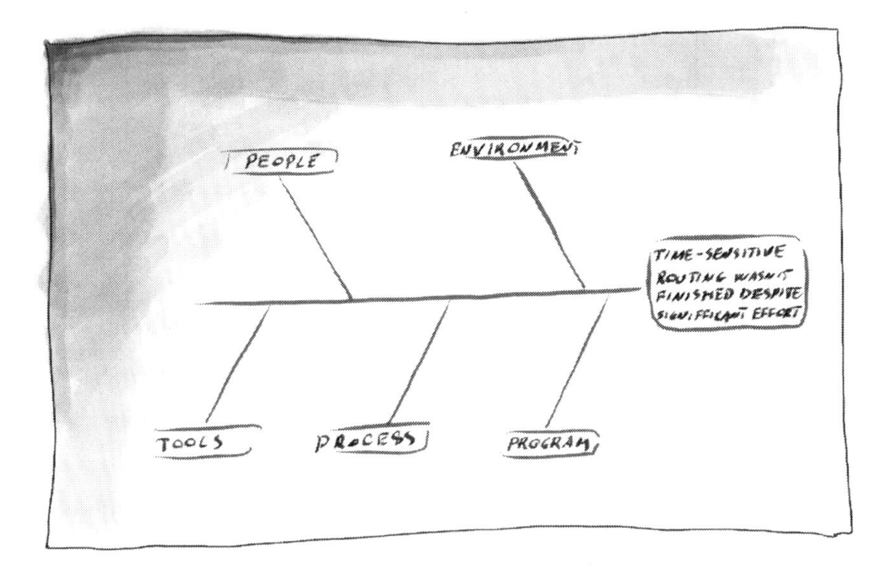

It was a little while before the group quieted their chatter and fully zoned in.

"Because, as it turned out, in order to realize time-sensitive routing, one would need the computing power of Watson for every user. That's insane," said a developer who wore one of those fancy t-shirts with a smart-ass slogan on it. The shirt said: 'You can't scale crappy code!' Of course it was printed in Courier font, the number one choice of old-school developers.

The facilitator added another bone to the spine and labeled it

'Insufficient computing power'. "Now, why do we think we need so much computing power?" he asked.

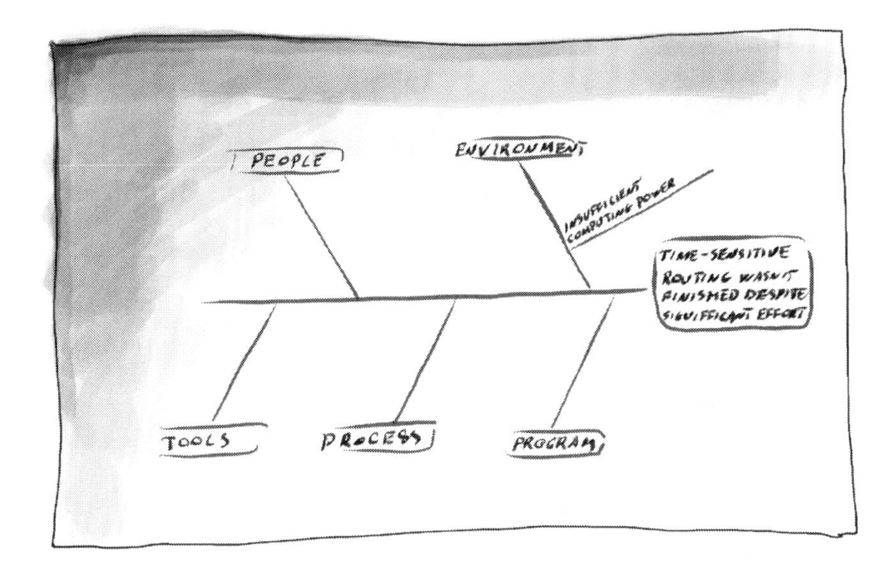

"Because time-sensitive routing has to recursively build-up a route, assuming that the user will be passing through each point on the route incrementally, at different times. The problem is that it creates a very complex scenario tree with more and more alternative routes at every step in the user journey. What might seem like a good future route now, may not seem so good in 15 minutes. To have a system that is able to calculate all those possibilities appears to be unfeasible. It's not only going to take a lot of time, but neither do we have a universal algorithm for it," said another person.

The facilitator added another bone, this one said 'no universal dynamic algorithm' on it. "Why do you think we couldn't develop an algorithm for this feature?" he asked, proceeding with his routine.

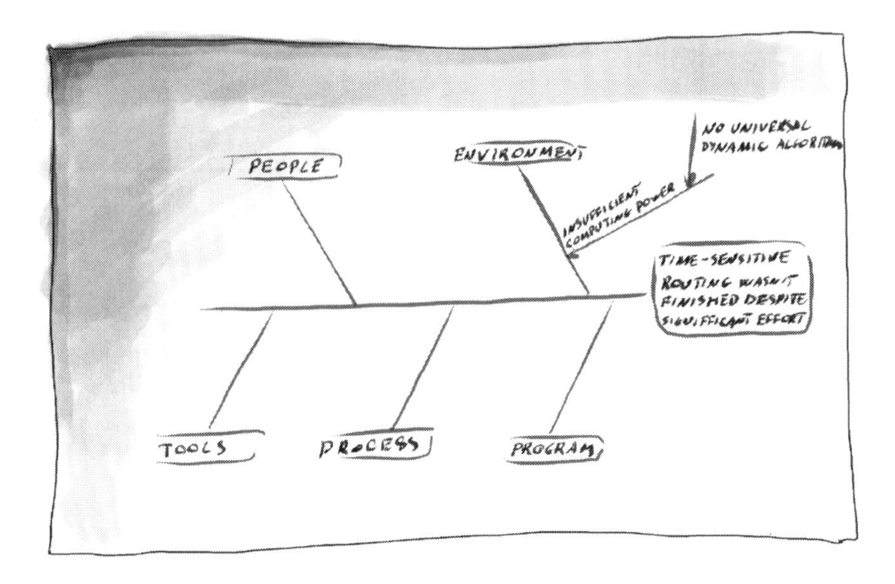

The developer that believes a person cannot scale crappy code raised his hand and said, "This feature is totally new. All we have is just the basic intent of what it should do, but we never really explored the algorithms or implementation strategy; we just blindly charged in. And we paid the price because complex things like this cannot be figured out on the fly."

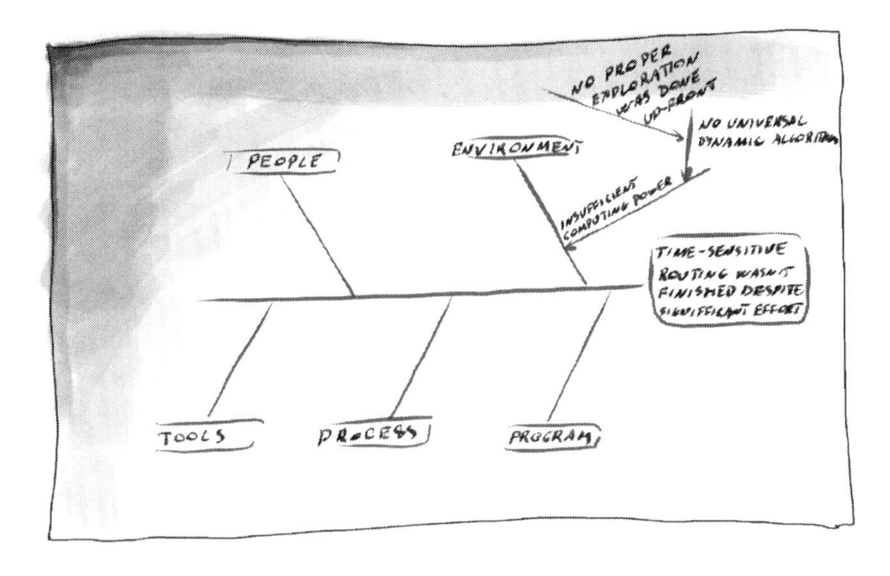

Another bone appeared on the board suggesting that 'no proper exploration was done up-front'.

"And you don't have to ask another 'why'," said the developer to the facilitator. "I think we all know 'why'. We don't have a good process for features that are brand new."

"Well, that's not entirely true," said someone. "We do have a process for features that are new, it's just that this feature was sort of a 'Black Swan'. It required a really complex algorithm, unlike the majority of new features, where we can derive a lot from what we already have and know how to proceed with development. What we don't have in place is a way of catching these 'Black Swans'."

Everybody nodded and she added another bone: 'No means to triage new work in terms of complexity'.

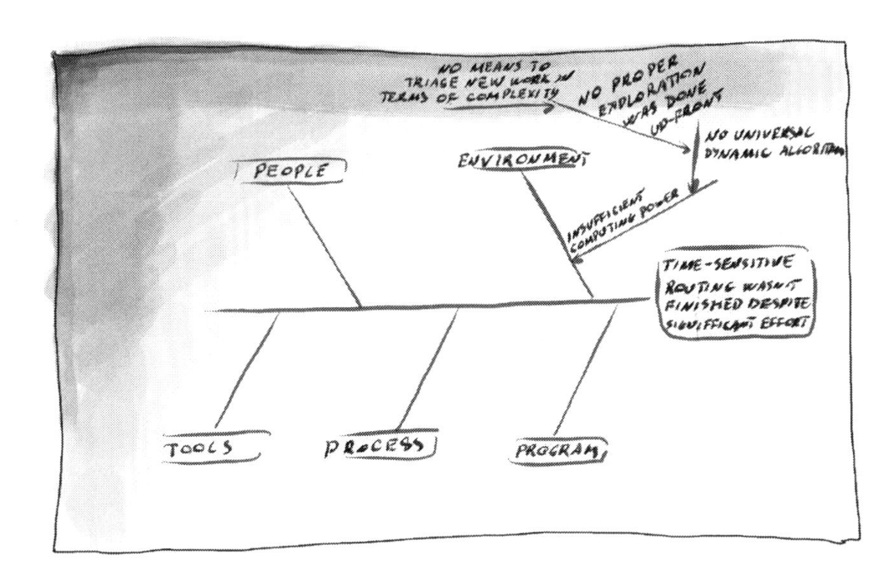

"I think this is it – we hit rock bottom on this one," said the facilitator. "What do you guys think?"

Everybody was in agreement. They then picked another plausible cause for the problem, and went through the same process of asking the magic 'Why's' until they had dug deep enough to stumble upon a root cause. After the third and fourth similar sequences had been identified, they stopped – there were no more viable ideas about what else could have led to this problem. And then they briefly swarmed around it, dot voted on the root causes, and came up with a winner – the one they thought was contributing the most.

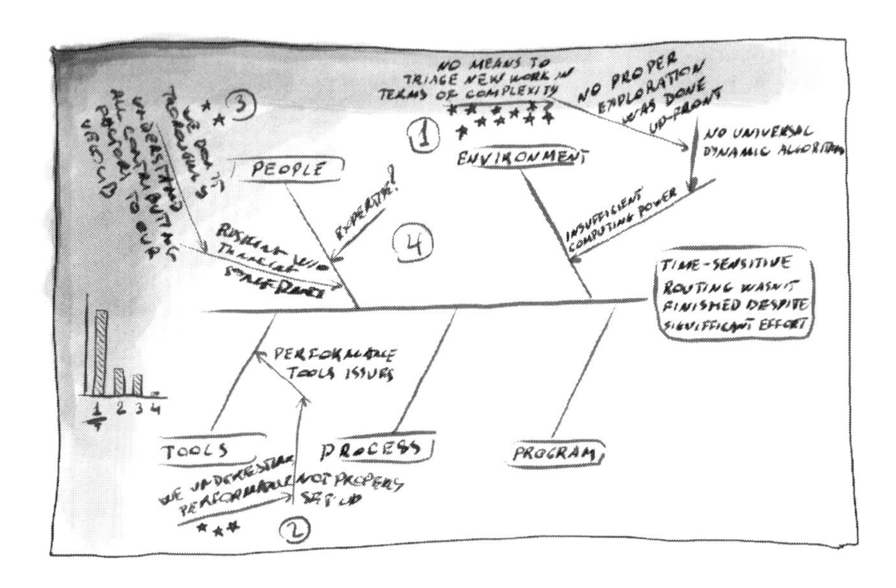

"Now we can drop the initial problem statement. Our actual problem is: 'No means to triage new work in terms of complexity'," said the facilitator. "We need to brainstorm better ways of identifying those 'Black Swans', guys."

And that's when this seemingly peaceful group of six people suddenly turned into a fireball of opinions, arguments, tough questions and bold answers. It seemed at times that they were about to explode and smash everything around them. But in about fifteen minutes they all calmed down and were patting each other on the shoulder, telling almost innocent jokes. Their job was accomplished for this session and they ended up with three orange stickies that represented the solution to the problem:

1. For every new feature, determine whether or not it can be fully realized using existing algorithms
2. As part of exploration, develop a functional prototype for every new feature that doesn't allow a 100% reuse of existing algorithms
3. Plan for prototyping time in the PI for the 'Black Swans' that are anticipated in the next PI

"Hey guys, who would like to present the outcomes of our problem-solving effort to the group?" asked the facilitator. "They are going to call for it in five or so minutes, I would guess."

When the time came to present, every working group described what problem they were solving, what the core root cause was that they had identified and, finally, two or three 'Improvement Backlog Items' as they called them, that they would like to add to their PI Plan the next day. And that was one great bunch of improvements. It was amazing what these guys were able to come up with...

"This skill does not come naturally to individuals and teams," said Mike, an hour later when he, Adi and I went out for dinner. "It took quite a bit of time to coach them on how to do it. Especially how not to get stuck on the way to the root cause. In the beginning, some of the folks would naturally fall into a vicious cycle of substituting a problem with its synonyms, instead of digging deeper and deeper, until the shovel hit precious stone – the root cause of the problem."

"Yes, it was quite a journey," agreed Adi.

Mike continued, "But even more so, it is critical that people don't re-invent the wheel. There are some practices out there already, some that have existed for decades – practices that work and provide consistently good results. Those are the ones you need to equip them with. Coaching teams during such events is priceless."

We had a great dinner, even though Mike was interrupted a couple of times by incoming calls from the 'restless product people,' as he called them, explaining to me and Adi why he had to step outside during dinner. Everyone was anticipating the PI planning; everyone stayed busy.

After my exposure to the Inspect & Adapt, I didn't have any expectations from the PI planning. All I knew was that I was going to learn a lot, and it turned out that in fact, that I learned a lot more than I could possibly have imagined. I wished Ed and the directors that report to him were here. I wished my boss was here. I wished I could show my entire enterprise what it means to do a full-fledged collaborative planning. It suddenly occurred to me how we, as an industry, managed to over-constrain ourselves to the point that we even backed away from the spirit of the Agile Manifesto. Somehow we decided that 'face-to-face conversation' as the best method of conveying information, should apply only to the team of six or eight people. And while our programs were wildly struggling from the deficit of Agile methods at that level, it did not concern us at all. Not a wee bit.

What I observed during the planning was the miracle of collaboration between management and teams, where both strictly adhered to the rules of the game. The rules are simple: business people decide what is more important and what is less so, but only the teams can say what actually fits into the plan and what doesn't. I had a chance to silently observe some of the most amazing conversations, which I currently cannot even nearly imagine happening at VeraComm. I witnessed a number of significant trade-offs that were made on the fly. Teams provided estimates and the management agreed to pull out some of the big, fluffy features in favor of more important things. The management considered it a sign of successful planning that they were able to use up the train's capacity in the PI for the items with the highest business value. "Are you sure you are not overloaded with all the enhancements to the road bike routing?" asked Ioana of the 'Sons of Anarchy', when they presented a draft plan at the end of day one. In moments like this, it seemed to me that these guys must be high on something. Otherwise how can you explain that the management, instead of trying to squeeze whatever they can out of the teams, are looking to not overload them instead. As Adi explained to me later, "Ethan, just so you understand... Ioana is no angel. She used to be a nasty product manager with a natural propensity for creating a false sense of urgency for all her backlog items. Because that, she thought, was the only way to have the teams accomplish anything. She and I had quite a philosophical debate one time," she smiled. "But look how she does things now... totally different attitude. I think she learned her lesson. Back then Mike pulled the right strings and we managed to have her stop making everything 'priority 1' that particular PI. That PI was this program's first successful one. She knows first-hand now that the peak performance of a program is when it's loaded according to its real, empirically proven velocity."

I also began to realize that this is the best way to build strong team cohesion at a larger scale. All of those discussions that they had, ad-hoc brainstorming sessions and so forth, building up a unique team formation that crosses the boundaries of conventional small teams. And from what I observed, the best way to build such a team is by letting them figure out the best ways of collaborating on the problem. Mike, and other facilitators that assisted him, were only creating the framework where the teams and their management could collaborate. At some point, when the energy in the room was going through the roof, Adi asked me: "What do you think you're seeing?"

"Well, teams, business owners... that's what the Agile Release Train is, isn't it?"

"Yes, but there's more than that," said Adi.

"Well, I have no doubt that there is."

"No, seriously, there's something important about what you see here. Look around you. People that you see in the room don't need anybody else to deliver the solution; they are self-sufficient. This may not always be the case: sometimes a solution may involve more people than a single train can potentially take on board. But Mike's case is interesting, and I want you to remember this example. What you've seen here is a *full value stream*: all the people that define, build, integrate, test and release the entire solution..."

I had a long flight home. Unfortunately, I wasn't able to find a direct flight. But during all of the travel, I was consumed by various thoughts. Quietly whispered by the impressions from the visit, and still echoing in my head, was the vivid image of the group that lived by some unique set of rules. They were completely defying, it seemed, the laws of physics, by which VeraComm or any other company I knew, operated. I was humbled by the immense power of servant leadership that the management and stakeholders of 'Silver Arrow' had demonstrated in the last couple of days. I'm stoked...

It was boarding time for my final flight, which I barely realized as my brain started to process a distant PA a few gates away from the terminal restaurant, where I was slowly finishing my lunch. Adi and I have to make this happen for VeraComm. I won't rest until it happens. Regardless of what it might take...

ETHAN'S DIARY

- *Agile Release Train is not merely a collection of Agile teams and their stakeholders. Agile Release Train is a self-organized team of Agile teams that rely on collaboration and face-to-face communication to produce maximum business value.*
- *ART contains all functions and roles required to deliver customer value.*
- *At the PI boundaries, Agile Release Train demonstrates a fully integrated system to its key stakeholders, that in their lingo, are called business owners. Business owners review the actual increment of the system and provide qualitative and quantitative feedback.*
- *Nothing strengthens trust between teams and business owners better than the PI System Demo.*
- *Program predictability measure shows how reliable a program's commitment is.*
- *"No demo, no numbers". If you can't demonstrate a fully integrated system, don't fool yourself with metrics. It's better to accept the defeat and focus on solving the underlying problem.*
- *Without System Demo every two weeks, you will hardly be able to have a successful high-profile stakeholder demo at the end of PI.*
- *Problem-solving is a critical part of Inspect & Adapt process. This is the train's chance to improve as a whole and escape the pitfall of local optimization.*
- *Root cause analysis, if done right, performs miracles. The output is critical: 2-3 actual improvement backlog items that will be loaded into the next PI plan.*

CHAPTER 4
Learning the Way

"If we apply Systems Thinking, things suddenly start to look quite depressing..."

–Nathan

"...I DON'T THINK THERE IS any other way out of this, Nerissa. This isn't a situation that can be handled by regular means. If the CTO can't make his own people deliver what we need, I will have to raise the issue at the next staff meeting," said the man in the dark suit with a subtle stripe. "I am losing patience, as you know. It's something I wouldn't enjoy doing, but I absolutely will do it, I swear, because this is getting way out of control."

"You're right, Zach," said Nerissa. "I've been saying all along that this company can't be fully driven by the technology people. *We* need to be more involved. And how about the lay-offs? Do you know if people in enterprise sales or in marketing are going to be affected?"

"No, no," Zach shook his head. "That is not going to happen, believe me. I told the CEO that this is not the right time to slaughter the goose that lays the golden eggs."

"So, what did he say?"

"He understands. Believe me, he is under enough pressure to be willing to listen. Now that the stock price is at its historic minimum, he is probably looking at a good chance of being let go by the board. At least no one would blame them if they did."

"But the lay-offs will affect the technology folks, won't they?" said Nerissa.

"Oh yeah! But think about it. If they can't deliver anything, maybe a little bit of purging in the ranks will help deliver the right sense of urgency."

"Looks more like decimation to me. And I just don't see how that is going to help anyone."

"Don't get hung up on it, Nerissa. We have work to do. This is the time when business development, and sales and marketing have to step up and save this organization from total collapse."

"How?" asked Nerissa.

"Let's ask a simple question: why are our customers so mad?"

"Well, they are not crazy about our quality and we lack some features that we just can't seem to deliver, no matter what," said Nerissa.

"Right. So, sometimes the strategy is just this simple: raise quality and deliver the freaking features."

Nerissa exploded in a fit of laughter that sounded a little bit insane. "Yeah, we might deliver a few features - in eighteen months, maybe. That may not be what our CTO will promise us, but that will be the actual outcome, you'll see."

"I will make it happen, Nerissa. As the executive vice president who is responsible for business development, I *will* find the right levers to bring this into motion: I report directly to the company's CEO. I hate to step over the CTO office, but I will do it if they can't manage their own people."

"I think I smell napalm in the air," said Nerissa.

"Come on, you know perfectly well that this is not sustainable," said Zach, pausing for a minute. "And there's also another thing - I need a meeting with you and your guys. I am going to invite product management to that event as well. We've been working on a big opportunity for the last seven weeks: potentially the biggest partnership we've ever had in the company's history."

"You're kidding, right? The biggest partnership in the company's history at a time when the stock price is the lowest in the company's history? That's really funny, Zach."

"It isn't," Zach said, smiling. "These guys know what they're after. They will acquire a significant share of VeraComm..."

Nerissa raised her eye-brows and they froze there for a few moments while her brain desperately skimmed through all the potential implications of what she had just heard.

"Who are 'they'?" she asked.

Zach remained silent.

"Oh, that's right. You can't tell anyone, can you?" she asked, smiling.

"Not just yet."

"Well, whoever they are, why would we agree to sell the shares?" she asked, but then quickly shook her head, "Wait. Why would they agree to buy? That makes no sense to–"

"Because the stock price will rise," said Zach, in a calm voice.

"Well, as a result of this partnership, sure it will kick it up a notch; but that's nothing compared to the hike we really need."

"That's not it, Nerissa. As part of this partnership, we are going to adapt our products to seamlessly integrate with their solutions, and together, we are going to penetrate into market segments that we could only have previously dreamed about."

"Like what?"

"Like HD telepresence for business, hazardous environments, and remote surgery, for starters..." said Zach.

"Are you serious?"

"Not to mention the government contracts," Zach proceeded. "Brace yourself. There will be an enormous amount of work."

. . .

With a great deal of persistence and a little bit of luck, I was able to get a meeting with a couple of people who, two weeks ago, were ready to hang me for introducing a new method. Rachel had accidentally given me an excellent idea of what to do. We were watching a movie the other day, the kind of movie I like most and that she can barely tolerate – with gang wars, police raids, stand-offs – in other words, a lot of action. The movie had a scene that turned the plot entirely. The protagonist went into a gunfight unarmed, and instead of catching a bullet, turned it into a parley and solved a problem that had previously seemed hopeless.

"This might be an extreme example," said Rachel, pointing to the screen, "but that approach is exactly what works best in our calmer, more civil environment."

And then it clicked. I suddenly realized that the antagonism between me and those I need to lure into the training room is preventing this company from succeeding. I need to do something about it. And really, what do I have to lose? Not much, as it turns out...

The day after that conversation with my wife, I sent out an urgent meeting request to all participants of the infamous meeting two weeks ago. Only five people showed up and my boss Brian was not among them, but that might end up being for the better.

"So, what have you got for us, Ethan?" asked Ed, who surprised me by showing up, and was glancing at his watch every few minutes.

"I need to talk to you guys," I said, trying to pick the best words to explain my less-than-obvious mission.

"Well, we understand that much," said the product manager – the only PM in attendance.

"Two weeks ago I invited you to a meeting where I had the opportunity to present a new method," I said, looking around the room. Nobody responded in the slightest. The thought crossed my mind that these guys were probably willing to sit on their criticism until after they had heard me out. That way it might be easier for them to do what they are going to do. But I proceeded, because like it or not, I'm at the point of no return. "Unfortunately, the way I presented the method to you guys, was far from optimal. I did not give you a chance to familiarize yourself with the method beforehand and because of that, we ran into a misunderstanding with respect to practices, that should have been discussed before. I take full responsibility for that."

I stopped. I wanted them to take a few moments and understand that I came here unarmed. I saw a little touch of surprise on their faces. Only Ed remained impassive.

"I invited you here today not because I want to explain the method to you again. I came with a different request."

Several people in the room began to look curious rather than concerned.

"So, what's the request?" someone from engineering management asked.

"I just returned from a trip to a company that applied this particular method. I wish you could have seen what I saw: teams that deliver value reliably, while their stakeholders have a chance to review the results and accept them based on empirical evidence. I wished I had created something like that for VeraComm. But I didn't. Nevertheless, I know the person that helped them. I would like to bring her over and have you talk with her. She will be speaking out of her huge experience of helping large enterprises adopt better development methods. I'm asking you to attend two days of training with her that we will organize here at VeraComm."

Nobody said a word for about ten seconds. Or maybe it was just two seconds that seemed to last forever.

"Gosh, we don't have that kind of time to waste," said the guy from engineering management.

Ed suddenly interrupted him, "Ethan, what my colleague here is trying to say is that we will find time, even if it requires us to rearrange our schedules a little bit. We all may have contributed to this misunderstanding. So, let's give it a shot. Right guys?" he asked, looking around the room. "Very good," he said without waiting for an answer. "Glad everyone liked the idea..."

I felt my heart racing insanely, fueled by the flood of adrenalin in my blood stream. So this is it, my chance to make this happen.

"All I can say, Ethan, is that your trainer better be good," said Ed, picking his laptop and leaving the room. Everybody else left the room too, leaving me alone to celebrate my little victory.

Time seemed to pass quickly after that meeting. Adi had a couple of back-to-back trips, so it was a little over three weeks before we were able to get her here. Everything in terms of preparation went pretty smoothly except for my boss Brian's actions. He called me and said that he 'had had enough of my B.S.' He said that he wasn't coming to the training and added that if it were up to him, I would long ago have been given a chance to apply my unmatched talents somewhere other than at VeraComm. That last phrase really struck me. Not because it was harsh or anything; I had no doubt that Brian would gladly fire me. No, I suddenly remembered that Raymond told me that my boss cannot fire me because I have a supporter who isn't going to let that happen. Well, either way, it's all good news. As long as we are moving forward...

. . .

Adi arrived in the afternoon of the day prior to the start of the training, and insisted that we let her into the training room to make sure that the room was properly set up. She was restless until she had tested literally everything.

Finally, the day of the training arrived. And it was a kind of moment of truth for me and Adi. A moment where it all either works out or it doesn't and then we have failed for good. If the training doesn't work out, I'm probably done. But it's too early to give up. And surprisingly enough, based on responses to the meeting invite, we're expecting twenty-four people. So, go figure.

The table outside the training room was covered with great stuff: oatmeal, two types of scrambled eggs, a couple of flavors of yogurt, a whole palette of cakes, coffee, tea and what not. One thing VeraComm does so diligently is good catering. Excellent catering, actually. It was 7:35 and two guys from the product management organization were already moving left-to-right along the table, entirely consumed by the process and probably only half-awake.

Adi was making her last-minute checks and looked fully consumed by that, too. The activity level was ramping up as more guys arrived, many of them from engineering management this time. They all dropped their backpacks at one table and followed the others to the breakfast area. A few minutes later Ed showed up with a couple more guys - Nathan, from engineering, Olga and John from product management. More than ten people! Well, not too bad. Except that it was 7:56 and Adi would be starting shortly.

"I'm going to give them ten more minutes, Ethan," she said, when the clock hit 8:00.

I didn't argue, but also didn't see why we should be so generous. This is probably all the people that were going to come anyway. I wasn't sure more people would show up, but it turned out I was wrong. Within the next ten minutes, all but one of the remaining participants had arrived.

"It's Shruti," said Nathan. "She texted me that she's stuck on 86th."

Wow. This is not what I had expected. How come nobody seemed to care at all and then, suddenly, so many people showed up - including many that weren't part of the previous meetings.

Consumed by these thoughts, I hadn't even noticed that Adi had started the session. They went through a quick introduction from everyone in the room and at each person's turn, Adi asked them why they had come to the training. Quite a few people provided fuzzy, not-really-sure-why answers.

"I'm here because what we deliver does not satisfy our customers," said Olga, one of the product managers who was sitting in the back of the room making notes on her tablet. Everybody turned to her and the room went quiet. "Lately we either deliver crappy releases or can't deliver at all. Other than that, we're just great."

Adi took a few moments to consider restating Olga's statement before putting it on the flip-chart, where she was trying to build some kind of affinity diagram of everybody's answers. But then she just decided to stick with the original form: 'Crappy releases or no releases.'

"Thank you, guys," said Adi. "Thanks to everyone for sharing your concerns." She tore off the sheet with the diagram and moved it to the wall. "Welcome to Scaled Agile Framework, or SAFe, as we abbreviate it. SAFe is a set of integrated practices for adopting Lean-Agile at scale. It was built to solve problems like those you identified a moment ago." Adi said, pointing to the wall.

Adi was on a roll and everyone in the room was actually listening. Although, truth be told, many wore quite sceptical expressions.

In the meantime, Adi moved to SAFe Principles. That's when I realized the power of those nine statements I had first seen on the bottle that Adi had given me back at the conference.

#1 - Take an economic view
#2 - Apply systems thinking
#3 - Assume variability; preserve options
#4 - Build incrementally with fast, integrated learning cycles
#5 - Base milestones on objective evaluation of working systems
#6 - Visualize and limit WIP, reduce batch sizes, and manage queue lengths
#7 - Apply cadence, synchronize with cross-domain planning
#8 - Unlock the intrinsic motivation of knowledge workers
#9 - Decentralize decision-making

Adi dwelled for a while on principle #2: Applying Systems Thinking. The idea of looking at the process as a system and trying to identify all of the steps in the flow of value came through quite well, but it wasn't until we discussed principle #6 that things started to come together. Adi asked every table to act as a team, and pass a batch of ten coins across the team members. The rules were that each person flips each coin, and once finished with all of the coins in the set, the batch moves to the next person, and so on. Each team recorded the total time it took them to perform the exercise. Then she asked the group to repeat the process, but in a slightly different way. The team members did not have to wait for the whole batch of ten coins at every 'station'. Instead, as soon as the first team member had flipped the first coin, the next person could pick it up and flip it, and so on. The difference in overall time for the same set of ten coins was almost twice as fast, on average.

"What did we learn from these numbers?" asked Adi, pointing at the flipchart where she was recording all of the teams' times for both rounds.

The group didn't seem to be ready to immediately answer any questions. For a while they sat still, as if something was preventing them from trying to reflect on what they had just done. Eventually people began chatting at their tables, some pointing to the flipchart.

"The second time was faster?" said a person from engineering, not sure whether that's what was initially asked of them.

"That's ingenious," said Olga, laughing. "What makes you think so?"

The rest of the group chuckled. Thank goodness! We needed a little bit of an ice breaker to get us out of that tense, unconstructive mode. I've been part of a couple of trainings when everyone is stuck in the negative zone. Somehow our company has traditionally had this interesting bias: people in the training think that they are doing an instructor a huge favor just by showing up. No wonder we are so un-teachable sometimes.

However, surprisingly, Olga seemed to enjoy this new development and proceeded: "Here's what's really funny. The first coin..."

"What about it?" asked Adi.

Olga picked up a coin and stared at it for a while, trying to get her thoughts together. "The overall processing time for all ten coins is certainly faster. Like two to three times faster," she said, pointing at the flipchart. "But the time it takes to get the first coin through all the steps is incredibly faster in the second round. Well..." she rolled her eyes up, as if reading the answer on the ceiling, "if we assume that four people were flipping coins and the fifth person was just recording time, the first coin reaches the finish line approximately seven times faster in round two, compared to round one!"

"Almost eight, actually," said Ed. "7.75, to be accurate... I just did that on a calculator, Olga," he said. The guys at his table chuckled.

"So, what does this mean?" asked Adi.

Olga delved into her thoughts again.

"It means that the customer receives the first chunk of value much faster, that's what it means," concluded Ed.

This is good. I noticed that nobody seemed skeptical anymore. At this point not only were people listening, they had also lost their sour expressions.

Nathan, an engineering director that works for Ed and a guy who had given me a hard time in our meeting a few weeks ago said, "It also means that we can validate our work faster. If something's wrong in the process, we're gonna know early on."

"So, Nathan, if I asked you to combine the takeaways from Principle #2: Apply systems thinking and Principle #6–specifically, the idea to use smaller batches–what implications would it have for an enterprise like VeraComm?" asked Adi.

Nathan took a while to think about it.

"We should make the batch size smaller everywhere in the process?" shouted someone from Olga's table.

"Yes," confirmed Adi. "The idea of smaller batch size must apply throughout the entire value stream."

Adi then moved on to the next principle and then the next. Gradually, people in the room became fully engaged in the process and had a lot of good discussions. It really began to dawn on me that all of the principles Adi talked about weren't really rocket science. Not at all, actually. It occurred to me that a different way of thinking was all that was required. Despite the many artificially created stereotypes in the industry, people don't fall into categories such as 'Agile, and therefore smart' and 'Everyone else, usually not as smart'. They are all doing sophisticated work, on a daily basis, which means that their mastery of these principles does not represent an intellectually inconceivable task. It's just that they never thought about these concepts in this way.

In the middle of the conversation around the last principle, Nathan suddenly interrupted and said. "So, that's why we have trouble releasing anything, isn't it?"

"What do you mean, Nathan," asked Adi. "How exactly do you link it to–"

"I'm sorry, Adi," Nathan said, shaking his head. "My mind is still spinning with the idea of combining Principles #2 and #6."

"Nathan just can't keep up," said Olga. "Nathan, you should spend a day with the product management team. I guarantee your life would change forever."

Nathan, however, didn't bother with an answer and proceeded. "Somehow, magically it seems, our features always get stuck somewhere in the process. We start them alright, but then we are never able to complete anything. Batch size is the number one offender."

Adi decided to not interrupt the discussion and Olga seemed to have had enough jokes for the day. Enough, at least, for her curiosity to be able to take over.

"Are you saying that we are operating with ten coins at a time?" asked Olga.

"It's worse than that," said Nathan, turning back to Adi. "Can I use the flipchart for a second?"

Adi nodded and Nathan drew a series of chevrons to represent the value stream. "This is our current process. We actually have Agile teams in place, right?"

Olga nodded.

Nathan labelled the steps. "Looks like our workflow? Yes, no?"

Most of the people in the room nodded and Nathan moved on. "Look, those Agile teams can really *only* develop and test in small batches, but everything before and after those two steps has a large batch size. So, if we apply systems thinking, things suddenly start to look quite depressing..."

The door opened and Shruti, a quality manager for this group, entered. "Sorry guys. The traffic is insane on 86th." She walked to one of the tables, surprised that nobody responded or even noticed her arrival, except for Adi, who nodded, but then quickly turned her attention back to Nathan's outline on the flipchart.

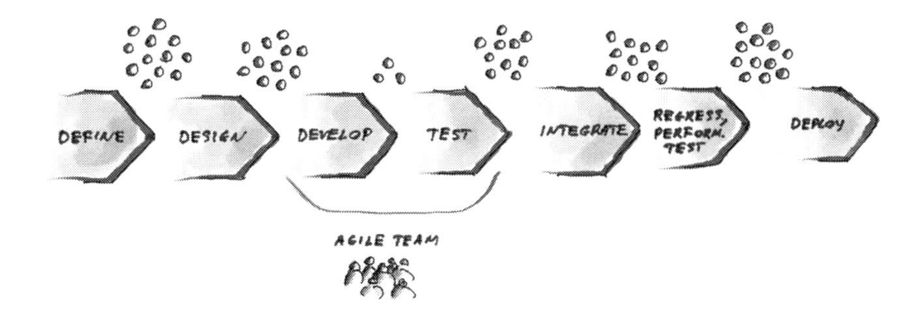

"Here is why we are so screwed up, Ed," continued Nathan. "Take integration, for example. That's a step nobody likes to do and therefore is repeatedly postponed. If it gets postponed, that means that we collect quite a batch right there. Same with regression testing, performance testing–"

"Nathan," Shruti interrupted. "Both regression and performance testing are executed that way for a reason. Performance testing, for example, requires a lot of setup time on behalf of QA. We can't do it in smaller batches."

"That just doesn't sound right to me, Shruti," said Nathan. "Things get stuck there and that causes us problems."

"I disagree!" replied Shruti.

"Well, I guess the rest of us here," said Olga, "can just wait until engineering resolves their problems."

"Oh no," Nathan said, turning back to Olga. "Not so fast." He pointed to the very beginning of the value stream and continued. "You guys are actually the worst. You dump requirements on us in enormous batches. Do you remember when you did that the last time, Olga?"

"Well, we don't hand it off to you frequently, you're right," said Olga. "And why would we? You guys can't deliver it faster anyway..." she said, laughing.

"Alright people, cut the horseplay," interjected Ed. "We are here to learn how to do a better job at delivering value, not to perfect our finger-pointing skills."

He's right and I'm glad he jumped in. But what he just said actually made me think more about it. It somehow occurred to me that finger-pointing, blame-game, and consistent misunderstandings could be a natural result of operating with large batches. It seems like batch size is not merely a matter of numbers. Yes, large batch size certainly slows us down, but apart from that, it also seems to produce negative team dynamic. Or rather, no team dynamic, per se.

"Thank you guys," said Adi. "I appreciate the honest conversation and we will have time to revisit the optimum batch size for each particular step, but let us not get stuck there. I would like, however, to point out that we should relentlessly apply systems thinking to all areas of our business. In this case it would be useful to think of us here as a system. And as such, we need to collaborate towards a common goal, which is the improvement of the entire flow of value. And to accomplish that we will be better served to learn not to take offense, but always to seek, offer and accept help. I understand that some of you have specific areas of responsibility as part of the flow. But at an even higher level, we have to set a broader common goal - improvement of the entire flow. And if you do not collaborate, don't expect your teams to ever work together on anything. Teams aren't capable of breaking the boundaries established by management. Think of what you do as something that entirely determines whether they will succeed or not."

That was a little rough and direct, but actually very helpful. Sometimes we need to call things what they are, otherwise we get stuck in counter-productive arguments, like the one that had just happened.

The rest of the day was even more fun. Adi described the notion of the Agile Release Train and the way she did it was brilliant: she simply built on what the guys had been discussing all morning - batch size and systems thinking. She defined the ART as a larger team construct that incorporates all of the necessary functions–and therefore steps–required for value delivery. She took a marker and drew what she had just described, looking up at Nathan's chart for the exact steps.

"If all of these functions work together as one big team, what do you think will happen to the batch size between the steps?" she asked the group.

It didn't seem that Shruti and Olga were happy campers today, so Adi looked around the room expecting somebody else to jump in.

"Well, all the batch sizes will naturally be much smaller," said Nathan. "That's like... obvious."

Once the definition of the train had been briefly made, and Adi described how the train synchronously and collaboratively develops and delivers value, we jumped into something unexpected, something that reminded me of my visit to Adi's client. Adi offered the group a chance to run a simulated PI planning session, just to 'get the gist of it'. I didn't know what to expect of it. The last time I talked about PI planning in this company, it ended poorly. But Adi handled it with a lot of confidence and to a surprisingly good effect.

She asked for a couple of volunteers to play the role of stakeholders and I volunteered. The rest of the group were teams on the train. Each team received a feature with some elaboration to it. In the next two hours we had to build, present and review the plan, as well as perform risk management and confidence vote. In other words, it was a nice little simplified version of a real PI planning session, compressed into two hours instead of two days, with the goal of simply helping us understand the flow of the event. The features were building up the functionality of an imaginary product; one so simple that anybody in the room could easily grasp it. And during this seemingly trivial exercise, something interesting happened.

"Our table is building the 'Book Browsing' feature," said Nathan to Adi, who had taken on the role of the Release Train Engineer for this imaginary company, called Geek Books. "We found a dependency on the search functionality. What should we do?"

"What is the simplest thing that comes to mind, Nathan?" asked Adi.

Nathan stared at her for a few seconds. "You mean I should just go and..."

"Yep," nodded Adi.

And indeed, Nathan simply walked over to the team that was working on the 'Book Search' feature. I wasn't able to hear what they talked about, but then they grabbed another person from Nathan's team and walked over to the team that did 'Book Detail'. Others also noticed what was happening and soon I witnessed at least six more examples of the same thing. The day was almost over and Adi decided to summarize the last exercise with the whole group.

"Guys, thank you for working hard all day and especially during the last exercise. We learned what an Agile Release Train is and how a train plans the Program Increment. I hope we all equally enjoyed it. Tomorrow we will dive deeper into how ARTs execute and release value, and then take a broader view on the enterprise as a whole, remembering that the Agile Release Train is just a building block in a larger, organizational context. Thank you everyone and I wish you *SAFe* dreams, because tomorrow we still have a lot of work to do."

Adi was busy disconnecting her laptop and switching off the projector. One or two people left right away, but many other folks remained in their seats and kept talking. Olga was explaining something out loud to her colleagues from the product management team, but all I could hear was 'feature', 'dependency' and 'risk' in her fascinating Slavic accent. Shruti was sitting at the same table and consistently nodding in support of Olga's preaching.

"Ethan, can I talk to you for a second?" asked Nathan, approaching me from behind and interrupting the idyllic picture.

"Yes, sure."

He took me outside. "Ethan, I... Well, I'm sorry for how things turned out back when you tried to get us going with this method the first time. We all went a little rough on you back then and for no real reason, actually. I wanted to apologize..."

"No apology necessary. You guys understand this method better now because of Adi's ability to deliver the message in a much more consistent and effective way. Yes, it was hugely disappointing to me when you guys reacted the way you did, but that caused me to realize that what I had needed was to bring her over here in the first place."

"Maybe. Either way, thanks a lot for doing this and for being persistent," he said, patting me on the shoulder. "See you tomorrow, Ethan," he said, walking out.

"Nathan, wait! May I ask you something?"

"Sure, go ahead."

"What exactly changed your mind?"

He smiled. "You know, at first it was that whole thing about taking a systems view. I think every manager eagerly accepts that. Because, if you think about it, a manager that doesn't want to adopt a systems view on the business simply isn't a good manager. It's a shame that we never happened to talk or think about our organization that way before. And you know what is most staggering?"

"Nope."

"Well, when I was a developer and was reading all those fancy books on object-oriented analysis and design by Grady Booch, Ivar Jacobson and others, I was totally aware of what we were doing there. We were trying to take a systems perspective on the solutions we developed. But it never really occurred to me that an enterprise requires a systems view as well, and then when we started thinking in terms of batch sizes and the other things Adi introduced, it was really easy to understand that this offers us a unique opportunity to identify bottlenecks in the process."

"Interesting..."

"Yes, it is interesting. But that isn't all, Ethan. The simulated PI planning was an even bigger surprise."

"How so?"

"Are you kidding? Now I totally get it. I really understand why you need all of the teams and stakeholders in the same room for two days. Look, we had such a simple system here as an example – a lousy online book store that isn't nearly as complex as the products we build for our customers. And yet, with all its simplicity and all the pre-elaborated data that you and Adi gave us, our team was able to identify plenty of edge cases that weren't initially obvious at all. And what's worse is, that the only way we were able to effectively do that was with help from other teams. No wonder we never even come close to our initial scope estimates in a release. We're simply used to ignoring the fact that all of these inter-team dependencies and program risks account for *a lot*, and without taking them into consideration it is simply impossible to have any level of predictability. Well, I guess I can only wonder why we never thought of such an obvious thing ourselves. But, it is what it is..."

I managed to not think out loud and kept the answer to myself. But the answer is simple: *it's all in the mindset*. And indeed, as Rachel said to me that night, that's where the rational meets the emotional. No wonder it creates the huge blind spots Nathan was referring to. Adi later explained to me why the mindset of a traditional management approach to product development is so deeply flawed by its nature. Traditional development methods do not rely on empirical data and that tremendously inhibits the learning process. "Don't get me wrong, they use more data than they need. Well, you know that, you're a PMO guy," she laughed and continued. "But that data isn't an adequate representation of the actual work progress. As a result, they develop a giant blind spot. Their mental model of the process is very far from the actual laws of physics in product development. But, there's no way they would know that because their model doesn't provide an effective learning mechanism. It teaches them the wrong things. They build their alternative reality and get seriously stuck in it."

And she's right. In our highly disjointed world at VeraComm, where functions don't communicate well and don't significantly collaborate, we fail to improve as a whole. Everybody seeks opportunities for improvement, but because we're separated from each other, the best we can do is improve our individual step in the process and no more. We fail to understand that problems at one step can be caused by fundamental issues at another. And with learning cycles as slow as ours–pretty much equal to the frequency of releasing, every eight or ten months–we just can't learn. Cause and effect are so widely separated from each other on the timeline that we simply cannot connect the dots.

. . .

Day two passed in seconds, it seemed. Lots of action and plentiful discussions, but the clock hit the boundary faster than I expected. Adi stayed for a while to address the remaining questions from the group and then took off to the airport for some insanely late flight.

When everybody had left, Ed approached me and said: "That was a good training session, Ethan. Really good training."

"I'm glad you guys liked it."

"We surely did. Hey, would you like to go somewhere and grab some dinner?"

"Sure. One thing though, Ed. I have a commitment this evening. I need to be home at 7 o'clock."

"Is it Rachel? Does she get jealous if you stay too long at work?" Ed said, smiling.

"Can't you accept that people may just want to spend time together? It's called f-a-m-i-l-y."

"Yeah, yeah, I get it," said Ed. "This won't take too long, I promise. You will get back to your lovely wife just in time. We'll go some place on 21st and pick the one that has the easiest parking option."

Wednesday night wasn't too bad in terms of traffic or parking or dining, per se. That's why Rachel and I usually picked Wednesday to go out to a movie theater. I'll have to keep an eye on my watch, because 6:30 is the absolute cut-off for me to make it home in time, then get to the movie theater without unnecessary haste. I want to make this evening with Rachel really enjoyable. Maybe I will be able to forget about work just for one night and simply be present for something else.

"So, as I said Ethan, good job organizing the training," Ed said, while cutting his enormously thick bison stake down one side. "But what you did," he paused as he finished cutting through the thick layer, "is like this cut." He raised a slice of steak on his fork and held it up: "It is just a first step, Ethan. And I want you to do more."

"Well, I'm glad you do, Ed."

"I like you, Ethan. I think you can go a long way with your persistence and your instinct, which is improving."

I have no idea what he's talking about or where he's headed with this. Possibly because it is really hard to concentrate at this point in time, after another day of intense training. And especially because Adi used me quite a bit today to help facilitate exercises. My head is like a tank: heavy and deflecting all projectiles that are coming my way.

"Also, just to be clear about something," he continued, "you pissed your boss off pretty badly, I have to tell you."

Interesting. Why would Ed bring that up? Perhaps this training is slowly developing into my next big problem. No wonder. Brian was mad at me already, and now he probably has the sense that something covert is happening behind the doors of that training room. But he chose not to come, so yeah, that's a real pity, but what the heck can I do about it?

"Are you aware that he wanted to fire you a few weeks ago, Ethan?"

Wow. So Ed knows. Well, of course he does. Brian is too chicken to fire me without talking to his bosses and it probably leaked out, so no wonder he knows. What a great topic for dinner conversation, though. I can't wait until 6:30. I want to get home, take Rachel by the hand and run with her to the car like we used to, back even before we were married. We used to create our own reality, with secret rules that only we knew. We still have plenty of stories, jokes, puns, and memes that only we understand. We are like one of those secret, underground societies that defy the rules whenever we see fit, yet adhere strongly to what makes us a family.

"Do you know why he didn't succeed with his intention?" Ed continued with the questions.

"Why?" I asked, now really curious.

"Because I actively campaigned against him firing you. His bosses owe me because I'm generally such a nice guy and have helped them with many things in the past. And now I called in their markers and asked that they put a restraining leash on him. I said I would go straight to the the execs and tell them that this organization is throwing away its last hope to improve the processes and our development capability, overall."

I almost choked on Ed's little speech. So this is the guy Raymond was talking about. But it makes no sense. Why then would he...

"Ed, why the heck did you bash me at that meeting along with everybody else? Why didn't you support me back then, when I really needed it?"

Ed smiled. "I needed to see if you had the guts to finish what you had started. I wanted to see if you were both serious and capable."

"But that's just–"

"Ethan... relax. Let me finish, at least. There's more to it. You're not the only person who wants this company to regain its power. There are people diligently pursuing that on the business side. And something big is coming."

"Big like what?"

"Nothing disclosable yet, Ethan. Forgive me, but there are things that I'm not at liberty to discuss until the time comes. Too much is at stake. You need to trust me on this. But here's something I can tell you today – your position is going to change."

"To what?"

"You are going to be the head of a newly created 'Transformation Team'. This is a director-level position. We didn't spend much time on the name. Feel free to come up with a better one, if you want, I don't care. But what I do care about is that you finish what you've started. And I will help you with that."

"What about Brian?"

"He's not your boss anymore. He has no authority over you from this point on. So just forget about Brian."

Gosh, I think I now understand why Brian declined the training invitation. What a turn of events!

"And who else is on the so-called 'Transformation Team' right now, if you don't mind me asking?"

"Nobody," said Ed, laughing. "But here's what's going to happen: tomorrow by noon, I need a list of people that you want on that team. You can pick several from the PMO group, but don't get too greedy. Whether or not you can go beyond the PMO itself, I can't say. Tell me who you want regardless, and I will tell you if it's feasible."

"So, am I now reporting to you?"

"Yep," Ed said, bursting into laughter again. "It's me, whether you like it or not, brother! So, congratulations and you can tell Rachel that you've got a fancy new title. You've also got a heck of a lot more responsibility, too. But you don't have to tell her that. Don't ruin your evening."

Ed was on a roll. And I wonder why is he so tense at times. Is that just the way he is, or is it because he knows more than he can tell? But it doesn't matter. This is a great promotion and it will help me achieve what I want for VeraComm. This is actually perfect. At least I will be, eventually, a legit change agent.

"I'm so proud of you," said Rachel, hanging on my neck as she usually does when she's in a mood to goof off. The more academic titles she gets, it seems, the more infantile she can be at times. I think there may be a direct correlation of some sort – hey, maybe that's a subject for a deep scientific study.

Just as we left our apartment, it started to rain. I reached for her and we ran all the way to the car, hand-in-hand. Today, it seems, I'm running everywhere. And now it's just Rachel, me, and a new movie on the big screen. Other people around us? Yeah, I think they will be there too, but who will be able to notice?

ETHAN'S DIARY

- *A successful change agent must ensure that there's no unproductive tension between themselves and the stakeholders. Any antagonism, even latent, may inhibit the transformation and must be promptly resolved. It's up to you to make the first step.*

- *Leadership training is a must and needs to be done as early as possible. It should give just enough initial momentum in order to proceed with the rollout.*

- *SAFe Principles are very important. They are the thinking tool, the wirepaths of our mental models of a Lean-Agile enterprise.*

- *Our goal as an organization is to learn how to work on smaller chunks of end-to-end value at a time, but deliver those more frequently. A systems view on the value delivery process is key to success, otherwise real bottlenecks might be overlooked.*

- *ART can be defined as a larger team construct that incorporates all necessary functions required for value delivery. Taking a systems view is at the structural foundation of the Agile Release Train. Putting all functions together, naturally decreases average batch sizes in the process and makes it flow faster.*

- *The traditional mindset progressively builds blindspots and inhibits learning. Surrounded by all kinds of numbers, we have no ability to really tell where we are in the process. Being separated into silos, we fail to learn and introspect as a whole. We need to put all the pieces of the puzzle together.*

- *Life is full of surprises: those that are supposed to be your enemies turn out to be your secret supporters? Sometimes it's best to accept things the way they are, without too much digging. In the end, it turns out surprises are great. Life is great...*

CHAPTER 5
The Prep

"It's like a bunch of very expensive bells and whistles..."

–SUNIL

"ED, COME ON IN," SAID Zach, offering Ed a seat. "Nerissa and I had a conversation recently and we decided that I should talk to you."

"Okay," Ed said in calm voice. "I'm listening."

"I'm assuming that you've heard that a big change is coming?"

"I did," nodded Ed. "But I don't know much about it."

"Okay. We can fix that. You should know more, and that's what I'm here for. QCell is buying a large block of our shares. But that's just part of the news. The other piece is that we are going to integrate most of our products into their solutions and thereby reinforce their positions in multiple areas. For us this means an exposure to brand new markets, which we could previously have only dreamed about."

"Frankly, Zach, it looks like part of this information might have already been leaked to the public," said Ed. "I'm sure you noticed the little uptick in stock price, didn't you?"

"Yes," Zach smiled. "Yes. Only it didn't leak, Ed. I mean, it did... but kind of on purpose. The public has more faith in us than we thought, as it turns out. And there's more growth coming Ed, that will make this enterprise successful once again. However, there are certain mistakes that we can't afford to make, and that's what I want to talk with you about."

"Go ahead," said Ed, still maintaining his poker face.

"So, I will be honest with you, nobody here believes that we can enter into a new partnership with the technology office like it is now. You know what I mean?"

"Yeah, I understand."

"I'm afraid that the changes in our business direction will trigger additional changes within our organization, including staff changes. It may all be quite disruptive. And that implies that someone will have to step up. Do you understand what I mean?"

Ed nodded.

"I thought you would," continued Zach. "But that's not all of it - there's more. I understand that you're eager, but this organization is going to enter into a different reality that, amongst other things, involves a lot of pressure on the technology office. A lot more pressure than there is now. The real question is, will you be able to step up?"

"And if I say that I'll step up, will that satisfy you?"

"No," said Zach laughing. "Not unless you answer the most important question of the day: what exactly are you going to change in your world that will make me believe that you're capable of handling all of this?"

"I don't think the use of future tense is necessarily applicable here, Zach. I hate to speak in slogans, but the future is now."

"That sounds great, Ed. Only I have no idea what the heck you're talking about."

"I am reforming my part of the organization as we speak. We are adopting a new method."

"Well, no offense Ed, but I think you guys have been taking on a new method every year or two, am I right?"

"This is different. In the beginning I was reluctant too, but now I'm fully invested in this."

"Oh, you'd better be, Ed... So, tell me more."

"The methods we used before were half-ass ways of applying a little bit of this and a little bit of that, without a consistent paradigm that would allow us to scale any local successes to the entire organization. But what we stumbled upon this time is a completely different solution. It's a consistent framework that is built for large enterprises with a single idea in mind: to build the ability of delivering large software and cyber-physical solutions in a fast and reliable manner. It's called SAFe or Scaled Agile Framework, and I actually have connections at a couple of enterprises that are using it. And so far, I've only heard positive feedback."

"What's the low-down?"

"The whole idea centers around applying the concept of Lean flow to the entire enterprise. The primary focus is on improving the flow of value, end-to-end. That simply means that we deliver customer value faster and more reliably, which translates to substantially better product development economics. This is achieved via building so-called Agile Release Trains–self-organized teams of Agile teams–around each value stream. Each train–"

"Okay, okay... So where are you with all this?"

"We are launching our first train in a week. We are very close to the first chunk of packed action," Ed said, pausing a second. "And here's the great news, Zach. You don't have to just trust me on this. In three months from the launch we will have a major demo and you will be able to come and see the actual results: fully integrated features, ready to be released. Consider yourself invited."

"What program are we talking about here?"

"We picked 'Mobile Solutions.'"

"That's actually a good choice, Ed, all things considered. That's a part of our business that will not be affected in the early stages of this partnership, so your hands are not tied. And I know that 'Mobile Solutions' is creating very bad optics. Not that they are worse than any other program at VeraComm, you know, but because of the nature of this program, they experience a lot of negative publicity as a result of undelivered features and patches..."

"You're exactly right. Plus, that program is perfectly-sized for one train. Currently there are ninety-six people involved. Thirteen weeks from now, they will deliver some of those long-awaited features."

"It's a little hard to believe, to be honest, but I guess you know best. And, frankly it's your ass at stake, not mine. I just want to be clear, Ed. If this thing doesn't work out, consider that you will have lost a once-in-a-lifetime opportunity. Not to mention that *I* will look stupid in the eyes of our CEO. I hope you understand," he said, pointing up with his finger. "The higher the rank, the lower the tolerance for failure. Now, which of your guys is driving this thing?"

"This young guy, Ethan. I pulled him out of PMO and created the Transformation Team. He's responsible for its success."

"Oh, I heard about that little brawl around moving eight or ten people out of PMO, and then a couple more from other groups. You guys created quite a stir with that. Nerissa said that Brian, the head of PMO, talked to her, and some other executives were complaining about it. Well, whatever. I'm good with it all, as long as it helps in the long run... Listen, once you launch this first program–and assuming that it is successful–what are you going to do next?"

"Yeah, so we already sent some of the folks from the Transformation Team to a special training for change agents. It was helpful; they came back quite enlightened."

"Good..."

"This week we are sending the rest of the Transformation Team. We want to make sure that they are well educated in terms of this method. And then, once 'Mobile Solutions' is launched, we are going to launch trains in other parts of the organization until everything operates effectively across the board. We will have all our local change agents there, as well as an external consultant, Adi – she's really good. She did the leadership training I attended; she will also be helping us with the ART launch."

Zach stared at Ed for a while. It appeared obvious to him that Ed really had a plan of attack. It was hard for him to say how viable that plan really was, but at least there was a check point coming up soon and that was a good thing. 'Being entirely realistic,' thought Zach, 'a partnership like this will take an investment of a lot of time at the take-off, and thirteen weeks will pass like a couple of seconds. So, there will be plenty of time to divert towards alternative candidates if this thing with Ed doesn't work out.' He finally decided that he had found out enough to satisfy his needs and that now he needed to move on to other affairs.

"Ed, don't let me down, that's the last thing I have to say to you. And also, keep what you've just heard to yourself."

"I understand."

"Maybe, you don't. I mean, seriously, you can't even tell your wife, you got that?"

"That's beside the point, Zach. She doesn't care anyway."

"Alright, Ed," said Zach, laughing–he clearly found the joke about Ed's wife entertaining. Or maybe it wasn't a joke, he thought for a moment, but then decided that he didn't really care either way. "Alright, take off, or I will be late for a call. One of those calls I have, you know, that determines the entire fate of this organization. But no pressure, right? Go!"

. . .

No matter how much time you allocate to the preparation of an ART launch, it will never be enough to be perfect. But as Adi put it, trying to make it perfect is actually a huge mistake. "The trick about the Agile

Release Train is that it continuously inspects and adapts. So it's not the starting point that matters as much, as it is the ability to understand the next constraint in the system and improve." She suggested that we focus on 'just enough preparation' and that's what we did. I have to confess that even this 'just enough' thing took quite an effort.

The preparation, however, provided a couple of very positive effects: it allowed the Transformation Team to acquire momentum, and to learn some basic ways of operating. We realized first of all, that we have to operate as a *team*. An Agile team, basically. Adi helped us to get started and she also advised me on what kind of people I should bring onboard. Adi is a good coach, which sometimes means she can be just as direct as you might imagine. "Bring people that have enough motivation to go through all the hurdles of the rollout. It's a tough job, so it needs tough people. If someone doesn't have at least the basic courage to hold their ground when necessary, and isn't able to overcome objections, doubt, and possible criticism from stakeholders or teams, then this job is not for them. It will hurt them and it won't help the cause. There's nothing more pathetic in this world than a resentful change agent that puts self-pity in the way of an organization's success. Instead, you must find those people that are restless, and we'll teach them how to be great change agents. We'll send them to the training to become SAFe Program Consultants, which will get them started. This team must be *unstoppable*."

Adi described to me some other important aspects of the team composition, structure and process. The one that significantly stood out was *connectivity*. The Transformation Team will not be any good if they aren't strongly connected into different parts of the enterprise. They must know what is happening in their organization. Apart from that, they need to have close relationships with the key decision-makers. "The whole idea of stakeholder management," Adi once said, "got completely bastardized by the pseudo-scientific paradigms featuring complex matrices that categorize your stakeholders this way and that way. They offer you a full sense of control while in fact, all they do is distract you from the most important thing you need to do, which is: to establish a reliable face-to-face communication cadence with your stakeholders – everything else will naturally emerge from there."

"In terms of stakeholders, my main one would be Ed, my boss in engineering," I immediately figured. "He will definitely agree to help, and he has quite a bit of influence in this organization."

"Well, that's great but that's not enough, Ethan," said Adi. "The Transformation Team must *directly* interface with the stakeholders in *all* areas of business that have an impact on development. This is a typical early mistake of many transformation teams. They follow the path of minimum resistance and fail to establish relationships with the people in product management, business development and so forth. As a result, they absolutely fail to address mindset and cultural issues. This failure eventually leads to tremendous disparity between development teams and their key stakeholders, destroying any hope of aligning business and engineering."

Luckily, in our case we had Ed, who was totally onboard with the idea and was able to connect us with the right people. He spoke to Nerissa and Zach, and had them assign director-level people from biz-dev and enterprise sales and marketing that would work with us on a regular basis. Apart from that, Zach and Nerissa promised to be there for the ART launch themselves. But even more importantly, Ed brought a product manager whom we were able to work with on specific aspects of preparation for our first PI planning.

Adi helped us to get started with our Transformation Backlog and a very simple progress board. Even though it looked overly simple, it helped us tremendously with the preparation to the ART launch. We were able to keep an eye on all of our initiatives inflight, to see where we're lagging, and what was left to do. It's amazing that such a simple thing can save you so much distress.

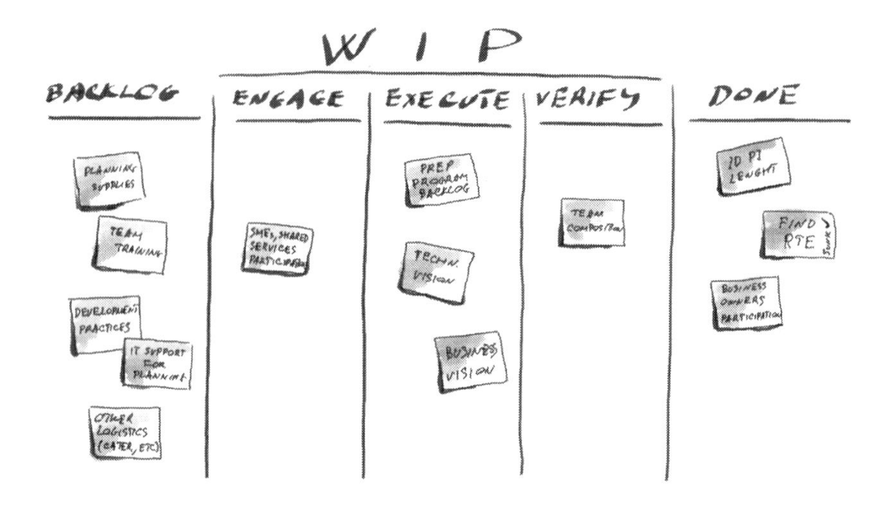

We built the board based on a simple observation: pretty much everything the Transformation Team does requires other people *outside* the team. We realized that we needed to reflect that aspect of the workflow in the structure of our board. Therefore, we split our 'WIP' step into three subservient steps: 'Engage' – for engaging those other stakeholders, subject matter experts, and so on; 'Execute' – for having them actually do what was required by a particular backlog item; and 'Verify' – which was for us to make sure that the result was what we wanted. This way we were able to see if, for example, an item got stuck because somebody outside the Transformation Team dropped the ball.

The prep was actually going quite smoothly. We quickly agreed on the cadence and identified all of the roles that were essential to a successful ART launch and execution. We decided that it would be wise to have one of the Transformation Team members take over the role of the Release Train Engineer. We also identified the Product Manager – the person with the ultimate authority over the program backlog. And we had two architects supporting the program and a few UX people. Ed and Nathan agreed to join Zach and Nerissa as part of the business owners team. Adi suggested that we have the entire Transformation Team in the room during the PI planning for educational purposes, and, if we would like to invite observers from other programs, that would be a very good idea as well. The practical reality of large-scale rollouts is such that demonstrating a process in action is the best way to propagate the method to others. People are sometimes resistant to change because they experience fear of the unknown. Having them observe how it works on a sister program is the best way to inspire confidence in the method. But also, as Adi said, "Make them jealous that their peers are doing something dangerously cool. Nothing drives large-scale adoption better than that." And even if it sounded like a joke in the beginning, I quickly realized that it's not a joke at all. All eleven observers, except one, had accepted the invitation to the PI planning. And the one that didn't had been previously scheduled to attend a tradeshow.

We didn't have much trouble addressing the team structure either: the teams had their key roles embedded, including Product Owner, Scrum Master, and developers and testers. We also took care of the logistics for the event: a big room was reserved ahead of time and supplies were taken care of, too. VeraComm is actually quite good at things like that.

Everything was going great, until we got to the program backlog. And that's where a big surprise happened. Olga, the product manager who appeared to be active during the training and fully onboard with Lean and Agile, suddenly began demonstrating a different attitude and things started to fall apart.

"*All* of these features are important," said Olga to Sunil, the Transformation Team member who took over the role of the Release Train Engineer, or RTE. You could tell by her tone of voice that she had started to lose her temper. Sunil clearly felt embarrassed by this unnecessary conflict. Additionally, there were two people from engineering. I'm not sure why we needed them, but Adi insisted on bringing in a few technical folks, so Sunil had no choice but to invite them.

"We can't select a subset from the backlog where everything is of highest priority," countered Sunil. "It's not helpful."

"*Arguing* about this is not helpful," said Olga. "I know this scope. I know how important it is."

Sunil was clearly stuck. He can be super insistent when needed, which is great, but he obviously sensed that pushing Olga any further would be counter-productive. At the same time, he was puzzled in terms of what to do next – how to keep the long backlog from slipping into the PI planning. Luckily, Adi jumped in.

"Olga, obviously the functionality that you have here on the screen is critical. I wonder if you could help me understand the nature of that importance in each particular case?"

"Yeah..." began Olga, not exactly sure what was being asked of her.

"Maybe we could take a few minutes and prioritize the features based on the cost of delay? Like we did during the training..."

"I don't know how you guys did that during the training. I was out for most of the morning of the second day," said Olga, shrugging.

That's right. I remember now that she wasn't there. She had a bunch of back-to-back meetings that morning, which explains a lot.

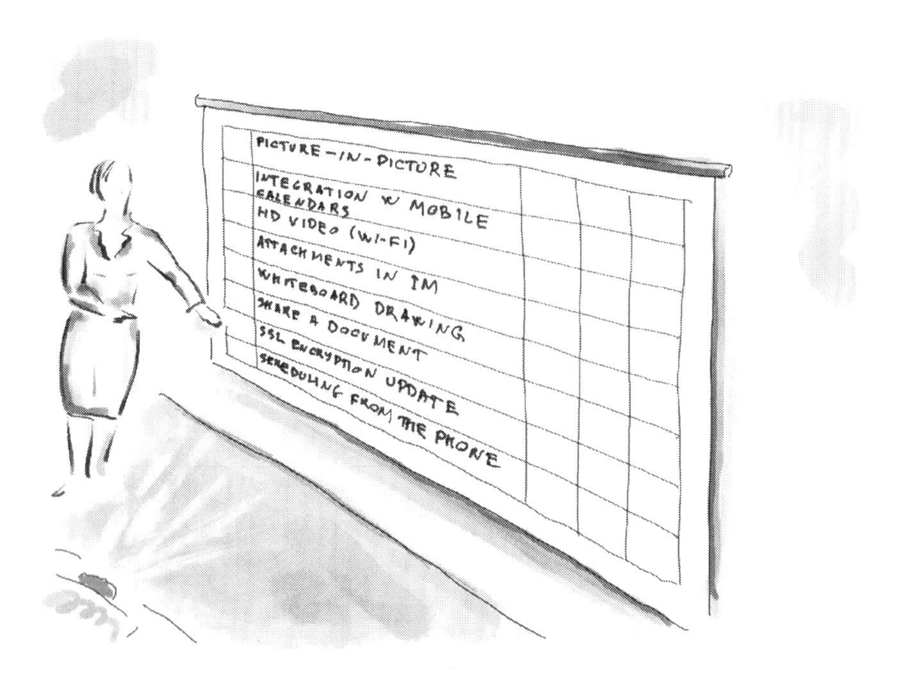

"Okay, but that should not prevent us from succeeding with this exercise," said Adi, approaching the projector screen. "Is it fair to say that all the features which you have on the screen should be delivered sooner rather than later?"

Olga nodded.

"That's good. Now, Olga, let me ask you a question: what exactly happens if these features are delayed?"

Olga looked up at the ceiling for a second, then at her list, and then back up at the ceiling.

"Well, different things would happen," she said. "Some features are strictly to catchup with the competition, and we are already late there - delivering those ASAP is critical. Another one is actually a security update due to SSL vulnerability, so you can probably guess the importance of that. A few of the other ones are new, and we'd like to push them to production as soon as possible, because that's an opportunity for us to get a bit ahead of the competition..."

"Okay, I think I've got the idea. Delaying those features is highly undesirable because they deliver certain user value, are time-sensitive, and may provide future opportunities, correct?"

"Yeah, that is correct," confirmed Olga.

"So, if I represented the cost of delaying a feature as a combination of those three factors, would that be a good approximation?"

"Yes."

"Olga, could you please create three new columns to the right of your list of features?" Adi asked, pointing at the screen. "And let's add the following titles to those: User (or Business) Value, Time Criticality and Opportunity Enablement."

Olga did exactly as she was told and gave Adi a 'now what' look.

"Let's start with the last column, Olga," continued Adi. "Which of the features has the lowest Opportunity Enablement?"

"The lowest?" Olga reconfirmed, and took some time to think. She scrolled back and forth through the list until her cursor stopped next to a specific row. "Attachments in IM, I would say. It's valuable to the end user, but once done, there's not much we can build on top of it."

"Great," said Adi. "So, let's assume that Opportunity Enablement for this feature will be our base, our unit of measurement, a 'one.' How much more future opportunity would 'Picture-in-Picture' provide then?"

"Oh," said Olga, "Much more. I would say three times as much as 'Attachments.' The thing is, that 'Picture-in-Picture' allows you to do much more with your tablet while being on a call. We believe that it will be our gateway to even more interesting features in the future. Also, nobody else is doing it yet, so if we are the first ones to implement it, we are going to earn some points for sure."

"Why don't you go over the rest of the features and do the same, and each time you decide on a number, just enter it into that column. And while doing so, try using a sequence that is slightly different than 1, 2, 3, 4, 5, ... etc. We call it a 'Fibonacci sequence' and it goes as follows: 1, 2, 3, 5, 8, 13, 21, ... Each number being a sum of the previous two. The progressive nature of the sequence prevents us from getting a false sense of accuracy..."

FEATURE	USER VALUE	TIME CRIT.	OPPORT. ENBL'MT			
PICTURE-IN-PICTURE			3			
INTEGRATION W MOBILE CALENDARS			2			
HD VIDEO (WI-FI)			2			
ATTACHMENTS IN IM			1			
WHITEBOARD DRAWING			8			
SHARE A DOCUMENT			13			
SSL ENCRYPTION UPDATE			1			
SCHEDULING FROM THE PHONE			3			
UX PARITY (DESKTOP–MOBILE)			2			

"I see," said Olga, starting her exercise. It took her about five minutes to go over all of the features in the list.

"How about Time Criticality now?" asked Adi. "Could you do the same as you did for Opportunity Enablement: find a feature with the smallest time criticality and then do the rest of them relative to that one?"

Olga began doing that and was done in about the same amount of time. "I guess I'm going to do the same thing with the first column now?" she asked, and began the same procedure without actually waiting for Adi's response. The User Value column took her a little longer, but in about ten minutes she had done all three columns for all of the features on her list. "What now?"

FEATURE	USER VALUE	TIME CRIT.	OPPORT. ENBLMT			
PICTURE-IN-PICTURE	5	5	3			
INTEGRATION W MOBILE CALENDARS	2	2	2			
HD VIDEO (WI-FI)	3	3	2			
ATTACHMENTS IN IM	1	2	1			
WHITEBOARD DRAWING	8	5	8			
SHARE A DOCUMENT	8	5	13			
SSL ENCRYPTION UPDATE	5	13	1			
SCHEDULING FROM THE PHONE	5	3	3			
UX PARITY (DESKTOP-MOBILE)	2	1	2			

"Add them up," said Adi. "Create another column, call it Cost of Delay, or CoD for short, and fill it out."

About ten seconds later Olga had built the CoD column and summed up all the values from the previous three.

FEATURE	USER VALUE	TIME CRIT.	OPPORT. ENABL'T	CoD		
PICTURE-IN-PICTURE	5	5	3	13		
INTEGRATION W MOBILE CALENDARS	2	2	2	6		
HD VIDEO (WI-FI)	3	3	2	8		
ATTACHMENTS IN IM	1	2	1	4		
WHITEBOARD DRAWING	8	5	8	21		
SHARE A DOCUMENT	8	5	13	26		
SSL ENCRYPTION UPDATE	5	13	1	19		
SCHEDULING FROM THE PHONE	5	3	3	11		
UX PARITY (DESKTOP-MOBILE)	2	1	2	5		

"Interesting," she said, scrolling across the backlog.

"What exactly is interesting, Olga?"

"...The way this cost of delay thing works. It's actually different for different features," said Olga, continuing to scroll back and forth. "So, let me guess," she said, "the ones with the highest cost of delay are the most important ones, right?"

"Not exactly," said Adi.

"What?" Olga said, visibly frustrated that the process took so much effort, but in the end did not seem to offer the desired answer. "Then why was I doing all this... stuff?" she asked, waving her hands around the laptop keyboard.

"We have only figured the *cost* of delay of these features relative to each other," continued Adi, "but we did not address the question of *how much* of a delay each feature will experience."

Olga looked at Adi for a few seconds without saying anything.

Adi proceeded: "What if your 'Picture-in-Picture' with the cost of delay of 13, would be delivered, for instance, in six months instead of two?"

"I see," nodded Olga. "The total cost of delay that the feature experiences would be three times as big. So, the time it takes to deliver a feature matters too, then?"

"Yes it does," said Adi. "On the one hand, you certainly want to start working on features that have the highest cost of delay. On the other hand, if any such feature takes a long time to develop, it will cause other features to wait a long time before even getting started, thus adding to their total cost of delay. That's why we are looking for a balance between cost of delay of a feature and the duration it takes to develop. We give preference to features with high cost of delay and low duration, which is expressed in a simple formula for feature priority: CoD divided by Duration."

"So now we need to find out the durations for these features," said Olga, creating one more column in the spreadsheet.

"I would suggest that before you do, we simplify a little bit. Actual durations may be a little difficult to figure. I recommend using *size* instead, as it is generally proportional to the duration and we know how to easily estimate that."

For the next fifteen minutes, the two guys from engineering provided some rough feature size estimates, basically following the exact same procedure as with the other columns. They picked what they thought was the smallest feature, and then estimated all other features relative to that one.

"Now that we have all the data we need," said Adi, "we can create the last column for the ratio of CoD and Size. We call this number Weighted Shortest Job First, or WSJF. So let's calculate it."

"That is interesting," said Olga. She finished with all the calculations and moved her cursor to 'Whiteboard drawing' feature. "I was expecting it to be my top feature or close to it. But now I see why it didn't make it to the very top: it's valuable and yet it's too big. So it seems everything that is too big will be 'penalized'? If that is the case, we will never deliver some features in our backlog."

FEATURE	USER VALUE	TIME CRIT.	OPPORT. ENBL'NT	CoD	SIZE	WSJF
PICTURE-IN-PICTURE	5	5	3	13	2	6.5
INTEGRATION W MOBILE CALENDARS	2	2	2	6	3	2
HD VIDEO (WI-FI)	3	3	2	8	3	2.7
ATTACHMENTS IN IM	1	2	1	4	1	4
WHITEBOARD DRAWING	8	5	8	21	5	4.2
SHARE A DOCUMENT	8	5	13	26	5	5.2
SSL ENCRYPTION UPDATE	5	13	1	19	2	9.5
SCHEDULING FROM THE PHONE	5	3	3	11	1	11
UX PARITY (DESKTOP-MOBILE)	2	1	2	5	5	1

"Not necessarily," Sunil said, jumping in. "I think I understand what the real problem is here. Let me ask you, Olga: what did you assume would be built as part of that feature in terms of the actual functionality?"

"Well, basic shapes, colors, different line thickness and style, erase function, etc."

"Ok – I see why it's not as high as you might have thought it should be," said Sunil. "Correct me if I'm wrong here, but the actual value of this feature is that it allows you to draw something while sharing your screen."

"Yes," said Olga.

"But then," continued Sunil, "it looks like all the functionality beyond basic drawing adds a lot of development effort, but much less total value. It's like a bunch of very expensive bells and whistles..."

Olga looked puzzled, but a moment later turned to the engineers and asked, "How much smaller do you guys think the feature would be if we just did basic drawing, black-and-white, fixed pen width?"

"I would say, maybe 25% of initial size," said one of the guys.

Olga turned back to the screen and looked at it for a few moments. "Yes, that's right," she said, pointing to the feature on the list. "If the denominator was four times smaller, it would significantly raise the WSJF value for this feature." She was quiet for a little longer and then said, "This is actually working very well... I like this WSJF thing a lot!" She looked around at Sunil and the rest of us: "You guys are not so hopeless after all..."

• • •

The preparation was almost over. We had a few days to finalize a couple more things which were mostly minor concerns. We knew that most of the work was done, and we could actually see the results: the program backlog was prepared, the business owners finished working on their presentations for the vision briefings, the team structure was addressed, various small adjustments were made, and all the program roles were assigned. Another important factor was having an RTE, Sunil, who was driving the overall preparation under Adi's guidance. The entire Transformation Team was assisting Sunil in every possible way–we had no higher priority than that.

"Just a few more to go," said Sunil, looking at the stickies left in the 'Backlog' step of the Transformation Team status board. As a team, we got into a rhythm of daily standups during the preparation to the 'Mobile Solutions' ART launch, and that proved to be a useful habit. It appeared that the more we got into it, the better we came to understand the key focus areas of the Transformation Team as such. Despite our first impression, the subject of process transformation turned out to be just the tip of the iceberg. The real subject was much deeper and harder to address. The true underlying issues were people, mindset, culture...

How did we come to know this? Because after the glitch that we had with Olga, we soon ran into another one. This time however, it wasn't a single person, but dozens of people. And of course it just had to happen when Adi wasn't with us: she had travelled back home to spend a few days with her family before the actual ART launch.

The last remaining backlog item that Sunil pulled into the 'WIP' area was 'Development Practices'. In all honesty, I have no idea why we put it on the back burner. Maybe that's how our brains work sometimes: they create blind spots that allow us to walk right into the problem which, if we were only a little bit more rigorous in our thinking, wouldn't have a remote chance of survival. But yes, I have the best hindsight out there, that's for sure. As my dad used to say: 'Running into a problem is inevitable. What matters is how you make your way out.' And it was the latter part of that maxim which we were struggling with the most.

To tell you the truth, I was never too psyched about our programs' ability to integrate and test. I guess that was one reason why Adi's original conference talk was right on the money for me. When she presented the basic rules of the Agile Release Train, the most memorable of which was the fact that the entire system has to iterate, it hit me right between the eyes. Well, how can you iterate as a whole if you don't frequently integrate? That's right, you can't...

"...We *are* integrating," said a developer that Sunil and I had invited for a quick discussion (along with a couple of other people from different teams). "We have an integration environment and we perform integration as a common routine. What makes you think that we don't?"

"I'm not sure," I said, trying to focus on what I knew about their actual process. These conversations with developers can sometimes unexpectedly develop into real holy wars. And these guys have had those wars in the past, triggered, by... well, by nobody knows what, to be honest. One recent example that comes to mind was this stupid dispute about which universe is better – the one where everything is written in Java, or the one where everything is in ObjectiveC. Nobody stays neutral: only wimps don't take a side in a debate like that. It seemed like it would last forever. But then something else, equally irrelevant, replaced it. So that's how they are... Other than that, it's an awesome, peaceful crowd. I know, because I come from inside those ranks. I have nothing but respect and awe for engineers, but today I am going to press on this topic of integration a little bit. And heck no, I'm not letting it degrade into any religious-like debate.

"It just surprises me," I continued, "that spotting defects is so difficult for some reason. Here's what I'm thinking guys: if the system is frequently integrated, most of the problems become visible upon a solid first inspection. I mean, correct me if I'm wrong, but it seems quite straightforward, doesn't it?"

The devs looked at each other with a smirk. "Integration is not for finding defects," said a developer with a long beard and braided hair. "That's why you have testing. Integration–I hate to be so obvious–is more for *integrating*. So, like I said, it sounds simple and stupid, but it's pretty obvious." He paused for a few seconds and continued: "Look, Ethan, there is daily build happening, and again, as much as I hate to resort to tautologies, it is happening on a daily basis. Who or what prevents our testers from taking it and knocking themselves dead testing it?"

"You are talking to the wrong guys, Ethan," said the other dev. "You should talk to the testers."

"Why does it feel like these guys have gotten away with it again?" Sunil said to me after the developers had left. He smiled. "I bet you, if we talk to the testers, we will hear a different story. Wanna bet?"

I don't want to bet. I just want us to be done with this and clear the way for the ART launch - that's what I really want. Yes, I do feel that something is wrong and it bothers me that I can't do anything about it so far, but we are going to proceed with the next step and see where it takes us.

"...Are you kidding me?" exclaimed Shruti, when we asked her why she thinks developers assume that it is testing where things really go wrong.

"Well, they think that the testers are not testing the builds early in the release cycle, despite the fact that those builds are being made available on a daily basis," I said to Shruti, hoping to get to the bottom of it with her help.

"On a daily basis?" she asked, becoming a bit agitated. "You know, we've heard this story before. That daily build system was set up some two years ago, if not more. At first we believed that it would actually work as advertised, and that we could test at will. And indeed, they would produce a build and we would test it and everything would generally be okay. Then they would produce another build and it would be okay too, and so on. This would continue up until late in the release cycle, and then suddenly stuff would begin to go wrong. Like really, really wrong. In the early part, those builds wouldn't even have much visible change in them at all, but later a violent influx of defects came along with loads of new functionality. If you want my honest opinion, I think our developers may be too idle for the bigger part of the release timeframe. I guess their conscience kicks in near the end of the release. I don't know how they get all of that functionality developed so fast at the end, but it's a fact: they do somehow. No wonder we have so many defects slip through..."

After talking to Shruti, Sunil and I decided to take a walk. The weather was beautiful. It was a little windy: just enough for the currents of air to comb the curly clouds and spread them along the horizon. The part of the sky that was covered with lengthy patches of clouds looked too colorful to be real. The palette that the wind splashed on the sky was fascinating, no matter how much pressure our work had created that day. I could just walk and know that all the trouble in the world could be cured by a single touch of the impeccable beauty unfolding high in the sky above us.

"Beautiful, isn't it Sunil?" I asked, magnetized by the view.

"What's so beautiful about being stuck?" asked Sunil, checking something on his phone.

"The view, I mean. Just look."

Sunil looked up for a second or two and turned back to me. "Adi just responded to my text from earlier today. She's in the mountains with her husband. She said that they were so deep in the boonies that this is the first time she has had cell phone coverage. Obviously, that didn't last too long." He said, putting the phone back in his pocket. "We are on our own, boss."

Well, so what have we learned? Not much, except that developers blame testers and testers blame developers. "Hey Sunil, you know what I don't like about this whole story?"

"I have no idea. It would be great to hear it," said Sunil.

"You know what bothers me even more than the fact that we don't know what's really happening with those builds?"

"No, no, Ethan. I don't know."

"Would you stop goofing around. I'm being serious. Do you want to know?"

"I can barely contain myself," said Sunil, with a fake serious expression on his face.

"The very fact that this blame game is happening just seems so wrong to me. You know what I don't understand? How is it that we put devs and testers on each Agile team a long time ago and now, three years later, they are still playing the blame game? I mean, just from a common sense perspective: does that sound like real team spirit to you?"

"You know, it does not really surprise me," said Sunil. "Based on my observations, even though developers and testers are assigned to each team, you don't see them hanging out together much. I went to some of their iteration planning sessions a while back and attended sessions for a few different teams. The way they planned the iteration was so bizarre. Imagine: they are in the same room, but they don't really plan together. They split stories into separate tasks for development and testing, and then reason about those and estimate them separately. There's never even a decent conversation between devs and testers on the same team..."

"Yeah, that doesn't sound right! Don't you think that if we launch the train but fail to address this issue, the teams will still remain pretty dysfunctional? In that case, what's the point of all this work?

"I'm not disagreeing, but how are we going to do it? Are you gonna wait until Adi arrives?"

"Not necessarily. I'm very eager to dig a little deeper into the mystery of builds. Why do those builds not change much during the substantial part of the release timeframe, but then have a massive turn later in the process? I can't help thinking that there might be some Parkinson's Law-like effect with those guys."

"Yeah, that may be true. The release cycle is typically quite long, so I totally see how that may create some false sense of comfort, resulting in the uneven spread of effort across the iterations."

"Here's what we'll do: could you please get all of our Scrum Masters together for a quick conversation? Let's talk to them. Not in the form of blame or anything; I just want to know if they can confirm our hypothesis here."

Sunil froze for a second with his phone in his hands. Only his thumbs were moving, frantically working the keypad. Then said, "Let's go back. I asked everyone who is available to come to our office. They shouldn't have any special meetings at this time of day... Not that I know of."

The thought that we may be two steps away from having discovered major inefficiency in our organization was in fact quite fascinating. That alone, if fixed, would significantly improve our ability to deliver. The thought of closing the deal so easily was escalating in my brain with every step up the stairs headed to our floor – the 'humility floor' as Sunil used to call it. Gosh, it's actually great that we got to witness all of that blame game today – it made us think about the potential root causes.

"This is a joke, right Sunil?" said one of the Scrum Masters after Sunil had carefully outlined our hypothesis.

"Yeah," said Sunil with a smirk on his face. "I just couldn't resist pulling you guys away from what you were doing because I have a great joke to run by you. Yup! That's how you do it."

"I think he is serious, Roy," said the other one. "Well ok, let's be serious then. You know what, I'm with my guys every iteration, every standup meeting. I see what is happening first hand, so trust me on what I'm going to tell you. Nobody's perfect on my team. And yet, every day there's a lot going on. They produce new stuff pretty much on a daily basis. I can't say that I see much difference in productivity throughout the release. And, truth be told, releasing is always stressful. But work-wise, those guys bust their humps all the time."

"Same here," said Roy. "Trisha, our Product Owner actually has quite a bit of new functionality to review at every iteration demo."

Well, that just makes no sense at all. But, these guys are not lying. It just doesn't compute.

"Let's schedule another meeting with devs," I said to Sunil as we finished the discussion with the Scrum Masters. "We need to get to the bottom of this. There is some kind of a mystery here that I must understand."

"No kidding," said Sunil. "I will send it out for tomorrow morning since it's 4:35 now, if you hadn't noticed. I think we should probably get testers in as well: that will get us to the crux of it much faster."

"Agreed. Let's get them in too."

On the way home, I kept thinking about the puzzle – I couldn't help it. In a way it's actually great that Adi is off for a couple of days. Sunil and I need to solve this problem. We have to be able to solve things like this, otherwise we will always be dependent on external consultants for basic things like... *thinking*. And that's absolutely not the goal that I have for this organization.

Rachel and I are going to watch 'The Martian' tonight. This time it will be at home. Who said you can't have popcorn at home? We like going to the cinema a lot, but sometimes a little change-up doesn't hurt. The TV is next to the window that faces northwest, which in the evening displays a very gentle streak of ambient, slowly dissolving sunlight. Catching that in your peripheral view when watching TV creates something magical. We both know it and we both love it.

"You are surprisingly on time," said Rachel, smiling and handing me a pack of popcorn. "Organic, non-GMO."

I think I would be dead by now, with my natural propensity to eat unhealthy food, if it wasn't for Rachel pointing me in the right direction every time. Or I might have three legs or perhaps one more head growing out of my shoulders or something...

"How's work?" I asked her, knowing that often my brain becomes occupied with my stuff, and I sometimes forget the simple things that matter most. Her job can be quite unnerving too. At some point, I realized that despite the fact that we were married, we were not really trying to understand each other better. I wasn't... at least.

The movie started and Rachel told me about a new piece of research that she's taking on and how much pressure there is because of the organization that funds the research, and how everybody gets edgy because of that. I think I know all her colleagues by name now. I've never seen them in person, but I know a lot about them. Sarah who always shows up late and leaves early; George that's a horrible team player, but smart as hell. I could go on and on: it's a lot of people, actually. I need this process with her. It proves that I'm not entirely self-contained and am willing to make a little room in my life for the person I care most about.

"Okay, enough of my job for the evening," said Rachel, pointing to the screen. "We can't pretend like we're watching a movie when in fact we're talking about academia and its ups and downs."

She has a good idea, only I'm not sure I can concentrate on the movie too much. My mind captures select snippets, but it's fully occupied with the problem, which I can't really seem to dissect. I wish I could problem-solve like Mark Watney and grow potatoes out of nothing.

Well, almost out of nothing. I wish cracking the puzzle with devs and testers was as easy as saving an astronaut stuck on Mars. That's the difference with real-life problems: *they are hard*.

"That wasn't bad, was it?" I asked Rachel, while she was still finishing her popcorn.

"'I'm gonna have to science the shit out of this'," she said in a funny voice, and then laughed. "You know what is wrong with it though?"

"What? The physics? Storms like that in the thin Mars atmosphere?"

"No, no. That's not what I meant," she said, with a totally serious expression. "Put yourself or anyone you know in his shoes. How would you feel if you were abandoned on another planet? How much of a sense of humor would you have left?"

Interesting. It is really interesting that I immediately thought about the special effects and other things like that, while she thought about a completely different type of reality – the one that is in our heads. Of course, she's right. I think any person would be deeply depressed and wouldn't seem as jolly as Watney.

Now, this is really interesting. If this is my default way of thinking, how much very important stuff did I miss out by considering everything but the human component? The way people perceive things is truly important. In a sense, it is the most important thing there is.

• • •

I had about ten minutes before the meeting and decided to run by the kitchen. "Oh look who's here – the Fourth Horseman of Transformation," said Raymond with a smirk on his face. He has that expression every morning until he either shoots off a nasty joke, or shares some unique news that nobody else in the organization knows but him.

"That's really funny, Raymond," I said, filling up my coffee cup.

"So, what are you working on?" he asked.

"Well. Preparing for launching the method in 'Mobile Solutions.'"

"Yeah, you guys are launching in what? Four days?"

Gosh, I forgot whom I'm talking to. "Raymond, if you know it already, then why do you ask?"

"Well, I don't know all the details. I've just heard the date, is all."

"Well, to answer your question about how it's going: it's going. We have some roadblocks, but overall we are moving inevitably toward the goal. How are you guys doing?"

"Well, business as usual." He looked around, "the whole thing with lay-offs is hanging over our heads, but nothing has started yet in that regard. It sucks to be sitting on a time bomb like this. Not that you would understand, Mr. just-promoted."

Yeah, the upcoming lay-offs... Why would Raymond remind me of that? Despite the fact that I know my newly created transformation team is in the clear, I feel really bad for engineering: some people will lose their jobs. I picture being in their shoes, and it's just horrible. Instead of coming home and having a good conversation with my wife and watching a movie, I would have to explain why we have to tighten our belts and switch to a different mode of spending. That wouldn't be any good, even though I'm sure Rachel would understand and support me in doing what I'm doing. It suddenly reminded me of one of my first jobs, actually my very first job as a programmer in a small company. Once their only customer started to experience serious challenges, they had to lay-off half of their employees, and I was in that half. I was too junior to be indispensable and I remember our team leader taking me out for a cup of coffee and telling me that I was among the first people to be laid off. I still recall the bitterness of that feeling, even though the lay-off ironically played a very positive role in my life, by giving me a strong forward momentum–a real kick in the butt, actually. It helped me succeed in situations where I would probably otherwise be helpless and entirely unprepared. But that doesn't change the fact that losing a job is always scary. I feel compelled to do whatever I can to help prevent or at least minimize that disruption. I think if we launched 'Mobile Solutions' ART and showed some results early on, it might convince the 'gods' to pull the plug on this terrible idea of layoffs. Raymond's folks will for sure be affected and we both know that. I feel for him.

"Any big initiatives in your world?" I asked.

"Well, yeah. The hardware teams are going through a tooling upgrade on the CAD side. That's taking up quite a bit of our time at the moment. You know, new tools assume a slightly different workflow, and we want to make sure that the way we set them up would make it convenient for them to–"

"Wait, wait, wait!" I said, feeling my pulse begin to elevate and my patience to suddenly disappear entirely.

"Wait what?" asked Raymond.

"Do you remember when you guys were setting up the daily build system for the software folks?"

"Well, not everything off the top of my head, but yeah, kind of. Every program got their Git set up for version control, as far as I remember. But then different programs insisted on using different CI tools. Why do you ask?"

"Do you know who would remember the setup detail for 'Mobile Solutions' and what they were optimizing for when setting up those environments? I bet it wasn't a single act, was it?"

Raymond began browsing through something on his phone. "You're right, it wasn't. We sustained that setup for quite a while, keeping an eye on it and tuning it up as needed until the tooling was well aligned with the actual process that the devs wanted. And yes," he said, putting the phone against his ear, "there will even be some notes in our communication tool about that, not to mention the standard configuration logs that are done every time."

As soon as someone responded on the other end of the line, he said: "Jess, could you please grab your laptop and find me in the kitchen? Thanks," and hung up. "Jess was the one who probably spent most of the time with 'Mobile Solutions' back then. I'm sure she will be able to help."

It took Jess a few minutes to show up in the kitchen.

"Oh, those guys? I see..." said Jess as Raymond explained what we needed from her. "Yes, I actually remember quite well."

"Jess, I'm trying to better understand what you guys were optimizing for when setting up the environments. I am currently working with this program in preparation for the next step in their process improvement, and would like to know more about their build process."

"Sure," said Jess. "They asked for an environment where they would be able to perform integration, so we spent some time with them to make sure they were comfortable creating new branches."

"New branches?" That sounded really interesting.

"Yes, they would create branches for every feature. We were working side-by-side with them, creating the scripts to facilitate the merging process: dependencies and other things, you know? They intended to do it frequently, so we couldn't call our job done until that process was fully set up and validated."

I don't get it. This makes no freaking sense. If they are working like mules and frequently merging their branches, I don't have a clue how is it that we have this influx of new functionality close to the end of each release. It just doesn't add up. It's like those guys are cursed: they do everything right, but the result is completely wrong. It can't be!

"Jess, could you do me a favor and describe the workflow in a little bit more detail? Especially what you guys were automating as part of it?"

"Yeah, there's not too much to it though. It's quite simple - let me try drawing it," she said, picking up a napkin.

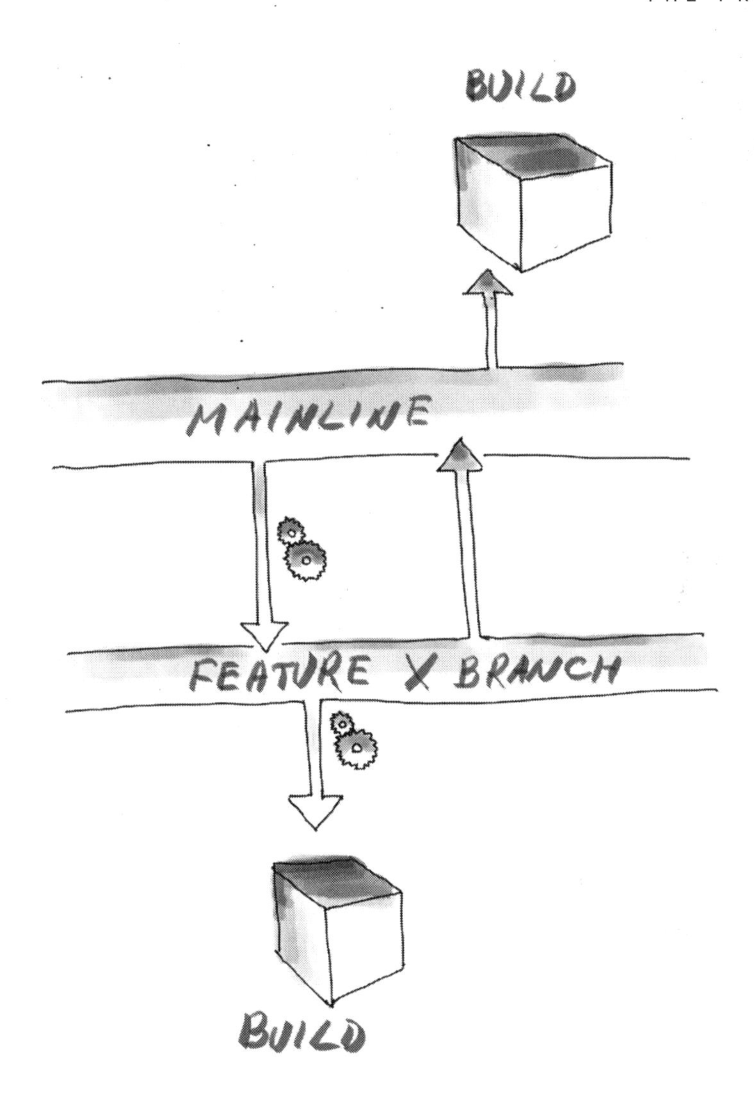

"The arrows show the direction in which source code moves," she explained.

"And this little thingy on the arrow?" I asked, pointing at the little cogs.

"That indicates that we did a great deal of automation to facilitate that step. You know, moving code and all the dependencies... And then we made sure that every developer could actually perform the basic smoke test for the build."

"Okay, hold on Jess, something looks weird to me in this picture."

Jess looked a bit confused: "What do you mean?–"

"Oh, there you are!" said Sunil, standing in the kitchen doorway. "The meeting has started, boss. Everyone is waiting for you."

"Come sit with us a sec, Sunil." I said, pushing the napkin in his direction.

"What's this?" he asked.

"This is the answer to our problem, Sunil." I said, barely able to contain my laughter. "This is the current workflow that 'Mobile Solutions' teams use to integrate their work across the board. The arrows show the direction in which code revisions move and these little cogs indicate significant automation effort to facilitate the flow."

Sunil stared at the picture for a while. Jess and Raymond looked puzzled, but didn't interrupt.

Suddenly Sunil jumped up from his chair and grabbed his head. "Un-freaking-believeable! But that explains everything!"

"Including the blame game," I confirmed. "Both the developers and the testers were telling the truth."

"U-n-b-e-l-i-e-v-a-b-l-e," said Sunil again, grabbing the napkin and disappearing through the doorway.

What a great morning! I feel like I just reached Mars' escape velocity and am racing towards my rescue ship. In your face, Mark Watney!

"What the heck just happened?" asked Raymond, who had obviously had enough mystery for one day. "Care to explain what all of that was about?" He pointed with his thumb back to the door where Sunil, fully charged and ready to move mountains, had just vanished.

"What was the model on the picture optimized for? Like literally, what could you do fast and easy?" I asked the two of them.

"Check out from the Mainline into a feature branch," said Jess.

"Correct. And what is not so fast and not very easy in that picture?"

"Checking it back in?" said Jess, staring at the wall. "But that is... that doesn't..."

"It doesn't add up too well, does it?" I asked, realizing that she was very close. "Every team is checking code *out* of the Mainline all the time, but barely anybody is checking stuff *back in*."

"So that means that the real change is only happening in the individual feature branches, while the main branch remains pretty dry most of the time," said Raymond, finally understanding what was going on. "Wow..."

"Yep. It remains dry until they get close to the release date," I said. "And that's where the real hell begins: they start merging their branches into the main one, causing enormous disruption and taking a huge amount of time to resolve all of the inconsistencies that have accumulated over the course of the release. By that time, every branch has grown into a universe of its own. And when all of those universes collide in the end, stuff gets ugly in epic proportions."

ETHAN'S DIARY

- *You can never be perfect with the prep to the ART launch. And you shouldn't. It's not the starting point that matters as much as it is the ability to continuously, at regular intervals, improve the train as a whole.*
- *Driving transformation is a tough job. Therefore members of the Transformation Team must have the courage to cope with the impediments, be restless and, in some ways, selfless.*
- *A Transformation Team must have strong ties to programs and key stakeholders.*
- *Invite observers from other programs to the first ART launch, especially to the PI planning. Being part of the action automatically answers a lot of questions and eliminates reservations.*
- *When organizing leadership training, make sure participants understand that they need to absolutely clear their calendars for two days. Otherwise it will be like it was with Olga, who missed the most important thing due to other meetings.*
- *Understanding the challenges with the current ways of working can be really tricky, and may take quite a bit of an effort on the part of the Transformation Team. It requires direct communication with the people that perform the work.*
- *When there are multiple 'truths' at the same time, automatically look for fragmentation and local optimization as a root case. It sits somewhere right in front of your eyes. Gosh, I still can't believe we cracked that nut...*

CHAPTER 6
The Launch

"To our eye it's just a leaf, but there is a lot more happening inside."

–ETHAN'S DAD

I GUESS ADI WAS RIGHT when she said that you can never be perfectly ready for an ART launch. We certainly weren't and that's okay. From what I observed at the PI boundary of 'Silver Arrow'–the train Adi took me to observe–the ability to continuously inspect and adapt is far more important than trying to have a perfect launching.

The ART launch itself is a relatively simple process that took us just a single week. Adi called it the QuickStart method of launching. The first two days are to train the teams on how to best operate as part of the train. Right after that the first PI planning basically gets the train started on a common cadence. And as for day five, well, we reserved it for different workshops with Adi; mostly to help us better understand how to go about PI execution.

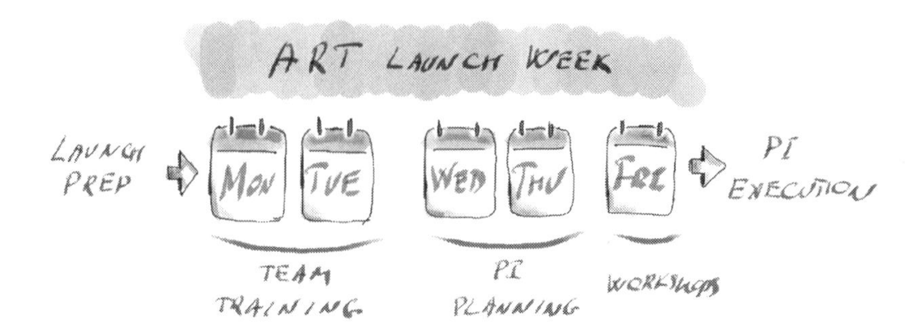

Sunil and I finalized the preparation and Adi returned and conducted the team training. In the beginning, the teams didn't even want to hear about any training, suggesting that they are already Agile and that there is no reason to waste time 'becoming Agile again'. It took a little bit of effort from Sunil and I to get them into the training room, but the result was quite surprising.

First of all, there was plenty of interesting information in Adi's team training that they hadn't been exposed to before. For example, discussion of the Principles. I remember how helpful the Principles were when we had a leadership class. That was where Olga and Nathan began to understand why Lean and flow are important. I didn't really expect, however, that the Principles would be of such great importance to the teams, but they were. In fact, tenets like 'Apply Systems Thinking' were of incredible value to those guys. We badly needed to move away from over-emphasizing individual teams and instead consider a different construct – Agile Release Train that can deliver end-to-end value. The 'Visualize and Limit WIP' caused quite a heated discussion between developers and testers. Once internalized, it allowed them to more clearly see how internal bottlenecks in the system may sit there for a long time, preventing the team from improving their throughput. But these bottlenecks would remain undetected under too much Work-In-Process.

Secondly, it turned out that things weren't nearly as great with the current process as the teams had thought. Quite a few teams were constantly delaying demos. Some teams, in fact, weren't showing anything in their 'demos', but simply reporting completion of their stories. Iterations were being largely 'waterfalled' by everybody. And while it may sound extremely weird that Agile teams would 'waterfall' the iteration, it's actually not as hard to believe as one might think. Here is how it happens for the teams: they work with large stories, they start with the development of all stories at the same time, and they test all developed stories when they are available (which is almost always at the very end of the iteration). As a result, they rarely make the stories fit. No wonder other things, like sticking to the iteration timebox or having a regular iteration demo, weren't working out either. For example, you obviously can't have a demo at the iteration boundary because there's simply nothing to demo.

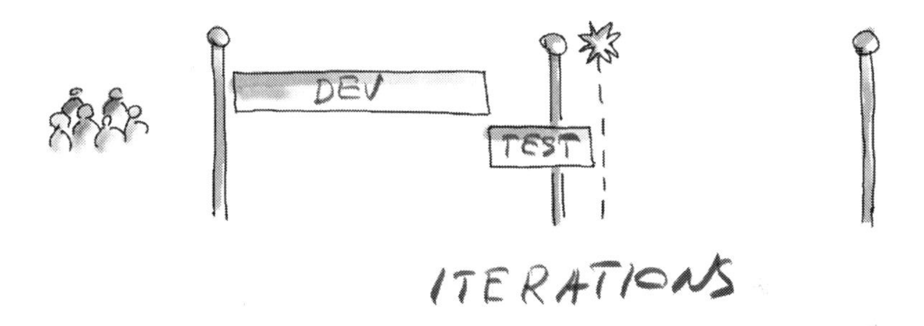

To address the problem of 'mini-waterfalls', Adi spent a lot of time with the teams on splitting stories. Every team experimented with story splitting at least to some degree. And other than a little problem with two engineering managers who didn't seem to really get it–quite frankly it looked more like they just didn't *want* to think differently–it was a good first attempt. "It happens," said Adi, "that sometimes people don't get this at once. We'll revisit the topic of splitting stories again soon, I'm sure - specifically, when executing iterations. Our goal however is clear: a few smaller stories at a time. Even if a team has problems with the iteration, they can still finish on time and have a bigger part of the iteration scope developed and tested."

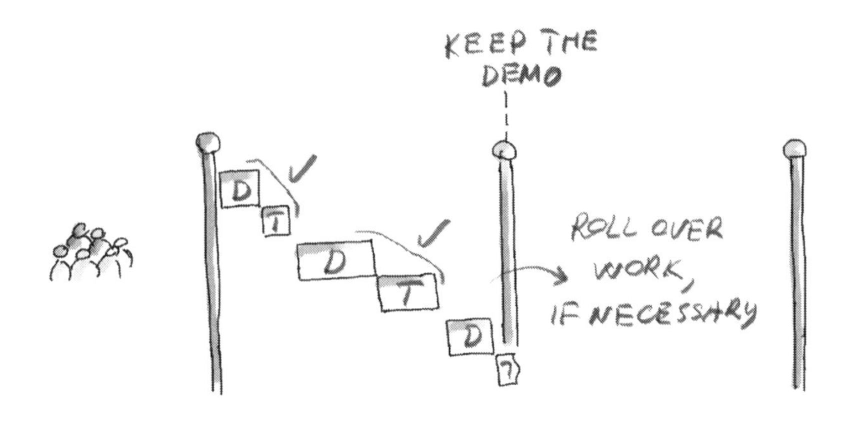

It was a real benefit that we had all the teams in the same big room for two full days of training. They all received the same message from the same instructor. Because the best way to scale something is to start by delivering the same message to all of the teams about the new method.

Engineering practices, which we also touched upon during the training, were a whole separate deal. A few days earlier when we had figured out the problem with the late merge, Sunil had a very honest conversation with the developers. I joined that meeting shortly after Sunil had rushed to the meeting room with the diagram on the napkin, but I didn't have to do too much myself. As the RTE, Sunil took over and managed to move the needle after a long series of discussions and arguments. It's interesting how our brains work: we sometimes develop incredibly big blindspots, which magically hide things that we don't want to account for. Rachel clued me in by bringing up a quote from a great French scientist, which has stuck with me ever since: 'As long as I do not see that I'm blind, I'm blind.' How can you otherwise explain that people who perform enormously sophisticated work on a daily basis–really smart people–can remain blind to such a simple thing as late merge (now a problem so blatantly obvious in hindsight). They have agreed to do something about it though, and that's good. More specifically, all teams on the train will merge their feature branches into the main branch at least once per iteration. That is absolutely mandatory regardless of the team, the area of the solution they work on, or the features they currently have inflight. Adi also suggested that we make sure the teams allocate some time to merging features. The teams had a chance to discuss the extra time for merging during the training, too. Everyone agreed to allocate at least 5% more time in the iteration due to the merge. Sunil was especially excited about it, because we were no longer looking at feature branches that would live their independent lives for months without merging back in. Now, in hindsight, I can't imagine how this program was able to blindly and systematically check code out, but not check it back in. I'd like to forget that nightmare...

The time for PI planning has finally arrived. The big room was almost empty - only a couple of people had arrived, looking for places to sit and quickly finding the name tents that I had insisted we create, the same way the 'Silver Arrow' train had done. When I told the guys about the name trick–TeamName@TrainName–they decided that they also needed a fancy name like that for their train. And after much heated discussion–and with the eventual blessing from Ed–it was no longer 'Mobile Solutions' but became instead 'The Arkenstone'. I remembered Ed shrugging and saying, "Well, they can call themselves whatever they want. As long as they deliver, I will indulge their every caprice." Soon it became apparent that the choice of the name inadvertently opened Pandora's box: the teams changed their names to match the genre, which is how we got to 'Rivendell', 'Misty Mountains', 'Erebor', 'Rohan' and what not @Arkenstone.

More people began to gather in the room and some of the tables filled quickly, everyone curious about what would happen next on their new journey. Sunil was working with the IT admins on the projection equipment, while Adi was explaining something to the rest of the guys on the Transformation Team. Ed and Nathan came in, followed by Olga.

At 7:35 the caterer finished setting up the breakfast table–which turned out to be as long as three regular tables in a row–piled high with oatmeal, waffles, various fruits, different kinds of yogurt, and quite a few other things. These guys were obviously going to spoil us, that much was clear to me. The smell of coffee rolled into the big room, reaching the most distant corners and compelling the still sleepy people to stand up and walk, like zombies, towards the tables in the lobby.

Adi asked that the food stay outside. The reason as it turned out was very simple: we needed the room perimeter freed up for planning needs. I noticed that the 'Silver Arrow' train had used the heck out of their walls for this type of event, and it was quite helpful in their case; so we attempted the same thing. And to simplify everyone's life, Adi and two guys from the Transformation Team created a PI plan template on one of the walls. That way everyone would have an example to work from.

In the meantime, it seemed that everyone who needed to be here had arrived. Prior to the planning, we had reinforced the importance of punctuality with everyone: do what you gotta do, but you can't show up late to this event. And it looked like folks had gotten the message. At 7:56 we were nearly ready to get started.

"It looks like we are ready," said Sunil. "I will briefly introduce the context of the event and the first presenter." He put the printout of the agenda on my table.

"We gave every team a handout listing the same agenda. Please keep an eye on us, boss. If we divert from it – wave!" Sunil said, smiling. He stepped to the stage and did a last check of the microphone. Meanwhile, we had reached the top of the hour and our first agenda item.

8:00 Business Context

"Hello everyone!" said Sunil. "Hello, 'Arkenstone'!"

The group responded in a loud mixture of "Hello's", "Hi's" and "Good morning's".

"Welcome to our first PI planning event," he said, moving to the PI planning agenda slide in his presentation. "In order to align to a common vision as well as to the actual content of work, we will have a series of briefings this morning. The first one is Business Context. I would like to invite Zach, our Executive VP of Business Development, and Nerissa, Vice President of Enterprise Sales to come up. Please welcome our presenters."

The group applauded while Zach and Nerissa walked to the front of the room.

"Guys, Nerissa and I appreciate the opportunity to speak to you," said Zach. "I think you all know that VeraComm is currently going through some challenging times." He paused for a few seconds. "But I'm sure you have also heard the good news: our stock price has finally begun to show small but steady growth throughout the month."

"Yeah!" ... "Yeah!" People from different tables began to cheer.

"This is all good news and more is coming soon, I can promise you that. But there is one thing this company must do, and it just happens that the people in this room will be the ones to execute this mission." The room went completely quiet and Zach continued. "We must regain our customers' confidence. It is critical that they once again believe that we can deliver and that what we deliver is valuable, quality stuff."

Nerissa chimed in: "We need to prove to the market that our solutions can not only do what the others can do, but more importantly, that we are able to move ahead of the competition by creating the mobile conferencing experiences of the next generation."

During the course of the briefing they talked about a lot of interesting things, which most of the people in the audience had no clue about. That should not be surprising at all, because all we had before was a kind of 'telephone game': Zach would come up with an idea and then talk to someone in product line management. That person would then grab a product manager who was closest to that area of concern and speak with them. The product manager would then put together a meeting with the product owners of the affected teams and, eventually, the product owners would bring new backlog items to the iteration planning, where the engineers would actually see them for the first time. This 'telephone' chain would sometimes have as many as 5-7 links. It's hard to imagine how much valuable information was lost or was distorted, and how much junk was added to the initial idea along the way. Such a process is the surest way to bastardize any good idea in an enterprise. The inevitable result is that teams drown in loads of scope, which rarely resembles the initial objectives.

They talked about where they think VeraComm could compete with other players in the market, what opportunities for expansion they envisioned, and so on and so forth.

"In a little bit, our product management will present some specifics on how to realize this vision," said Zach, concluding the main part of their briefing.

"Are there any questions?" Sunil asked of the group.

Silence. Are they quiet because there really are no questions, or are people just uncomfortable asking anything? Well, either way, what a culture we ended up with, eh? It seems you can't get too far just on good intentions while sitting in full isolation. This level of interactivity and transparency is all new to us. New instincts, like those I observed at SilverArrow's PI planning, are simply not available to us yet.

"Guys, our whole purpose here today," said Sunil, who like me was concerned with the problem, "is to be able to communicate and collaborate. None of this can be achieved uni-directionally – it has to go both ways. These two days represent a perfect opportunity to go through all the questions that are currently unanswered or which will come up during the planning process. Please use this opportunity – both Zach and Nerissa are happy to address your questions. We still have a little over ten minutes in this timebox."

Zach and Nerissa nodded, but the audience remained unmoved. I noticed Adi approach Sunil and whisper something in his ear, while Zach stepped forward to demonstrate by his posture that he was completely willing to address the teams' concerns, if any exist. It was getting both a little awkward and worrisome.

"Hey guys," said Sunil. "By a show of hands, how many of you were creating new functionality or enhancing the existing one in the last release?"

Almost everybody raised their hand.

Sunil continued, "Please keep your hand up if you understand what business goal that functionality was supporting."

Most of the hands went down. A few of those still up also went down moments later, leaving literally just a few people with their hands up.

"Okay, thank you. *Now*, do any of you have questions for Nerissa and Zach?" asked Sunil.

A few seconds later someone raised their hand.

"Please," said Sunil, pointing to a person at the 'Rivendell' table. Somebody handed over the second microphone to that developer, who stood up and asked: "I have heard that there will be more interactivity offered to mobile users. Is that true? And if so, what exactly do we expect it to do for us from a business perspective?"

"Thank you," said Zach. "That's a really good question. Olga, your product manager, will show you guys the specific functionality that we would like to be built. But let me address the bigger aspect contained in your question: what business benefits do we expect from enabling more interactivity for mobile users? In the last couple of years, we've seen more and more people perform a significant amount of their business tasks on smartphones. Moreover, the latest trend of 'tablets that substitute for laptops' is acquiring more and more momentum. As more sophisticated apps become available on mobile devices (including both general-purpose apps, as well as vertical cloud solutions), they allow for easy data access from mobile devices. That means that accessing and sharing data, and showing and even creating a diagram in real time, are just a few examples of what our users should be able to do on mobile platforms, just like they do on the desktop today. The 'mobile' trend for enterprise employees throughout the world is acquiring such strong momentum that it made us realize a simple thing: if we manage to surf this wave amongst the first, it will get us really-really far."

"Thank you," said the 'Rivendell' team member, clearly happy to hear such an elaborate explanation.

"Any more questions?" asked Sunil.

Four hands went up immediately.

"'Rohan', please," said Sunil, pointing in the direction of the next person.

"I was wondering about the licensing," said a lady in a t-shirt that I had noticed earlier in the morning. The t-shirt had the opening '<BODY>' tag printed on the front and the closing '</BODY>' tag on the back. "You guys mentioned earlier in the presentation that we would like to enable mobile users to perform most of the standard scenarios. Well, one of those is 'Scheduling a Call'. But in order to do that, one needs to be a licensed user. If that's the case, we need to have an easy option to make them licensed users in the first place. Do we plan on achieving this via the mobile interface? And will that be a separate app or an in-app purchase within the exisiting application?"

Lots of folks in the room turned in her direction, indicating the topic's obvious interest.

"Wow, that's another great question," said Zach. "Nerissa, would you like to take this one?"

Nerissa gave a very good briefing on how they would address this issue. Frankly, it was all news to me as well.

Zach and Nerissa managed to address three more questions before the timebox for Business Context closed, but there still were a couple of hands up. Sunil suggested that those questions be asked during the lunch break or even during team breakouts, insisting that it was important to stay on time and move to the next briefing.

9:00 Product / Solution Vision

Olga took the stage and walked the group through specific points on the plan of intent for the next quarter. She presented a list of features, prioritized using the Weighted Shortest Job First. She also addressed questions, that in her case were coming from all sides; it seemed like it would have no end. But the discussions around the questions were actually incredibly helpful. The members of the teams came to understand what each feature is for, what the business benefit is, and what scope was initially envisioned for each feature.

We had spent quite a bit of time preparing this briefing. Apart from the whole story of prioritization where Olga originally took a stance pushing everything she had in the backlog into the planning, there was another important aspect that Adi pointed out. We had Olga spend some time with the Product Owners from each team to see how those features would split into stories. It was a very rough initial cut, deliberately left incomplete. The goal wasn't actually to get to the stories, but to simply better understand the features themselves. We learned that splitting is a very good exploration method. And rather than running into too many unknowns at the planning, we took care of them during the preparation. "But don't go too far with this either," said Adi. "You don't want to split every feature into very small stories during the preparation session, because that way you risk locking yourself down to a potentially wrong solution. Without the teams in the room, going into too much detail means going in the wrong direction."

In the meantime, Olga finished the Q&A portion of her briefing, and Sunil took everyone to the next step in the process.

10:30 Architectural Vision & Development Practices

"In our first PI we will have a certain gross capacity allocation to architectural initiatives," said Anand, one of the train's architects. Anand is a super smart guy, but unfortunately he can't build readable slides, so we had to spend quite a bit of time getting where we wanted to be during the preparation. Sometimes it takes a village, but it's good when you have a decent result at the end. And we finally did, once we convinced Anand to stay away from PowerPoint and just tell another person what is it that he wants to communicate. "We would like to spend around 20% of our capacity as a train on building certain architectural capabilities for our near-term needs. More user interactivity significantly changes the landscape. Some of the initiatives include: connectivity and real-time import of objects from cloud providers, building layered user workspace, and building canvas capability for real-time drawing."

He also talked about some nonfunctional requirements that have increased in importance, especially cross-domain security associated with access to cloud-based file hosting services. System performance was another critical topic, as some of the new features Olga was talking about were built on the assumption of HD video and sharing of the user workspace.

Then we talked a bit about engineering practices. The presenter – Nathan – reminded everyone that in light of the recent discovery of our less than adorable branching practices, it had been decided that we would integrate all feature branches in every iteration in order to be able to produce system demo every two weeks. Since it had already been discussed at length, today was just a summary of that decision and a reminder of why is it so crucial to our success. Without that change, we would simply 'waterfall' the entire PI, which is the last thing we wanted to do. What initially attracted me to SAFe at a first glance back at the conference, was its ability to scale Agile to the entire program, not just at the team level.

"What functions of the layered workspace are we going to build in this PI?" asked someone from the 'Rohan' team.

Anand dragged in a flip-chart and briefly sketched a diagram that quite nicely outlined the core functions; such as document readers, layer switching and a navigation bar. Needless to say, Anand was much better at creating ad hoc sketches than slides. After a couple more questions, Sunil called this section done as well.

11:30 Planning Context & Lunch

This was Sunil's timebox and he did a great job going over the rest of the planning process, the planning artifacts, and so forth. Adi's faith in him was obvious given that she had decided to have him do everything, and was only making discrete suggestions here and there.

"The goal of Day 1 is to build your draft plan. And the main part of that is your team PI objectives. You build your objectives by splitting your features into stories, sizing them and placing them into the iteration plans. You do that for as long as your capacity allows it and then put together a summary of the plan – those are your team PI objectives."

"For those stories, Sunil," asked someone, "should we define the acceptance criteria?"

"No, we should not be doing that," answered Sunil. "We are pursuing a higher-level goal at the PI planning, which is to get aligned in general on what and how we are building in this PI. Getting to the level of individual user story acceptance criteria would get us stuck in the weeds when we need to acquire a bigger picture." He quickly added: "You will have your iteration planning for that level of detail."

It took about twenty minutes to go through the rest of the process and the remaining time was allotted to lunch. Sunil asked all of the teams to make sure their planning sheets were all set up and that they had convenient access to space on the wall.

1:00 Team Breakouts

All of the teams started to set up their areas, and once done, returned to their tables. Most just dove into their computers and started writing stuff on stickies. In the meantime, Sunil set the timer for one hour. "That's the timebox till our first check-in, the Scrum-of-Scrums," he told me before going over to the corner to work on the SoS checklist.

I stood up and walked around the room, wondering how the teams were doing and, in fact, what they were actually doing. The sound in the room had become complete white noise: all of the conversations, it seemed, had collided into a thick, un-parseable flow of group consciousness, which nevertheless carried significant value.

The first thing the teams were working, following Sunil's advice, was understanding their capacity in each iteration. Adi did a great job during the training (prior to this planning session) of helping the guys internalize a new method for estimating and planning. Nothing new really, just a large-scale-friendly variant of the story point-based estimation. The idea is simple: align the notion of a story point across the board so as to enable easy and straightforward estimation at scale. Sounded simple, and yet it triggered violent resistance from some teams during training the day before.

"This is unthinkable," said one of the developers during the training. "We have our unique notion of a story point that developed naturally and is perfectly tuned to our team context, and we are not going to give it up!" Her teammates fully supported her, and the situation became even worse when some of the other teams started to comment on it, too.

"You can't make us do that," said someone in the back of the room. I, quite frankly, wasn't expecting them to make such a big deal out of something as trivial as story points. But at the same time, I knew it could be really important to them: story points are used for their specific estimation base and now we are basically pulling the rug out from under them. None of us would be thrilled about it either.

Adi, however, wasn't prepared to give up. She waited until the folks had finished their comments and where ready to listen. "I totally agree with your every word," she said. "But I have a question, just a little one, if I may?"

The group was quiet.

"Thank you, I'll take that as a 'yes'," she continued. "Let me ask you this: you all use story points to express your team's velocity, but how about the velocity of the entire program?"

Everyone still remained quiet, although their expressions had started to change. It was an interesting question indeed.

"We could figure the multipliers each team should apply to their velocity to make it comparable, and then just add up those adjusted velocities," said someone.

Others shook their heads. "That doesn't sound very practical," said the lady who had commented on normalizing story points in the first place. "But I think I know what we should do instead," she continued with a smirk on her face, "we figure velocity for the program based on features, just the same way we do locally as a team with our stories."

That really sounded like a good idea.

Adi smiled and picked up a large sticky. "Imagine that this is a feature," she said.

The lady at the 'Erebor' team table nodded.

"Size it," said Adi. "Size it..."

The lady took a little bit of time, but soon came up with an answer: "What I would do is look into our backlog and pick the smallest feature first. I would call it a '1' and then estimate the size of this one relative to that 'unit of measure', so to speak. Then, at the end of the PI, I would look at the total amount of points achieved in all features and that would be our velocity."

Many people nodded in support. And rightly so, as it seemed quite logical. That is until Adi unveiled an unexpected angle.

"Let me ask you another question," she said, "And for that, if you don't mind, I would like us just for a moment, to move away from the program level and back to the team level. So, here's my question: why can't the other teams in this room use *your* current team's notion of a story point?"

"Well, because they... well, I don't know the right way to say it... they must, in a sense, own it, they must feel it, you know. It has to be *their* story point; the unit of measure they constantly think in, otherwise they will not be able to operate with it. It's like asking me to tell you the temperature in Celsius."

Everybody laughed.

Adi laughed too, but she was the first one to regain her serious, connected expression. "Great point," she said. "That's a really great point. And who do you think is going to own or feel those different 'points' for features?"

The lady looked puzzled. She turned to the ceiling for the answer, then to her desk, and then to her teammates, but despite her to this point flawless record answering, luck had suddenly abandoned her. The entire group seemed to plunge into some sort of deeply introspective, existential blues.

Well, that was some wizard craft from Adi. I always wondered how people did that. I remembered watching Ronda Rousey or Fedor

Emelianenko magically turning the course of a fight from a seemingly inconvenient position into an arm bar, and then the inevitable victory. I was always amazed and puzzled at the same time how do they do it. Well, during that conversation, I witnessed an instructor with real champion mentality fulfilling a critical learning objective without once resorting to her instructor authority. Rather, she took over by reasoning with her students, treating them as equals, showing real respect, and gently bread-crumbing them toward the right answer.

That turn solved the problem once and for all. Of course there was no viable answer to Adi's question. Someone has to own the 'point' and think in that point as their main 'currency'. But that someone can't be a team, because they already have their own 'system of measure'. And indeed, operating with two different systems is similar to handling the US and Metric Systems at the same time, which, many would agree, seems practically insane. So, if the teams can't own that magic point, who can? The answer is simple: the only option left is management and their select subject-matter experts. These guys would ultimately own it for the train. Of course the teams didn't like the idea of being pushed out of the estimation process. It suddenly occurred to them that aligning on the same story point across *all* teams and then using that universally for both stories and features would totally solve the problem. Normalized story point estimation was not constraining them. It was, in fact, enabling and empowering them and they eventually came to realize that. As a result of that heated discussion, they came to respect Adi and then thoroughly supported her throughout the rest of that two-day class.

Having such a thorough resolution helped a lot at the Team Breakouts during the PI planning. Every team used a simple formula: 1) start with ideal days as the initial unit of measurement to align across the board, 2) once started, use them as abstract story points and never come back to the notion of a day again. In practice, this meant that in a two-week iteration, every engineer on the team–developer or tester–would normally have 8 days of capacity (which roughly speaking equates to 10 business days minus time for iteration planning, stand-ups, demo, retro and so on). Instead of referring to those as 8 days, they would simply treat those as 8 story points and add them up to understand the team's estimated capacity. So, a team that had four developers and two testers, like 'Erebor', would have a capacity of (4 + 2) x 8 sp = 48 sp. The only remaining step would be to connect capacity with the size of stories. That was achieved by picking one or several stories from the backlog, estimating them initially in days, then dropping days as a unit of measure and estimating the rest of the backlog relative to those select few. That's it, nothing could be simpler.

It was 1:40 pm in the the PI planning day and some of the teams already had all of their capacity numbers written on their sheets. Many were already busily working on splitting their features further into stories and estimating those, in the same, normalized units. As I walked further around the room, I saw that the teams were still mainly at their tables, writing on stickies, discussing the size and other variables in the stories they had.

"So how do you like what you see?" asked Adi, as she and Sunil approached.

"I like it," I said, "but I'm not sure that they've gotten too far with it - unless I'm missing something."

"Well, you may not remember exactly what was happening at 'Silver Arrow's' PI planning over a month ago, but here's a rule of thumb: you don't usually see much stuff on the wall until after the first SoS. It's usually in the last two or so hours that things really start to happen. Now we need to give them some breathing room, especially given that this is their first PI planning," said Adi.

"There you go," said Sunil, pointing to the 'Rohan' team wall. "Those guys already have some stories in iteration one. It's not all that bad, boss."

Meanwhile, the clock hit the top of the hour.

2:00 Scrum-of-Scrums #1

"Scrum-of-Scrums!" shouted Sunil, keeping the mic a little further from his mouth this time, for the sake of everyone's eardrums. "Scrum-of-Scrums! Scrum Masters, please join me in the Scrum-of-Scrums area."

"Sunil," said Adi smiling, "rather than yelling while keeping your microphone so far out, have you tried speaking normally and putting the mic closer?"

"Very funny, Adi," said Sunil. "I had not thought about that, no." He walked towards the SoS area while Adi and I followed. We decided that it would be best if Adi ran the first SoS to demonstrate the process and then let Sunil take over that ceremony for the rest of the planning.

It took a couple of minutes for all of the Scrum Masters to gather.

Adi took the mic and said, "This process is incredibly simple. Here's a set of questions that will allow us to track our planning progress today. The columns represent teams. I will go question by question and will need you guys to pay attention so that we can move fast with the simple things here. When I call out your team name, help me understand where you are regarding a particular question." She paused for a few seconds. "Ready?"

Everybody confirmed that they were ready to proceed.

Adi turned to the whiteboard and started the process. "So, the first question for you guys is whether your team has capacity estimated for all iterations in the PI. 'Rivendell'?"

"Yep," said the 'Rivendell' team Scrum Master and Adi made a corresponding mark on the board.

"'Erebor'?" she continued.

"Yes, done..."

She went through all of the teams and then moved to the next question: "Are all features split into stories? 'Rivendell'?"

"Still splitting one out of three," was the reply.

Adi did the same for all of the other teams and then moved through the rest of the questions. In fact there was no need to go through all of them because the teams, understandably at this point, hadn't gotten any further than question four.

SCRUM OF SCRUMS

	RIVENDELL	EREBOR	MISTY MOUNT	ROHAN	SHIRE	GONDOR	IRON HILLS	ICE BAY	LONG LAKE
CAPACITY ESTIMATED FOR ALL ITERATIONS IN THE PI ?	✓	✓	✓	✓	✓	✓	✓	✓	✓
ALL FEATURES SPLIT INTO STORIES ?		✓			✓	✓	✓		
ALL STORIES ESTIMATED ?		✓			✓				
HOW MANY ITERATIONS PLANNED ?		•			••				
DEPENDENCIES IDENTIFIED AND RESOLVED ?									
GLOBAL RISKS IDENTIFIED ?									
TEAM PI OBJECTIVES WRITTEN ?									
READY TO PRESENT THE PLAN ?									

"Okay, guys," said Adi. "The next Scrum-of-Scrums will be at 3 o'clock. I strongly recommend that in order for all of us to stay on track, you have most of your iterations planned and are ready to write PI objectives by then. Now we are going to have the meet-after. Are there any outstanding topics or questions?"

"Yes," said the Scrum Master of the 'Iron Hills' team. "My team just identified a significant dependency. I'm trying to think of the best way to manage it..."

"That's simple," said Adi, "As Sunil said in his presentation earlier, write the dependency on a red sticky and attach it to the story that requires other team's help."

"That's it?"

"Almost. Then you have to go to that team and let them know that you are expecting certain things from them. A dependency is taken care of if, and only if, you have the other team's confirmation that they have put the corresponding stories that acknowledge their part of the dependency into their PI plan."

"Makes sense," said the Scrum Master.

Nobody else had any questions or topics for discussion, so Adi let everyone go. "Next SoS is yours," she told Sunil.

"This is amazing," said Sunil sometime later. He looked around the room where, by that time, every team was busily writing more stickies, discussing what they wrote, moving things around, and discussing, discussing, discussing...

Some teams were laughing at barely appropriate jokes, which no one would ever remember later, others were engaged in heated debates, trying to dig to the very bottom of things too important to be discussed in the comforting, calm manner of kitchen talks.

"I'm going to walk around a little bit," said Sunil. "Some of the teams may need help." He walked towards the closest team–'Gondor'–and just quietly joined them. After listening a little bit and discussing something with the 'Gondor' folks, he moved on to 'Ice Bay' to do the same thing.

In the meantime, more stickies had begun to appear on the teams' plans here and there. The whole picture suddenly caused something to click in my brain, opening a gateway into the most precious reserve of memories that my subconsciousness keeps so carefully guarded. I was reminded of my dad's orchard in early spring, when just a few of the boldest buds would burst with the unstoppable desire to tell the world that they are alive. Ready it seemed, to trigger a chain reaction of leaves popping out of nowhere to the applause of every soul in the universe, that are carefully watching the awakening of the world. I remember those times very well, even though I was only about four, I think. I also recall asking him once: "Why don't those leaves pop up all at the same time?"

Dad always treated my questions very seriously. "Ethan, what do you see here?" he asked, gently bending one of the long cherry branches down so I could see it up close.

"Leaves," I said.

"Yes, well, there is more going on here than just the visible leaves, buds and twigs," he said, pointing to a leaf with his finger. "To our eye it's just a leaf, but there is a lot more happening inside. It consists of many-many little parts that feed from the branch; the branch in turn feeds from the stem through lots of little pipes. The stem pumps sap from the roots, which go deep into the ground, splitting into a myriad of small branches. Some of these branches are almost as thin as a hair, and reach the water and other nutrients that are vital to the tree. Different leaves have different little pipes that deliver the sap. Some are better, thicker pipes, while others are smaller – sap doesn't flow through them as fast. Those that have better pipes grow stronger much faster than the rest, springing out first."

That day was very memorable to me; not because of the amazing blue sky and sizzling sun, with hardly a single cloud on the horizon. All of my early childhood memories are like that. I think, maybe, that's just the way the brain augments reality in our very distant memories, by embellishing them with the finest wallpapers available. No, I remember that day so clearly because it turned my perception of things upside down, once and for all. A certain curiosity was triggered that day, maybe enough to last for the rest of my life. This curiosity extended to everything that surrounded me, impacted me or bothered me in one way or another. What's inside a vehicle's engine? Why do clouds fly in the sky? How are raindrops formed? Why are people so different and why do I exist? Those buds from my father's orchard 'blossomed' into a lifelong sense of curiosity, reaching to the very depths of my life. This fundamentally defined my personality and kept me hungry for knowledge and always eager to unveil that which is hidden.

"There is a little problem here," said Sunil, approaching me from behind, looking a bit concerned. "I'm going to grab Adi. There is a problem with one of the teams, I think."

And indeed, the 'Iron Hills' team had a plan that looked a little... weird. Their numbers were not quite adding up.

The numbers in the load for all of the team's iterations seemed to be within capacity. Actually, at one level, everything looked pretty good.

Sunil however, looked restless. And after approaching the team's plan, said: "When I add up the estimates on these stories to figure out the iteration load," he pointed to iteration 1 and continued: "I get more than the team has indicated for that iteration..."

"We can explain that," said one of the team members. "You see, this story," he said, pointing to a sticky at the top of the sheet, "is a little bit too big. So, we are simply assuming that we will do part of it in iteration 1, while the remaining portion will be finished in the second iteration."

Sunil remained quiet for a while, then shook his head as if trying to get rid of some uninvited thoughts. "Wait a second. That's just gonna kill the whole idea of incrementing the system..."

"Would you please explain what you mean by that?" asked another team member.

"Yes, I will," said Sunil. "See, the point of iterating is to produce an increment at the end of each iteration. But in this case," he grabbed a flip-chart and a marker and drew a simple picture, "you guys simply have a Work-In-Process spread across multiple iterations. It defeats the whole purpose of incremental and iterative development."

"Yeah, but it's just too big to fit in one iteration," said the team member. His teammates nodded in support.

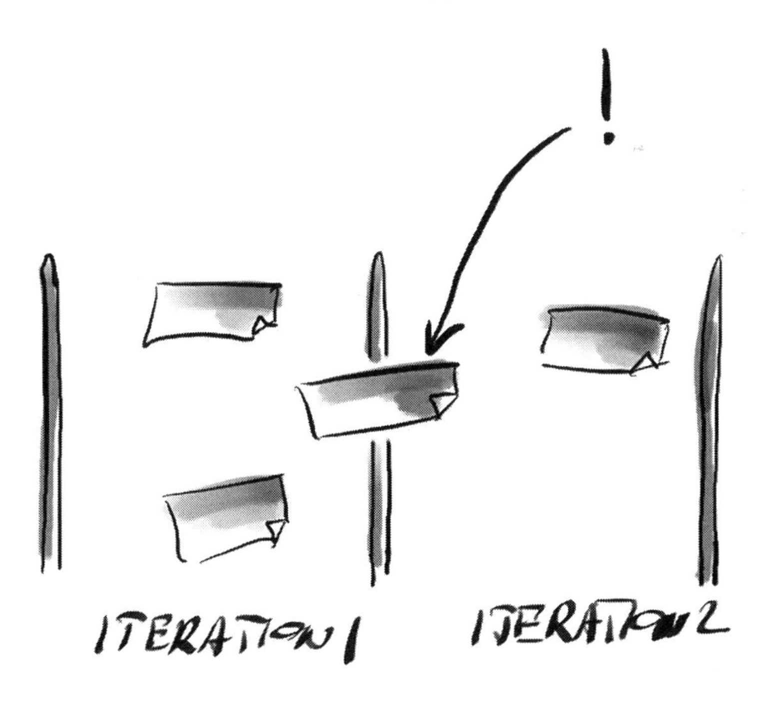

"Well split it guys, come on..." said Sunil with the expression of a betrayed child.

The team member shrugged. "How?"

Sunil himself was stuck and stared at the story for a while.

"So, 'Word document rendering,' would you tell us a little bit more about that story?" asked Adi, jumping in.

"Sure," said the team member. "In order to share documents from a mobile device during a conference call, they need to be rendered somehow in user workspace. We will be using a third-party library for rendering, so the story basically assumes that we will be hooking up their rendering capability inside our workspace window frame. The problem with splitting this story is that it's a binary process: you either hook up the renderer or not."

A couple of the other team members smirked after 'you either hook it up or not.' Adi stared at the sticky for a few more moments and said: "Have you used this function before?"

"No," said the team member. "We haven't; this is our first time. We read about it last week though, knowing that it was coming."

"How do you know it will work?" she continued.

"Well, we don't know it 100%, but from what we read in the specs of this library, we think it will do what we need."

"Have you considered any alternatives to this option?" asked Adi.

The developer paused for a second. "No." He looked at his team members for thoughts.

"I think we need to preserve some time to figure this out," said another team member. "It's true that we don't know if it's going to work or not. But then, what are we going to do with that backlog item?" he asked, pointing to the story.

"If we all agree that a bit of exploration is needed upfront, let's create a separate sticky specifically for that. We call it a *spike*, an effort to figure out something you don't yet know how to do," said Adi. "Also, for that, let's use a yellow sticky. That way it is much easier to navigate through the plan. You will see that all your new functionality is on green stickies and all research and exploration is in yellow."

The team created a new sticky and added it to iteration 1. They gave it a rough estimate and turned back to Adi. "But now we still have this giant story," said someone, pointing at the backlog item that had caused the issue in the first place. "Why shouldn't we just assume the scenario we have, knowing that the outcome of the spike may potentially change it, should something go different with the initial plan?"

"I like that," said Sunil. "Plan for the scenario you know, assuming that it's not necessarily the only one out there. But we still need to split it, guys. It's gigantic. We need to have something executable after iteration 1."

"Yeah, but as we said," continued the 'Iron Hills' team member, "it's a binary thing, this story. You either do it all or otherwise you get nothing. There is no middle ground."

Adi picked up the sticky from their plan and looked at it, saying, "How is the system going to render a document? Could you guide us through that process?"

"Sure," said the team member as he picked up another clean flip-chart from the stack. "First, we receive a file stream object from the system. That's just a raw file stream. Then this object is going to be passed to a library function that will render it. In order to render anything, the library functionality needs to know the container frame. It will then pick it up and render the document inside it."

"How would you test it though?" asked Adi, "to ensure that it is properly operating?"

"Well, we would test different document features such as styles, scrolling and so forth," said the test engineer. "We would also verify the user's ability to zoom in and out, select a portion of the text, etc."

"By the way," said the developer, "rendering is one thing, but this whole deal of interacting with the document is a totally different business. The library cannot do everything on its own. It requires us to hook up user events to its own view handlers. Assigning handlers to events can be a tricky business because there can be overlaps with the handlers that already exist in the workspace. Assigning handlers for instance, accounts for quite a considerable portion of the estimate."

"Wait," said his teammate. "That's perfect; we can split this story based on that. First we can develop the functionality that only renders the document. You can't scroll or zoom or do anything else yet, but you can see the first page or whatever part of it appears on the screen by default. And then the second story would involve all the interactivity."

Other team members joined the discussion and in a matter of two minutes they ended up with two like-sized stories, each one going into its own iteration.

"Great job guys," said Sunil, walking towards the Scrum of Scrums area. Adi followed in the same direction – it was almost time for the next check-in. Olga, the product manager, was talking to one of the teams, but as she noticed Sunil and Adi walking towards the SoS whiteboard, she looked at her wristwatch and proceeded in the same direction. Nathan was in the far corner, participating in an active discussion with the 'Gondor' team. They were pointing at their plan and passionately explaining something to him. I didn't see Ed or Zach anywhere in the room. It is not so easy, however, to spot a person in a room filled with more than a hundred people, so it's possible that they are simply somewhere where I can't see them. Oh, well, a needle in a haystack it is. In the meantime, the haystack was fully on a roll: the teams appeared to be so busy dealing with their stories and iterations that seemingly nothing could divert them from that course of action.

It was now Sunil's turn to lead the Scrum-of-Scrums. "Scrum Masters, please join me in the SoS area," he said into the microphone without too much effect. The mic was pretty loud, but it seemed like the teams were way too deep into their plans to be so easily distracted.

"Scrum-of-Scrums! It is Scrum-of-Scrums! All Scrum Masters, please join me here..." Finally, some of the Scrum Masters could be seen headed in Sunil's direction. The crowd, it seemed, lived by its own laws of physics, accelerating when they saw fit or showing inertia in other cases. Our world had definitely begun to change...

• • •

"Well, quite a bit of action out there, isn't it, Ed?" said Zach, offering Ed a chair. "It's much quieter here in my office, though. You know, when I moved into this office four years ago," he said, poking the back wall with his finger, "I asked them to make these walls sound-proof. And guess what? They did," he smiled. "When I'm on a call I can't concentrate if I hear noise from outside of my office – I get aggravated. And when I'm aggravated, I'm not so good to deal with. You feel me?"

Ed nodded, not entirely sure where this was going.

"Ed, I'm telling you this because I'm getting aggravated as we speak."

"How come?" asked Ed.

"You see, my nice little plan to sign the deal of the century with QCell is suddenly at risk." Zach turned to his monitor. "This is one of their VPs writing me back. Just listen to this stuff: 'Zach, it was pleasure to have you on the call last week. I see how much you and your company have invested in this deal. I think you have shown how committed you are to the idea of expanding your organization's landscape and to helping us all achieve a mission that neither of our companies could accomplish on their own. Unfortunately, my attitude is not shared unilaterally across my organization. I have to inform you that as a result of the Board meeting on Wednesday, it was decided to put the deal on hold. This is unfortunate news for both of us, as I had great hopes for a tight and productive collaboration.'"

Zach shook his head while still looking at the monitor. He began poking and shifting his keyboard from one side of the table to the other. Kids play that way with little car models when they feel like having fun. Adults do not play that way; they let their steam out when they feel stressed. Zach finally turned back to Ed: "He then explained why this had happened further in the email. A new person joined their Board a couple of weeks ago. She felt quite uncomfortable with QCell entering into a deal with VeraComm. Her biggest concern is, as she put it, that 'VeraComm has proved to have very poor delivery capability. We can't bet our future on a partnership with someone who cannot deliver to their customers.' Unfortunately, a few other Board members voiced support for her concern, which is what got us here."

After reading the final section to me out loud, Zach remained silent for a short while. "You know, I'm looking at the wording and I'm seeing the word 'Unfortunately' being used three or four times. You know what that tells me?"

Ed shook his head.

"It tells me that he is onboard with their skepticism too, that's what it tells me." Zach's voice became more tense. "This deal is slipping away, my friend. I wouldn't be surprised if the next time I poke them they tell me to forget about any future partnerships." He moved the keyboard as far away to the other side of his desk as he could. "Look, I don't want to go to the CTO with this because we both know that it will be of little help. I need you to save this company from losing its only chance to survive. Save the deal for me, Ed, and I will make sure you get what you want. You can trust me on that. Help us both here, Ed!"

"Okay..." said Ed, but his 'okay' did not carry too much confidence.

"Okay?" asked Zach. "Everything is at stake here. We are talking about you guys not being able to deliver. And all you have for me is 'okay'? I would understand if it was a bulletproof, passionate 'okay'. But, honestly, your 'okay' is very uninspiring, Ed. I don't know what you're thinking, but I expect real action from you, not a lousy 'okay'."

"I'm thinking here," said Ed, "you guys already have a bunch of yes-men in this organization and how far has that gotten you? I *am* going to take action, but I'm not going to B.S. you while doing it. If I have doubts, trust me, acknowledging them will help in building a strategy that is going to work for us."

"Alright, alright!" Zach said, smiling. "Take it easy. I know you understand what's at stake. But as your fearless leader, I thought I would emphasize the urgency a little more. That's all," he said, smiling again. But then Zach turned serious. "Any immediate thoughts you would like to run by me? Feel free to bring them up now. I have time."

"Well, yes, there is one idea. Something that might help us solve the problem at its core..."

ETHAN'S DIARY

- *The QuickStart ART Launch model is a single-week, full-immersion experience, preceded by a few weeks of prep, of course. QuickStart consists of team training, two days of PI planning, and 1 final day for various orientation workshops to help prepare the train for PI execution.*

- *Don't rely too much on the fact that teams are already Agile. That 'Agility' may contain multiple anti-patterns, when you take a closer look. Align all of the teams on the train to the same process. Train them in a consistent way of operating across the board. They may be reluctant at first, but in the end they will appreciate it.*

- *One typical problem to be aware of: 'waterfalling' the iteration. Operating with smaller user stories and frequently integrating will get you out of that vicious loop.*

- *It may happen that certain forms of interaction are not customary; for example: asking questions of the higher-level stakeholders. As sad as that is, it may be true. Facilitators have to pay attention to such things and trigger the right levels of interaction. The way Adi suggested it was simply fascinating.*

- *Morning briefings on day one of the PI planning turned out to be simply unbelievable. As soon as the teams felt completely comfortable asking questions and offering opinions, it became the most exciting session, involving both the teams and higher-level management. As I write this line, it occurs to me that it might have actually been the only such session that I can remember. Unbelievable. And we were wondering why we can't do anything right? Sure...*

- *Adi made the right call by co-facilitating with Sunil and generally giving him significant elbow room. We need our own RTE; one that will be able to help keep the train on track. The only true way to learn a new craft is by doing it.*
- *As a facilitator and coach you will be spread thin across the teams during the PI planning. So pick your battles and offer help where it's needed most, but keep an eye on the clock.*
- *It's fascinating how quickly the program learns new collaboration scenarios during the PI planning. And that's just day one!*
- *It is critical that teams stick to the simple ruleset defined at the planning. When a team does not follow basic rules of the game, it may be because there is a serious problem that they are not even aware of. As in the case of 'Iron Hills' and their giant stories.*
- *"'Iron Hills' and their giant stories"? Seriously? I realized the ambiguity only as I put it on paper. I think Tolkien would be laughing his rear off, reading my diary.*

CHAPTER 7
Fun with Planning

"It's not tight, it's basically impossible..."

–ED

3:00 Scrum-of-Scrums #2

This was Sunil's first Scrum-of-Scrums and his first encounter with a serious problem that needed to be addressed. All of the Scrum Masters discussed their current progress and subsequently the SoS board reflected where the entire train was with respect to the planning process. The picture however, wasn't too attractive.

Two teams–'Gondor' and 'Ice Bay'–had only completed planning the first iteration, while the other teams had done at least three. "You guys are behind," said Sunil in a slightly irritated voice. "This isn't what we would expect to see two-thirds of the way into the team breakout process..." He shrugged his shoulders and shook his head. Adi however, moved in quickly to cheer up everyone, suggesting that the best way to proceed would be to meet with both of the lagging teams and help solve the problems preventing them from progressing with their PI planning. They decided to attend 'Gondor', but bring the 'Ice Bay' Scrum Master into the discussion to share the learning.

SCRUM OF SCRUMS	RIVENDELL	EREBOR	MISTY MOUNT	ROHAN	SHIRE	GONDOR	IRON HILLS	ICE BAY	LONG LAKE
CAPACITY ESTIMATED FOR ALL ITERATIONS IN THE PI ?	✓	✓	✓	✓	✓	✓	✓	✓	✓
ALL FEATURES SPLIT INTO STORIES ?	✓	✓	✓	✓	✓	✓	✓	✓	✓
ALL STORIES ESTIMATED ?		✓	✓	✓	✓		✓		✓
HOW MANY ITERATIONS PLANNED ?	••••	•••••	••••••	•••	••••	•	•••••	•	••••
DEPENDENCIES IDENTIFIED AND RESOLVED ?		✓	✓				✓		
GLOBAL RISKS IDENTIFIED ?			✓				✓		
TEAM PI OBJECTIVES WRITTEN ?									
READY TO PRESENT THE PLAN ?									

"Hello guys!" said Sunil as they approached 'Gondor's' planning area. "Looks like you guys could use a little help maybe?"

The 'Gondor' team members looked a little puzzled and not particularly thrilled about so much outside attention, as Adi, Sunil, another team's Scrum Master and I intervened in their world.

"Well, we are runing out of time," said a team member looking askance at the clock on the wall across the room, far behind Sunil's back. "It just takes a lot of time to figure these things out."

Sunil made a step forward to take a better look at the plan. They had iteration 1 fully planned and three stickies in iteration 2, suggesting that yes, the process was indeed slow for some reason.

"What are these?" asked Adi, pointing to the bullet points written on individual stickies, attached to each story in the plan.

"Those are the acceptance criteria," said the Product Owner. "We need to know exactly what is going to be delivered with each story."

"I see," said Adi, looking around at the rest of the team. "It looks like you guys have plenty of dependencies here, too."

"Yeah," said a team member. "These are mostly the dependencies on two teams: 'Rohan' and 'Iron Hills.'"

"It's good that you guys know that," said Adi. "Have you had a chance to discuss the dependencies with those two teams?"

"No, we have not," said the team member. "We've been busy writing the acceptance criteria."

Sunil said: "You guys shouldn't be doing this. We discussed this before as a group. Someone even asked a question about it this morning. You can't work on the acceptance criteria during the PI planning," Sunil continued, frantically waving his hands. "There will be iteration planning every iteration. That's where we can do this, but now you are just holding everyone else back." I had noticed before that when Sunil gets emotional, he waves his hands with the passion of a drowning man who has one last chance to be spotted by a life guard. He kept talking from behind the team members, preventing anyone else from getting a single word in.

Meanwhile Adi, very carefully and on the sly, walked over to Sunil and deliberately stepped on his left foot. Sunil suddenly stopped his excited rant and quit waving his hands.

"Guys, let me ask you something about your stories," said Adi. "Let's start by picking a story that has a dependency... This one for example," she said, pointing at a particular story. "Without going as deep as acceptance criteria, how do you know that the story itself is feasible?"

"Well, we've done similar things before," said one of the developers on the team. "This story, in fact, doesn't have any significant unknowns as far as I know."

"Yep, that's true," said another team member, while a couple of others nodded in support.

"And yet it has a sticky attached to it, doesn't it?" said Adi.

"It does," confirmed the developer, pointing at a red sticky attached to the story. "This is a dependency on the 'Rohan' team. They have to build a fairly trivial API for us to make this whole scenario work."

"And the dependency is unchecked?" reconfirmed Adi. And indeed, the sticky did not have a check mark on it; so she's either right about it being unchecked, or the team just forgot to mark the dependency as having been taken care of. Either way, that's probably the case with all the other dependencies - none seemed to have a check mark on them.

The developer looked at the other team members. Finally, a lady holding a big black cup of coffee with a VeraComm logo on it, said: "They'll do it. They've done stuff before. They know what they're doing..."

"I believe you," said Adi. "Or to be more accurate, I believe that you genuinely trust 'Rohan' to do that work for you. You guys may hate me after this, but I have to strongly recommend that we, together, verify that's the case, okay?"

The team members weren't thrilled by Adi's suggestion, but chose not to respond.

"With your permission," she continued, "I would like to bring the Product Owner from 'Rohan' over to confirm what you guys just said." She quickly walked to the corner where 'Rohan' had deployed their planning sheets and just as quickly came back.

"No, no," said the Product Owner after Adi had explained to him the nature of her request. "There is no way we can do anything for anybody in iterations 1 or 2. We have a lot of work to do with the user workspace for document sharing and that needs to happen early in the PI, otherwise we may run into a problem. It's a risky new feature anyway, so a lot is at stake. Listen, guys. We would love to help, but there's no way for that to happen anytime in the first two iterations. The best we could do is to put it in iteration 3. Even that might require us to make a call with respect to some other stories, of course, but at least in the 3rd iteration it is not impossible."

Team 'Gondor' went silent. It was at least a minute, it seemed, until 'Rohan's' PO broke the silence: "Do you guys have any other dependencies on my team in your plan?"

The team's Scrum Master nodded and silently pointed to two additional red stickies; one in the same iteration and another among the two stories of iteration 2.

"Well," said 'Rohan's' PO, "what can I say... come by at some point and we'll talk. I'm sure we will be able to accommodate some of it in the later iterations." He looked at the wall clock: "Now, if you don't mind, I need to get back to my guys. We just started writing our PI objectives. I need to be with the team for that." He quickly walked towards his team's corner.

The developer from 'Gondor' pointed to the remaining iterations: "we have no idea how many more surprises like this one are in there... This isn't about story detail, guys. First of all, we must validate more important assumptions: are the stories even possible to execute, and what iterations do they fit in, given all of the dependencies and load that other teams have in their plans."

"That's absolutely right," said Adi. "That's exactly what we are trying to achieve as a train during the PI planning: understand higher-level assuptions. In every iteration, each team will have an opportunity to refine their stories further. Nobody has cancelled iteration planning. Today and tomorrow, however, we are trying to align to a common plan of action as a train. So, understanding cross-team dependencies and program-level risks represent one of the key goals for the planning session."

The team quicky swarmed around the plan and began actively working on other iterations, while two other team members went over to the 'Iron Hills' team to negotiate dependencies.

"Sunil," said Adi, "Can you spare a second for me, please?" She beckoned to him, inviting him to join her off to the side. Sunil went over and they talked about something for a while; I couldn't hear anything from where I stood. After that Sunil looked at Adi, sighed and nodded. A couple of moments later he went over to 'Gondor' and briefly talked to the team. I noticed that some of them patted him on the shoulder and the lady on the team, the one that had been talking with Adi about dependencies a couple of minutes earlier, gave Sunil a hug.

"What did he say to them?" I asked Adi when we were back together.

"What would you say to them after you had had a rant like that?"

"Oh, I see. I would apologize too. Good call..."

"It is and he handled it well. He's gonna make a great RTE one day, I'm sure. He has the passion for sure," she said, smiling. "But all joking aside, he actually has one of the most important skills of an RTE..."

"Which is...?"

"He's good at identifying the important things in the middle of chaos. Being selective in terms of where to apply one's major effort is vital to an RTE. Otherwise you'll be spread very thin and that's a very bad recipe at scale like this."

While Adi and I were talking, I noticed Ed and Zach entering the planning room and heading towards us.

"Ethan, can we speak with you for a second?" asked Zach in a very polite manner. "It won't take too long, I promise."

"Sure," I said, following them to the lobby. As soon as we had found a quiet corner, Ed said: "What we're about to share with you is highly confidential. Don't tell anybody, don't explain anything to anyone, do you understand?"

"Yes, yes, I got it. What's going on?"

"We need your help," said Zach. "I'm gonna tell you what I've already told Ed, so listen carefully." He proceeded to tell me about QCell and the deal that they thought was going to be signed, but which had suddenly been jeopardized as a result of one of their new Board member's scepticism about our ability to deliver.

"Our idea," continued Ed, "is this. If there is any chance for VeraComm to deliver anything quickly, it would only be with 'Arkenstone' – the other programs are in really bad shape, but here we probably have a chance if this method really turns out to be safe."

"...No pun intended," said Zach, grinning.

"I see," I said, realizing that by taking such a path, we would create unnecessary pressure on the newly launched train. Not taking such a path, on the other hand, would equate to losing the only chance this enterprise had to thrive again, like we once had, many years before.

"I know I may regret this one day, guys..." I said, realizing that the choice was quite obvious.

"Ethan, you can trust me," said Zach, "if you help us save this deal, you will never regret your decision: I give you my word. Just tell us what you think 'Arkenstone' can specifically do to help this matter."

"As you know, Adi invited me to visit another company with her. Based on what I saw there, I can tell you that the one thing that will help restore QCell's confidence in us, would be having their people come over and attend our PI System Demo, the cumulative demo of the train's work in the PI. Nothing builds trust better than that degree of transparency. Showing them a real increment of the solution will help create the ultimate visibility into what we do and how we do it."

Zach stared at me for a while and then smiled. "I like that." He then looked at Ed and said again, "I like this idea. Do you think these guys will be able to pull it off?" he said, pointing towards the planning room.

"I do. To be clear, there are always risks, but I have confidence in the process."

"Good, good," said Zach. "Ed, any thoughts?"

"Well, I like it too," said Ed. "I think we should just review the scope again to be sure that what we load into this PI will best demonstrate our delivery capability. We want it to look really exciting."

"I think we will have a chance to do that in just a little bit, Ed," I said. "In less than an hour, we are gonna have a Draft Plan Review which will give us a rough idea of the entire program's plan."

"Good, good," said Zach, turning to me: "I may need you on the call with QCell if we have any problem convincing them to pay us a visit. Someone needs to be able to describe the benefits of this new process to QCell and that's gonna be you, my friend," said Zach, now pointing at me.

Ed tapped me on the shoulder, "See you in a little bit. We'll be back to review the draft plans."

Well, this raises the stakes. And at some level it seems to be a good thing. The fact is that a sense of urgency might push us through all the bumps in the road faster. I'm beginning to realize that more attention on the program is only helpful when adopting a new method. One way or the other, we will see how it all works out as reality sets in.

In the meantime, the 'Gondor' team was clearly progressing. They had filled most of their iterations with work so far. The 'Ice Bay' Scrum Master, who had also had the same problem as the 'Gondor' team, went back to his teammates to help solve the common issue of getting stuck in too much detail at the story level, while failing to spot the bigger, glaring holes in the plan. Sunil took the microphone and gave everyone a 30-minute warning about the upcoming presentation of the draft plans. The machine was definitely accelerating towards the next station.

4:00 Draft Plan Review

The room looked like a beehive: the teams were making the final changes to their PI plans, walking around, discussing things among themselves... Someone ran across the room to confirm something with another team and then quickly jogged back with the good news to their team; or at least that seemed to be his teammates' reaction to the sticky he had brought back. Sunil's early attempts to drag everyone's attention to the next step–the draft plan review–didn't seem to have any affect on the crowd. The room felt busier and smaller than before, packed to the brim with stickies. It seemed as if the scope, initially captured in the top features for this PI, was being brutally dispersed into every corner, filling up each gap in understanding, shedding the bright light of color-coded meaning over the deceptively simple initial assumptions about the scope. The room was calming down very slowly, as if there was a reluctance to transition to the next step. It was as if the hive was trying to savor the moment of ultimate alignment.

"G-u-y-s!" Sunil shouted loudly. "Thank you," he said when nearly all of the chatter had stopped and the teams were back at their tables. "We will be presenting our plans now. Please keep in mind that there's not much time allotted to each team: you will have five minutes, including the Q&A. In order to accomplish that, we have to stay at a high level and stick to the simple presentation format. The format is as follows: first we ask you to go over capacity versus load in every iteration of the PI, then present your PI objectives, then talk about global impediments and risks, if any have been identified. Then comes the Q&A. First, each team will have to address the questions from the business owners," he said, pointing to Zach, Nerissa, Olga and Ed, who were all standing close by and obviously ready for action. "Then anybody from any team will be able to ask their questions, as well. Let's start here with 'Gondor' and then move counter-clock-wise along the wall until we are done. So, 'Gondor', who's presenting? Please, take the stage!"

One of the developers from the 'Gondor' team stood up and approached the wall where their plan hung. "I will be presenting," he said, trying to gauge the optimum distance to the microphone. "My name is Josh and I am Steward of Gondor."

Everyone chuckled, but Josh quickly got right to the topic. "Our capacity in iteration 1 is 52 and the load is 49; iteration 2: capacity 47, load 45; iteration 3: capacity 56, load 60; iteration 4: capacity 50, load 55; iteration 5: capacity 54, load 54. Iteration 6 is the Innovation-and-Planning iteration, so we didn't load anything except for a couple of spikes for what we know will be our future features."

Ed made a few steps forward. The numbers had clearly drawn his attention to the 'Gondor' plan.

Meanwhile, Josh moved to the sheet with his team's PI objectives and continued: "In this PI we will be aiming at the following: the whiteboard drawing feature, which will allow our users to share visual representation of ideas with other people during a conference call. The next one is saving and sending whiteboard drawings in meeting minutes. Once a call is finished, a user will be able to preserve a graphic and share it with the participants of the call. Next up is rendering plugin engine. This is the foundational functionality that will allow our team, and a couple other teams on the train, to hook up specific plugins that know how to render different file formats, such as Word, Excel and PowerPoint documents, plain text, pictures, etc."

He went through all of the objectives and then moved on to impediments and risks: "We've only got one item here. We know that the 'Server-side' guys are going to deliver an update in three weeks. This update is essential to screen sharing and image processing, and is optimized for mobile clients. To be on the safe side, we need to make sure we know the exact new APIs for that update, otherwise there may be surprises..."

Sunil made a note, and then asked: "Business owners, any questions for 'Gondor'?"

"Yeah," said Ed who had grown a little impatient by this time. "I'm sitting here looking at these numbers, guys... Let me pick an example of an iteration that looks tricky to me: capacity of 56 story points with a load of 60? How are you going to deliver that?"

"Well, we admit that it's... tight," said Josh.

"It's not tight, it's basically impossible," continued Ed. "Look, I'm not criticizing you guys or anything. Just the opposite. I am trying to make sure that whatever you commit to, you can reliably deliver without overstretching. From the past we have plenty of examples where commitments were made and we were just not able to deliver. Or even if we did deliver, it was usually something of horrible quality."

Well, this is interesting. Ed seems to be doing exactly what we had wanted him, and other Lean-Agile leaders, to do in cases like this all along: protect the teams from overloading at all cost. As Adi pointed out during the leadership training: it's not enough that the leadership stops overloading the teams with too much scope. The teams *themselves* can have flawed instincts and regularly take on more work than they can actually accomplish. This leads to a very strong cognitive bias, which many of us have: we are unable to adequately assess our actual productivity. And for some magical reason, even after finishing every timebox with roll-overs, it fails to plant the slightest seed of doubt in us with respect to our delivery capability. More precisely, we are probably chronically underestimating work or overestimating our ability to deliver, which is the same concept only stated two ways. Obviously, it takes substantial effort to reverse that dynamic. The good news is this: we seem to be past the resistance on the part of management. The bad news: our teams still have old habits that they need to drop.

"Guys, that's a fair concern," said Sunil. "That is something you will need to take care of tomorrow, when refining your plan further. Otherwise it just won't be a plan that you can realistically execute."

He turned to the business owners: "Any more questions, guys?"

"Yes, I've got one," said Zach. "The 'Rendering plugin engine'... What is it really? Why is it important? How big is it? It sounds to me like one of those technical things I could never understand, and why should I care about it anyway? Besides, do we have to do it in *this* PI?"

Wow, that's like fifteen questions in one. And poor Josh has to answer them all, doesn't he?

"I totally understand where you're coming from," said Josh. "It may indeed appear as quite a bit of extra work, I can see that. But the fact is that if we don't do it, it will cost us a lot both in this PI and in the future."

"Please explain," said Zach, still looking puzzled.

"Allow me," said Ed, jumping in. "I know what this thing is. In order to share a Word document, a PowerPoint presentation, or a JPEG image, it needs to somehow be rendered in the VeraComm application workspace. That's because unlike on the desktop, in the mobile world you can't easily share your screen if you are switching between apps. So, in order to render different types of documents inside the workspace of the VeraComm application, we need to use different libraries–sometimes from third parties, sometimes developed by us–to make that happen. Each of those libraries have different APIs. If we use them as is, it will make the code absolutely impossible to maintain in the future. But even in this PI, after adding one or two document formats for rendering, we will be spending a lot more time adding each new format. It's far easier to develop a sort of universal interface for all third party libraries. Such an interface would allow you to 'attach' a new library using configuration capability, rather than coding your way in every time in a unique manner, which only creates more and more problems."

"Okay, I think I've got it," said Zach. "We're gonna pay one way or the other, but this way you guys are saying it will cost us much less overall, is that correct?"

"That is exactly right; we pay a bit now to avoid excessive debt in the near future," said Ed, turning back to the teams: "Guys, our Executive

VP of Business Development and I just spoke in his mother tongue for a quick moment and now we are back to normal..."

The teams laughed. And Zach, also very happy, turned back to everyone and said: "Well, someone has to count the money in this enterprise and find out where we can earn more, or at least where we can lose less," he said, pointing to the 'Gondor' PI Objectives.

"Alright, thank you guys," said Sunil. "Any questions from the teams?"

Someone from 'Erebor' raised their hand.

"Please, go ahead," said Sunil, passing the second microphone to the 'Erebor' team table.

"We will be working on the video renderer for the same purpose," said the team member. "We would like to find out more about the plug-in APIs to see if what you've got so far will be good for video streaming."

"Good point," said Josh, looking at his teammates.

One of the 'Gondor' developers at the table turned back and shouted out, "We will have to talk to you guys. We haven't specifically considered sharing a video file as of yet. There may be some difficulties with the current model we plan to use. Check back in with us on that, please."

"You had me worried," said Josh. "I don't think we are necessarily addressing the APIs required for video streaming. There may be surprises with buffering. That's the first thing that immediately comes to mind."

"Okay guys, take it offline because your time's up," said Sunil. "Let's give them a hand, guys. They have done a great job so far. That plan allowed us to see some risks and inconsistencies, and that's why we're all here, isn't it?"

'Arkenstone' applauded the 'Gondor' team, while Sunil and the business owners made their way over to the next team.

"Alright, next up is 'Rivendell'," said Sunil, as he invited the next presenter.

'Rivendell's' PO was the one to present. He went over the capacity and load for every iteration in the PI. The picture in their case looked much more encouraging than 'Gondor's' had: capacity and load were much better balanced across the PI.

Next he presented their objectives and risks. The business owners liked the plan, but people on other teams spotted an interesting problem.

"How are you guys going to implement the 'Save' function?" asked someone in the back.

"We are going to use our own mechanism for that," said the 'Rivendell' PO.

"Well, from what I know, 'Gondor' is going to use the operating system capabilities to do that as part of one of their objectives," said the developer from the back. "I believe that they are going to build a feature in this PI which will allow the user to save a snapshot of the whiteboard. The way they do it will also allow you to save to disk or multiple cloud options, like Dropbox, Box and what have you. Am I right guys?" he shouted.

"Yes, you are," Josh from 'Gondor' shouted back.

"We will have to look into that," said the 'Rivendell' PO. "We don't need two competing persistence mechanisms in the system. But at this point we don't have enough info to know whose is better yet."

"Alright, take it offline with 'Gondor'," Sunil said to the PO. "Guys, give them a hand!"

The room exploded in another round of applause and cheering. It was hard to say why they were so psyched. Was it only a show of support for the team that had just presented their plan? Or were they so enthusiastic because their new horizons were rapidly expanding far beyond the team boundaries? Well, who wouldn't be excited? Especially when it seemed that the new process had unveiled many gotchas that would have previously prevented the teams from succeeding with their work. I think every team member is absolutely tired of being unable to deliver on their commitment. There's very little fun in that.

It took a bit more than an hour to go over all the teams on the train. But the result was astounding. Zach, Nerissa, Olga and Ed were really happy to learn what the teams were capable of: just what they could and could not do, and why. Suddenly it began to change the underlying rules of the game for all of them. After the teams had finished, Zach approached me and said: "I have come to realize that those of us in management don't necessarily understand or appreciate the level of complexity these guys are dealing with. Now it will be much harder for me to blame them when something gets screwed up," he said, smiling.

We were finished with the Draft Plan Review. Sunil addressed the whole train: "Teams, I'm really proud of you and the work you've done today. All of the teams managed to get to draft PI objectives today. That gives us all the ability to understand where we're headed as a program. Thank you for your great work! Drive home safely, have a good dinner, and sleep well because tomorrow is another big day of planning and we need your brains fresh. I ask that the business owners, other program stakeholders, POs and SMs stay a little longer for a Management Review and Problem Solving meeting..."

5:00 Management Review and Problem Solving

"The format of this discussion is going to be simple," said Sunil when most of the team members had left and everybody had circled up. "We will go through a number of items that I have noted as outstanding issues. And anybody else may feel free to bring up other items too, if I missed it in my notes. Once we're done with that, we will capture the adjustments, if any, and socialize them with the teams tomorrow morning.

"So, for starters, some of the teams are obviously overloaded." He continued: "'Gondor', 'Erebor' and 'Ice Bay' are all over capacity. Adi, based on your experience, do you have any suggestions about the best way for us to proceed?"

"There's no general rule for this kind of problem," said Adi. "But let me suggest some things that are often helpful. First, you will want to look into the scope itself. Some objectives may not be as important as others in a team's plan. Tomorrow we will have teams identify what we call 'stretch objectives', and that will help us tremendously. Second, some of the other teams may be able to help. I noticed that two of the teams had quite a bit of excess capacity, but I don't remember which ones exactly. There's a chance they could help, if the skillset allows for it..."

The group decided to revisit the issue when working directly with the teams the next day. The exception was one team that badly needed help with a high-priority feature. 'Rivendell' would help that team, everyone agreed.

"I have another note here," said Sunil. "It's about the dependency that 'Gondor' had on another program - the 'Server-side'. 'Gondor' needed more info on the APIs. And as you probably noticed, a few other teams brought up the same thing."

"Well, we all know those guys, right?" said Ed. "Let's just call someone there and find out who could help us get the API specs."

"Yeah, but it's 5:15 pm," said Nathan, looking at his watch.

"I know someone who never sleeps," Ed said, smiling. He pulled out his phone, dialed the number and switched it to speaker.

"This is Bonnie," said a female voice on the other end of the call.

"Hi Bonnie! Ed here."

"Oh, hi Ed. How are you?"

"I'm fine. I have you on speaker here with about twenty other people in the room."

"Oh wow! Should I be worried?" she said, giggling.

"Well, I don't know yet. But let's give it a shot. We need your help."

"Go ahead..."

"So guys," Ed continued, "to those of you who don't know Bonnie, she's a system architect in her program, working on the server-side functionality. These are the folks creating and maintaining the web services that we and some of the other teams in the organization use for the core functionality that VeraComm offers for calling, sharing, etc." He turned back to the phone: "Bonnie, we are planning our next... quarter. Several teams mentioned that they don't really feel comfortable committing to any development objectives without knowing the exact APIs that you guys are going to release in three weeks. Is there any chance you could guide us in the right direction? Maybe you guys have a description or could at least auto-generate some remote method signatures for us when you have a chance? Or provide any other helpful guidance...?"

There was no sound coming from the other end. "She's probably on mute," said Ed. "Hey Bonnie, are you–"

"I'm not on mute," said Bonnie. "I'm surprised you haven't heard yet... but that release is not going to happen as we anticipated." She paused again for a few seconds and then continued, "It will not be delivered in three weeks. It will take us at least two and a half months to finish everything we initially promised to deliver."

"What? Why?"

"Well..." continued Bonnie, "for starters, we always have estimation problems. And now there are a few things that we hadn't expected to occur, so we have to deal with those. Second, well, our program is... shrinking."

Ed looked around the room then got back to Bonnie: "Can we call you back in five?"

"Sure," she said, sighing. "Standing by here."

"Hey guys," said Ed to everyone in the room once he had hung up the phone, "let's take a break for a few minutes."

He grabbed a few people, including the business owners and Adi and said: "This is bad. Zach, I think we need your help. Bonnie's program is clearly the first one on the list for lay-offs. That sucks for at least two reasons. If those guys–he pointed at the Product Owners and Scrum Masters–figure it out, imagine what that will do to team spirit when we are in the middle of an important development. But, even if they don't figure it out, we can't let this happen to the 'Server-side' program, simply because it will take them *forever* to deliver what we need. We can't afford to wait ten weeks! We absolutely need it in three weeks, otherwise we're hosed." Ed looked Zach in the eye and continued, "I need you to go to the CEO with this, Zach. We only have one shot at this. If the lay-offs continue, we will have precisely a zero chance to close the deal with QCell."

Zach didn't seem to be very happy to hear that bit of news. He stared at the wall for a while and then said, "What is this, Wednesday? I can talk to him tomorrow, in the morning. But I will need to come to him with something constructive as well. I need a strategy that is sound and is well-thought-out. And I will need to show him that this brilliant strategy has but one impediment – lay-offs."

"Adi?" Ed turned to her and asked, "any ideas? Sounds like we are gonna need a plan. Zach needs a concrete strategy to take to the CEO. How should we go about managing this dependency on the 'Server-side' folks?"

"Well... in fact, I do have an idea," said Adi. "Tomorrow we will have another breakout session where the teams will be able to better understand and manage the dependencies they have on each other, and on external parties like the 'Server-side' program, in this case. But it's far more important that you bring them over..."

"Bring who over?" asked Ed.

"Bonnie, and possibly a few other engineers from the 'Server-side'. Also, if possible, someone who is making the scope decisions for them."

"What do you mean by bringing them over?" Ed asked.

"We will have a much better chance to succeed tomorrow if they are with us when we discuss the adjustments with the teams. Then during the team breakout, they can plan with us just like any other team. If possible, I would even keep them for the final plan presentation, risk management session and team commitment. I can assure you that after planning with us, they will head back home with plenty of stickies to complete in the next couple of weeks. That is the basis for the strategy you are looking for to halt the lay-offs... Just get them in here, Ed. Everything else will naturally stem from that collaboration."

"Done!" said Ed, "I'll make it happen. Okay, let's get back to Bonnie while she's still available." He dialed her number again. "Hey Bonnie. We have some good news for you. But it's conditional good news: for good stuff to happen, we're gonna need your help. We think we can make the case upstairs to stop the lay-offs in your program."

"You can? How?"

"We'll take care of the details on our end."

"Okay. So, what do you need from me?"

"We need you and a couple more folks to clear your schedules entirely for tomorrow and spend the whole day with us."

"But that's–"

"Bonnie, you have to trust me on this. I have Zach here and he's anxious to have you guys plan with us tomorrow. And when Zach is anxious, you know, it means... a lot."

"Hi Bonnie," Zach jumped in, "Ed is right. I am very anxious and he's right about what it means. I want to help you guys, but you need to help me here. Can you do that, Bonnie?"

"Yes..." she said after a moment of silence. "Yes, I will come and bring a few guys. You better have some doughnuts for us, though..."

None of the rest of the issues seemed very important. The meeting was over in another ten minutes. Zach told us that he would be back at about 9:30 or 10 am the next day, hopefully with good news. And with that everyone grabbed their backpacks and left the room.

• • •

"You look tired," said Rachel as I arrived back home.

"Busy day," I said, trying to remember where I usually drop my car keys, "really busy day."

"How did it go overall?"

"Well, there's hope, I think. How was your day, honey?"

Rachel was about to say something, but she suddenly pointed to the table where my phone was performing a peculiar dance.

"You will probably want to pick that up..."

"Hello?"

"Hey Ethan, this is Ed. Sorry to bug you at this time of the evening..."

I shrugged to Rachel and pointed into the ceiling, which made her smile. I guess whatever Ed was going to say would not change my mood at this point.

"It was a really crazy day," he continued, "and I forgot to let you know that it's all been arranged..."

"What's been arranged?"

"Oh yeah, I'm sorry. I'm talking about QCell. They agreed to jump on a call with us tomorrow at four our time. We'd better be done with the planning by then. Zach performed his magic by getting them on a call earlier today, we just forgot to tell you – crazy day, as I said. Now we need a little miracle from you so they will start liking us again," he chuckled, but then continued in all seriousness: "I'm not kidding, Ethan. VeraComm's destiny is pretty much in your hands right now. If Zach is successful tomorrow in his talk with the CEO, your mission will become even more important. You understand why, right? Imagine if our CEO reversed his decision on the lay-offs, but the deal with QCell didn't work out. How damn awkward would that be?? The thing is, Zach and I will support you as much as we can, but at this point I think it is pretty much all you."

He wished me a good night, as if that mattered. I felt like I still had some ambient noise from the planning swirling around in my head. It was as if the teams were in my living room, but that the volume was cranked down a little bit, allowing me to hear my own thoughts occasionally.

"Is everything alright?" asked Rachel.

"Oh, it's nothing," I said. "It's just that tomorrow I have to save the freaking world. Other than that, everything's just great. But I would still love to hear how your day was..."

ETHAN'S DIARY

- *Respect for people is key to the learning process. A facilitator must understand and fully embrace that. Part of being a successful RTE is being patient with people who are gradually mastering new skills.*

- *The goal of the PI planning is not to go into depth on each story, defining acceptance criteria, etc. The goal is to understand the bigger picture view, and for that, focusing on dependencies, program risks and objectives is key.*

- *Dependencies need to be managed explicitly via collaboration with the other teams during the planning. Assuming that a dependency will be taken care of by someone else is basically equal to failing that dependency.*

- *By the end of planning day 1, all teams must get to draft PI objectives. They may be rough, but if any of the teams get stuck and don't have objectives at the Draft Plan Review, the overall program will have no idea where it is and what adjustments should be made.*

- *One of the main goals of the Scrum-of-Scrums meeting is to see if anyone's stuck in the planning. These teams might need help.*

- *Draft Plan Review performs miracles: as teams continue to present their plans, business owners begin to recognize the multiple complexities involved in the development process. This enhances trust and mutual respect. Teams also begin to better understand the thought processes of program stakeholders.*

- *A simple check of capacity vs. load is important: it allows bottlenecks to be spotted in the plan.*

- *Management Review and Problem solving aims to address outstanding key issues that remain open at the end of day 1 of the PI planning. Reviewing solution options and preparing adjustments to be announced the next day are typical for this meeting.*

- *Do not expect that external programs and teams will deliver as earlier promised. Check these out. Chances are, there may be big surprises.*

- *If you manage to get back home unscathed after day 1, switch off your phone completely. I mean it...*

CHAPTER 8
On Doughnuts and Commitment

"The team is where the collaboration happens."

–JOSH

THE ROAD TO THE OFFICE unexpectedly led me through the mountains this morning. I wasn't lost, it's just that sometimes we subconsciously create an alternative plan of action, in opposition to our habitual way of doing things. This little scheme sits tight under the radar until the blueprint decides that it's time to materialize. And then, as long as the brain is kept busy with something else, the secret plan begins to unfold, quietly controlling the muscles in order to execute the plot. So it was this morning, when I woke up earlier than usual and took off for work, having a chunk of extra time. But as I was driving by the canyon and thinking about the transformation and what our next steps are to be, I unconsciously turned west, as if it was scripted from the very beginning of the day and I had no choice but to comply.

I drove further and further up until finally the road began to bend and meander downward. And there I stopped, at the last trail head that

I was familiar with; the one that sits right on top of a steep drop-off that had no observable end. The cliff was the last frontier, the entry into a large valley, perfectly formed to unveil a panoramic view of the Rockies. The distant peaks it seemed, were cast of a completely different ore and shaped into an ensemble of sharp edges – a monumental reminder to the fragile life in the valley that above 10,000 ft, a callous desert discourages visitors from entering into its frozen kingdom. This year's autumn had barely touched the Front Range, but high up and across the valley, the 'Fourteeners' were already fully covered in cloaks of white. Only on the ridges, and following no discernable pattern, could bulges of grey-blue streaks be seen here and there, tearing apart the white party costumes along the weak seams. But even those will be mended in a matter of hours if the weather shows sympathy to order and style. Far away in the skies, where the peaks cut into the cream of the clouds, something new was building up. A myriad of tiny drops held the entire valley hostage, while deciding what to do next. Will they stay as they are or swarm into perfectly shaped crystals, powdering the last islands of bare rock? The drama of indecision resonates in the air, backwashing the Front Range with intense gusts of wind. Right above my head it toyed with the strong pines that seemed at first to reject the temptation, but eventually gave in to the flirtation, and fully tamed, bent their heads under the next ardent gust...

I could stand, watch, listen, and stay as fascinated as a child for another hour or two, but it was time to get back in the car and head to a different place of drama. Too many things had to be done, and finishing the PI planning was only one of them, and probably the most straightforward task, at this point.

8:00 Planning Adjustments

Sunil briefed the group on the changes that had stemmed from yesterday's late afternoon discussion.

"'Gondor', 'Ice Bay', 'Erebor', you guys will have to check with the rest of the program to see if they can help you with your excessive load," he said. "As far as we know, 'Rivendell' may have some spare capacity to help. Other teams may as well. Keep in mind that some fluctuations in scope may still happen during the planning today, so keep your eyes open."

He turned a page in his notebook and pointed to a group of people that sat quietly at a new table and were finishing a big box of doughnuts. "'Gondor', do you see those 'Server-side' folks that are celebrating their sweet life?"

The people from 'Gondor' team nodded.

"That is Bonnie and company. They have kindly offered to work with us today out of a mere... sense of guilt," he said, squinting at Bonnie who grinned in response as she bit into a big chocolate doughnut. "We are still waiting for an update on some variables from our stakeholders, but I would suggest that you not wait. Start digging into dependencies with the 'Server-side' guys. If there are no more questions, I think we should all get back to planning. Our goal is to finalize the plans. The next SoS will be in about an hour. Go!"

8:39 Team Breakouts #2

The teams spread out, getting back to their plans on the walls. Many team members were walking around the room, talking to their peers from other teams, discussing various things, gesturing with their hands, alternately laughing and being very serious, patting each other on the shoulder, and exchanging stickies.

"Oh, this is it!" exclaimed Ed, staring at his phone. "Zach is calling," he said, looking at me with a somewhat uncertain expression. Sunil froze, quietly staring at Ed as if everything in his life depended on it. Then Ed picked up the phone and just listened for a while without saying anything.

"What?" whispered Sunil, waving his hands in front of Ed, "What is he saying?"

Ed just quietly turned away from Sunil and covered his other ear with his free hand. Sunil shook his head and walked around so he could see Ed's face again. Another minute passed like that. Finally, Ed hung up the phone, put it in his pocket and turned back to us with his usual stone-faced expression.

"Well, guys, here's the thing," he said in calm voice, "that man deserves a monument..."

"Yes! Yes! Yes!" exclaimed Sunil, performing a 'moonwalk' around Ed. I could only guess what all this looked like to the people who hadn't been let in on our special mission here today.

"Sunil, people may be watching," said Ed. "I'm sure they are standing around wondering what a bunch of weirdos we are!"

"Who?" asked Sunil, looking around. "These folks, you mean? The ones that insisted on calling themselves elves, dwarves and what have you? Oh, I'm sure they're just fine..."

"Could you elaborate?" I asked Ed.

"What is there to elaborate on?" shrugged Ed. "It just feels awkward when somebody performs the 'moonwalk' dance around you, that's all..."

"I meant your phone conversation with Zach."

"Oh, right. Sure." He scratched his forehead. "The CEO agreed to roll back his decision on lay-offs, effective today! No exceptions, everything's back to how it was."

"That's awesome news. Zach really did his magic."

"Yes," said Ed, becoming graver. "But there's one little thing, Ethan..."

"What is it?"

He put his hand on my shoulder and said in very official tone, "If QCell does not agree to move forward with our deal, he will have no choice but to resort to layoffs again, with one exception..."

"What's that?"

"If the deal doesn't work out, he will revise the lay-off quotas, and the revision will not be downward..."

"But why?"

"He is convinced that information about the cancelled deal will eventually get out and he doesn't want to be caught unprepared. Zach said that the CEO was actually really unhappy with where this whole deal is going, suggesting that it exposes us to unreasonable levels of danger at a time when taking these kind of risks is highly unnecessary."

Well, that's just freaking great.

"So, my dear friend," said Ed, winking, "this adds a bit more spice to our little mission today."

I had somehow overlooked that all of this would automatically put me in a horrible position. Indeed, today we'll have the call with

QCell where we... or more accurately I, will have to perfrom a miracle of some sort. Well, if I ever happen to have grandchildren, I would like them to know about this day. The day on which I was Bruce Willis, Chuck Norris and Sylvester Stallone, all rolled into one, to save the freaking world; except that in my case, the happy ending is not at all guaranteed by the script. Well, that's what makes my life much more exciting than a predictable Hollywood movie. It's a fight worth taking on.

Meanwhile, Adi approached us. "It's time for our little walk," she said to Sunil. "Let's grab all of the business owners."

"We don't have Zach," said Sunil. "Did he say when he's gonna be back?" he asked Ed.

"Yeah," Ed nodded. "He said he will be back as soon as he takes some time to decompress."

"From what?" asked Adi.

"From another of his dazzling successes," he said to her. And he continued, turning back to me: "Ethan, this is quite a packed day. Let's make sure we stay focused on what matters and not get distracted."

"Okay," I said, wondering if he really thinks that I couldn't figure that much out on my own.

In the meantime, Sunil, who had quietly disappeared a few moments earlier, was already speaking loudly and waving his hands in front of Bonnie and her guys. Then they all suddenly stood up and walked as a group over to 'Gondor', where Sunil repeated a similar choreographic composition with his hands, passionately explaining something to the 'Gondor' team. Good for him, because occupied by the thoughts about today's call with QCell, I had completely forgotten that our guests from the server-side portion of the development organization were blocked, and so was the 'Gondor' team.

Suddenly Sunil beckoned to us.

They were in the middle of an intense discussion. "What's up?" asked Ed, as we approached.

"Tell them," said Sunil to Bonnie. "Tell them what you just told me."

"Well, we are having trouble with the part of the plan where we have to deliver the update in three weeks," said Bonnie. "That's hardly possible, I'm afraid..."

"But I thought you guys were constrained on people. Now you have people – I hope Sunil updated you on that," said Ed. "So why can't you guys do it for us? Without your help we will completely fail the whole document sharing feature, and more."

"That is correct, Ed," said Bonnie. "We are not constrained anymore in terms of people. But unfortunately we already lost a couple of weeks when we shifted priorities, knowing that there would be...," she paused, "...constraints. Plus as I told you yesterday, we underestimated the scope in the first place. Realistically, what we can do is to deliver it in seven or eight weeks, at best."

"Bonnie, yesterday you told us that you could do it in two and a half months and that was without any remediation in your headcount issue. And now, when you know that you have more people, all you can do is to speed it up from ten weeks to eight?"

"Look, Ed, we are tired of underestimating our work, too. How fun do you think it is to always fail to meet other people's expectations? It doesn't add much to our job satisfaction, to tell you the truth. Enough underestimating for us! 7-8 weeks is at least a realistic figure."

"Well, that's just great," said Ed. "I'm so proud of you guys for suddenly becoming dedicated to mastering the art of estimating work. I'm thrilled."

"I have an idea," said Josh, a developer from 'Gondor', jumping in. "Why don't you guys do what 'Iron Hills' did with their backlog items? They had a big story that spanned across two iterations and instead of keeping it that way, they split it."

"I don't get it," said Sunil. "How that will help us here, Josh? Split or not, it still takes eight weeks."

"Well, let me restate it differently," said Josh. "Obviously, I didn't make myself clear. I'm not suggesting they split their work just to have a nicer, more incremental execution. Building screen sharing capability is a *priority* for us, would you agree?"

"Oh yeah!" confirmed Ed, who was obviously imagining how bad it would be not to have such a killer feature for the PI demo with QCell. "We need to do everything we can to make this happen. It is very, very important."

"So," continued Josh, "if it is so incredibly important, then I suggest that Bonnie's team strips down their scope of work to *only* the functionality that we need from them for optimized image processing and transmission on the server."

Bonnie had been listening quietly all this time, but finally decided to jump in. "I'm not sure I follow," she said, putting down her doughnut, "are you suggesting that we dump the release we have been working on all this time?"

Josh nodded, but then raised his index finger: "Dump it, but not entirely. Dump everything but the APIs we need."

"That's insane!" exclaimed Bonnie. "We can't do that!"

"Bonnie?" Ed gave her a look. "We helped you with something really-really important today. So help us. Be open-minded, please..."

"Gosh!" she said, grabbing her head. She looked to her teammates, who simply shrugged without saying anything. Then she turned back to Ed and said: "You know, guys, this is not going to work anyway."

"Why not?" asked Ed, with a touch of irritation in his voice.

"Because we have quite a few features in progress right now, none of which are completed."

"So?" asked Ed.

"So, nothing is executing... Even if we decided to follow the path you suggest, we would have to finish our current features as part of the exercise. Otherwise we wouldn't be able to make an executable build with the APIs you need."

"Oh, that's just adorable, Bonnie," said Ed.

"Wait," said Josh, "It doesn't have to be that way. I have an idea about what to do."

"What now?" asked Bonnie with a skeptical expression on her face.

"Roll it all back."

"Are you nuts?! That's weeks of work down the drain!" Bonnie exclaimed, even louder. "Am I dreaming, or is this person actually real?" she said, pointing her finger at Josh. "Because if it's a nightmare, now would be the best time to wake up." She pinched her forearm with exaggeration.

"I'm serious," continued Josh. "This will get us where we need to be: something tells me that if you rolled back to your last stable release, you could probably get us what we need in three weeks or even less, what do you think?"

"It's actually not a bad idea," said Ed, patting Josh on the shoulder.

"Are you all serious?" Bonnie asked, visibly trying to not explode with frustration.

"We are," said Ed. "Bonnie, I understand that it may seem disappointing to you guys, but that is actually an effective, although rough, strategy. How much time would it take you to start from scratch and just build the new APIs that these guys need?" he said, pointing at Josh.

Bonnie stared at him for a while and began to realize that there was no escape from this path. She began to mutter something that only she could understand and after a long minute of keeping everyone in suspense, finally said: "He's actually right about the timing: if we do it that way, we can be done in about two weeks, I think; a maximum of three."

"Here," said Sunil, handing Bonnie flip-charts and a pack of stickies. "Why don't you guys find yourselves a spot on the wall close to the 'Gondor' team, and start building your plan? That way, together you will navigate through the problem much faster. I would also like you to present your plan along with the others, when the time comes. We need to know the plan of intent across the board. We all depend on you for our success."

The 'Server-side' folks deployed to the left of 'Gondor' and soon after, began to write stickies and post them on the sheets.

Zach showed up shortly afterward and, with the other business owners, they began circling the room, visiting team after team. They started with 'Gondor' because there was a lot of interest in their plan, due to all the uncertainty with the server-side functionality. First they ensured that the team had identified stretch objectives – a safety buffer that consisted of goals for development that may or may not be achieved as a result of the PI. Next, they assigned relative business value to every PI objective, using a range from 1 to 10.

"You know guys," said Olga, the product manager, "I'm looking at this plan and something is bothering me here."

"Like what?" asked the 'Gondor' Scrum Master.

"Look," she said, pointing at the sheet, "three out of five of this team's objectives have ten points of business value."

"Yeah?" said Ed, looking at her with puzzlement.

"So it reminds me of our little exercise during the program backlog refinement in the preparation to the PI planning. Only that in that case, I assumed that everything was critical and it turned out that it wasn't. Here, on the other hand, I'm looking at the objectives and I'm realizing that they are all really, really important. It almost feels like these three objectives are not only the most important ones on *this* team's sheet, but that these are the most critical things for the entire program."

"I still don't follow," said Ed. "What are you trying to say?"

"Oh, I see," jumped in Sunil. "Three very important things for the entire program all happen to be on one team's plan."

Josh scratched his forehead and said, pointing at the sheet, "I hear you guys. I'm looking at our plan now and it doesn't look as good to me anymore. It's actually worse than just my team owning the three most important items for the entire program. These two objectives," he said, pointing at 'Rendering plugin engine' and 'Basic client API', "these are critical to other teams, as well. Without them, they will not accomplish their objectives in this PI."

"Well," said Ed, "I hate to say it, Josh, but I think it's even worse than that. In order to build your client APIs for the screen sharing, you need those guys to succeed on time." Ed pointed at Bonnie and the other 'Server-side' folks, peacefully working on their plan.

Josh smiled awkwardly. "You're right. This doesn't sound good. Plus, we have to make sure that the 'save' function in another objective will be reusable by other teams," he said, pointing at 'Saving and sending whiteboard drawing' and continued: "During the draft plan review yesterday, we discovered that others need that functionality, too."

"...Which means that it can't really be a stretch objective," concluded Sunil. "Which in turn means that you don't have any stretch objectives at all in your plan..."

"Not good," said Ed. "This doesn't look like a realistic plan and we've only just gotten started. Problems like this one may also be lurking in other teams' plans."

Zach approached the 'Gondor' team's plan on the wall. "We can continue agreeing that this is all bad or maybe, just maybe, we go ahead and do something about it. No? ...Never mind, just asking."

Yeah, right. When the Executive VP is 'just asking', what you certainly want to do is to 'just answer'. I was beginning to realize, however, how helpful all of this interaction is for everyone in the program. To the teams, it affords a great opportunity to make adjustments just-in-time, because their key stakeholders are a handshake away and eager to help. To the business owners, it provides a unique opportunity to see why sitting in the office, and planning and committing the organization to a certain course of action without critical information, is not going to work very well. There is no way either party can figure out all of the hidden traps in the plan on their own. As it turns out, the secret recipe is so simple: get them all in a room and lock the door behind them, and make them stay together until they figure out what they are going to build and how they are gonna build it in the next Program Increment. It is fascinating to see how quickly they were able to spot problems when they are all together–"

"Class, class? Bueller? Bueller?" asked Zach, trying to steer everyone back to his original question.

"I have an idea," said Sunil. "I don't know if it will help us solve all of this, but I think it will allow us to see into the problem a little better."

"What is it?" asked Ed.

"I think we need to map out all of the significant dependencies we have in the program, all in one place. Clearly guys, we're only at the first team of the walkthrough and we've already found a lot of surprises. Furthermore, we don't even know if this team's case is the toughest we'll see today. So, what I suggest is that we build a consolidated dependency board and see where the weak links are in our overall plan."

"Yeah, yeah, I like it," said Zach, smiling. "At least someone is taking my jokes seriously."

"How you gonna do that?" asked Ed.

"Well, look," Sunil continued, pointing at the red stickies on the 'Gondor' iteration sheets. "Every team has dependencies identified and written on red stickies like these, right? The only problem is that we have never put them all together, into a consolidated view."

"Oh, I see. So you want to take all these red stickies and put them in one place?" confirmed Ed.

"Yep. Maybe we just ask every team to duplicate those stickies rather than physically move them from their plan to the dependency board. They will of course need those in their plans, one way or the other."

"How are you going to know which dependency is in which iteration?" asked Ed.

"Well, we just write the iteration number on each stickie, I guess," said Sunil, shrugging.

"I have a better idea," suggested Josh. "The problem with iteration numbers being written on the stickies is that, at some point, nobody will be able to navigate through all that. Instead, why don't we build something similar to each teams' plan that has iterations going left to right. Then we can just stack those on top of each other. So, for instance, 'Rivendell' would appear as the top row with their iterations listed left to right; then comes 'Erebor' underneath, just the same way; then 'Misty Mountains' and so forth. That will give us a much better visual of which item is to be done by which team and where it appears on the timeline."

"I like that", said Ed. "It's essentially a simple table, with teams as rows and iterations as columns."

"But wait," said Olga. "Every dependency is a matter of at least two teams. How will you know who is the provider and who is the consumer of a dependency?"

"What if we just connect them?" asked Sunil.

"Connect what? How?" asked Olga.

"Connect stickies. Look, if for example 'Rivendell' needs 'Save' functionality from 'Gondor', we put a red sticky for 'Gondor' in their row and another sticky, let's say a blue one, for 'Rivendell'. The red sticky shows what the dependency is while the blue one shows which feature it is. That way we will also better understand the impact of those dependencies in terms of the overall PI outcomes. And connecting them can be as easy as just attaching them to each other with a string."

"I like the fact that there will be features on the board," said Olga. "Although I would like to see it in action. Can we just do it?"

"Yes, we are going to do it." said Sunil. "You know what, guys," he said to the business owners, "why don't you just proceed, doing what you're doing. And once you're done with team 'Gondor', move to the next one. In the meantime, I will grab a few observers and use their help to build the board. It should take us about ten minutes, I suppose. By then it will be time for the next Scrum-of-Scrums anyway, and I will work with the Scrum Masters on filling out the board after the SoS. Adi, could you please back me up here?"

Adi nodded and Sunil moved towards the free space on the wall where he intended to build the board. In the meantime, the business owners, led by Adi, moved to the next team.

After going through the regular routine at the Scrum-of-Scrums, Sunil described the intent behind the dependency board and asked the Scrum Masters to bring dependencies from their teams to the board. The Scrum Masters, it seemed, were swamped in the breakouts, talking to their teammates, looking into the plan, then talking some more and writing more stickies. First came the Scrum Master from 'Rivendell' who brought a dependency on 'Gondor' to the board. Sunil found red yarn somewhere in the office, brought in scissors and tape and that was all they needed in order to proceed. Soon, two more Scrum Masters joined the people at the board. More and more yarn was deployed, and it all jelled into a peculiar pattern, weaving its pathways further and further, revealing the hidden dependencies in the PI plan that had already started to raise some fundamental concerns.

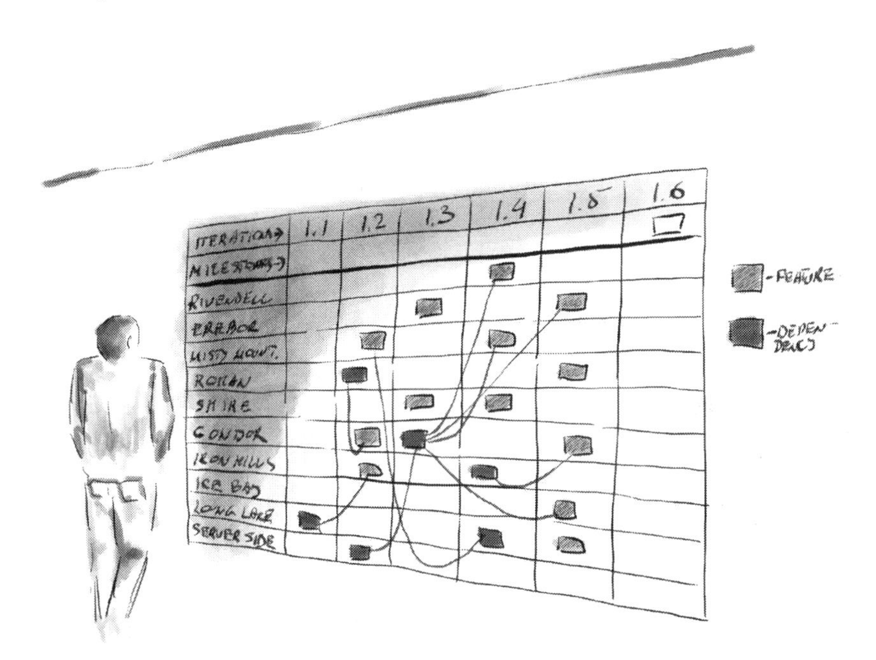

Meanwhile, Adi and the business owners were finishing their walk-through, talking to the last team in the sequence and basically ready to wrap up.

"Ethan, hey," Ed shouted out as he and Sunil and the Scrum Masters approached us. "Guess what? We're done. How's this thing with the board going?"

"It's going," I said, eager to find out their impressions after talking to the teams. "Can you tell us more?" I asked. "How did the business value exercise go?"

"Well, you oughta ask him," he said, pointing at Zach.

Zach smiled and said, "Whoever invented this 'business value' thing with relative numbers 1 through 10 is a freaking genius. You think it's gonna do one thing, but it actually does something completely different. Somehow those numbers make you think much deeper about the scope, and instead of just assigning the set of cyphers and moving to the next team, you begin to notice a lot of tricky things about that team's plan. Ed, am I right or am I becoming unreasonable?"

"No, no," said Ed. "You *are* right!" Then he added after a second, "...And reasonable."

"So, what exactly have you discovered?" I asked.

Zach continued: "Well, in a few cases we spotted some objectives that were pushed to stretch, while in fact, they were of a higher business value than other objectives above the line."

"Yeah, not to mention that in many cases those objectives were really fuzzy," added Olga. "It sounds fine when they read you those objectives, but as soon as you ask yourself exactly what business value a particular objective represents, it suddenly turns out that there are serious inconsistencies. So, sometimes you expect that they would include certain functionality as part of an objective, but they actually don't. And sometimes it's the other way around: they have some stuff in their plan that you would not necessarily expect–"

"And it's not that those divergencies are always bad," said Ed. "In quite a few cases they offered an interesting perspective that allowed us to look at things differently. Also, while making all those clarifications with the teams, we realized that the plan was sometimes too aggressive."

"So, what did you do in those cases?" I asked.

"...Pulled something out, what else? Miracles only happen in make-believe. We are in the real world and therefore need to be realistic. It was painful to de-scope things, but we did it. Also, Zach is right; it's bait-and-switch," he said smiling. "You think you are defining simple numbers, but in fact you are actually building alignment with the teams. Without those numbers, many questions would remain unanswered simply because they would never have been asked..."

"Alright, that's enough about us. Tell us what *you've* got here." said Zach, looking at the dependency board that definitely required a closer examination and a great deal of discussion. "So, help me understand again, what are these?" he asked, pointing at a piece of yarn that was connecting a red and a blue sticky.

"The blue sticky is a feature," I said, pointing at the feature that was connected to the same piece of yarn. "The row in which the sticky appears indicates the *team* that owns that feature. The column where that sticky is placed tells us in what *iteration* the feature will be finished. A red sticky is a dependency: some work that another team needs to do for this feature. And just like with the blue sticky, the position of a red one indicates who is fulfilling the dependency and when."

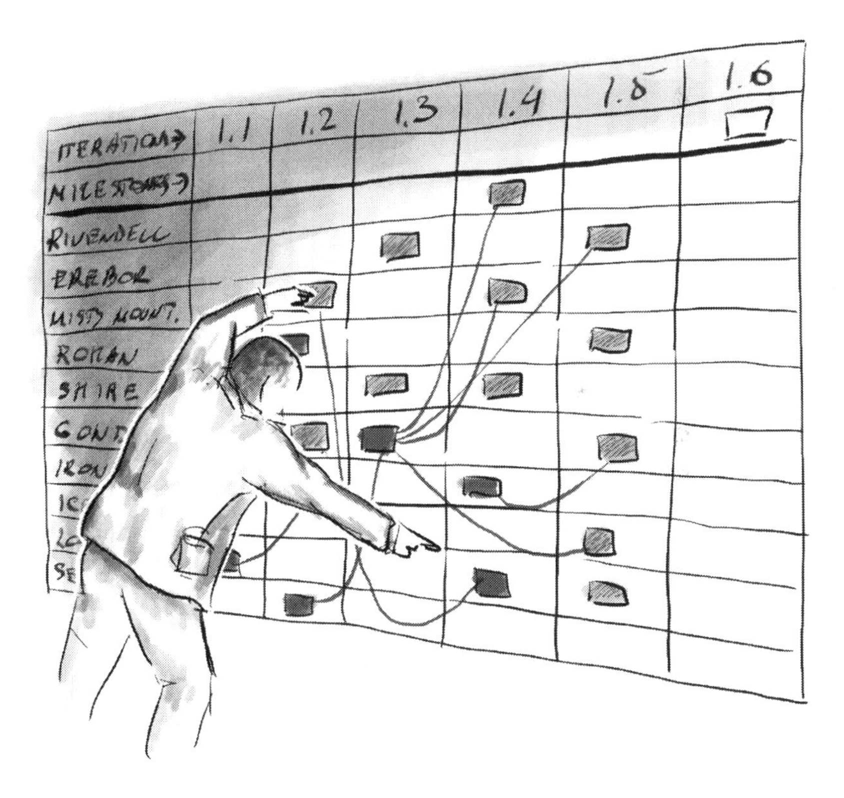

"I see, I see. That's good," said Zach as he started to follow some of the pathways with his index finger. "How is this going to work out?" he asked, pointing at a specific dependency.

Indeed, that dependency looked weird. What was weird was that the feature itself appeared in the plan earlier than one of its dependencies. That definitely was not going to work out too well. Zach was right.

"Gosh, did we not joke about things like that when building the board?" said one of the Scrum Masters. "And yet we missed one of those, sitting right in front of us. That's hilarious."

Ed stood side-by-side with Zach, looking at a different area of the board. "This is even trickier," he said, pointing at the area around team 'Gondor'. "They have a dependency on the 'Server-side', but look what happens right afterwards – an explosion. Four other teams require what 'Gondor' is building. Wow! And look how tight it all is. One mistake by these guys and everything else comes down like a house of cards."

Everybody agreed that it was a big problem. We were approximately half way through the Team Breakouts timebox and had already learned so much about the upcoming PI. The guys swarmed around the problem and, together, managed to drive it home. They worked with 'Gondor' to strip their plan of everything, but a couple of very important items, so that they would have enough elbow room to deliver the critical stuff. To get there, some unpleasant but very necessary decisions had been made, one of which was to pull the 'Save and send' feature out of this PI. That not only helped 'Gondor', but also cascaded further downstream, nullifying some objectives on other teams' plans, and creating more breathing room for them as well.

"We like it. I like it," said Zach, looking at the program board after a couple of significant improvements had been made. "What do you think, Big Head?" he asked Josh, the developer from 'Gondor' who had been incredibly instrumental during the whole exercise. Josh looked at the board and tried to sip some coffee, but quickly realized that his cup was already empty.

"Oh, let me take care of that for you," said Zach taking his cup. "Ed and I wanted to go get some coffee from the lobby anyway, right Ed?"

"Uh, sure..." said Ed, trying to not look surprised.

They walked towards the door while Josh remained standing in place, staring at the board.

"So, really Josh, how do you feel about all of this?" asked Sunil and added, "especially now that this company's top management is going to serve you coffee..."

"Yeah," said Josh, "I do feel good, and not because of the coffee thing, exactly. That is certainly nice, but I think this whole idea of being a team member has begun to acquire new meaning."

"How is that?"

"You know, I think it just sucks to be blind. It sucks to pretend like your team of eight people is all there is. The process we've gone through demonstrates that drawing artificial boundaries hurts you more than it helps. I think at some point, as a team you inevitably become selfish; you think you can just work on your stuff, hit your targets and that's it. But as it turns out, it isn't like that at all..."

In the meantime, Zach and Ed returned with the coffee and Zach handed Josh his cup, filled with fresh, fragrant, bittersweet goodness.

Josh took the cup, nodded to Zach and continued: "A few years ago when we were adopting Agile as a team, some of us struggled with it, failing to understand that being a team means collaboration. Eventually we were able to get past the struggle as a team. But now, as I'm looking at this board, I can't help but realize that the context for collaboration is much broader. It's no longer just 'Gondor'," he said, pointing at all the connections surrounding his team as well as the others. "The statement remains true; the team is where the collaboration happens. But *this* is the team," he said, spreading his arms to indicate the entire board. "The 'Arkenstone'..."

11:00 Final Plan Review

Sunil kicked off the review – and one by one, the teams began to present their plans. The process was very similar to the Draft Plan Review from the day before. However, this time around the primary focus was on the next level of detail of the PI objectives; namely the committed vs. stretch objectives and business value assigned to each one of them. Also, as part of this review, the business owners had to explicitly accept each team's plan. The process was moving at a good pace, as team after team presented. Each time a team plan was accepted, Sunil would ask them to take their PI objectives and global risks and stick them on a separate wall, specifically allocated for that purpose. Finally, when all the plans had been presented and accepted, and there were no big open questions left, Sunil pointed to the wall that contained all the objective sheets: "This is our plan of intent. This is what we think we are going to do as a program in the next PI. A few more things need to be done here, though...

"After lunch, I would like to ask you guys to return promptly so that together we can get rid of all the red stickies out there," he said, waving his laser pointer across all the risks underneath the PI objectives.

I automatically followed the crowd to the tables where lunch was being catered - everything smelled so enticing. Or maybe we were all just so hungry after lifting such a heavy load above our heads. Somehow I couldn't think about anything else but the mashed potatoes, the grilled meat–at least three different kinds–and the green salad with various dressings, obviously making it less healthy. However, I think the least healthy thing right now would be delaying the lunch itself, no matter what it happens to be.

Olga, far ahead in the line, was pouring some soup in a bowl and explaining to a couple of developers that the best soup in the world is called Borscht. She went on to explain how it is misspelled and how it is actually not a soup at all and that nobody calls it 'soup' in the part of the world where it came from.

"So, it's like the Duality Principle in Quantum Mechanics," said Josh, who was in line next to Olga. "As long as you are not trying to taste it, it's a soup. But as soon as you sip a little, it suddenly loses all its soup properties and all you are left with is a bowl of Borscht."

The guys at the front of the line chuckled, busily packing their plates with the very precious energy. Olga just shook her head without saying anything.

"...And you know why it is the way it is?" continued Josh, who wasn't ready to give up on the subject so easily. "Because the broth that is used in that 'soup' is made from Schroedinger's cat."

"That wasn't funny at all!" said Olga to Josh, who was cracking himself and his peers up. They were taking over merely by quantity, out-laughing Olga's attempts to recover.

"Can I talk to you for a second?" Ed asked, materializing behind my back it seemed, from nowhere. "Once you get your plate fixed, of course..."

I finished filling my plate and followed Ed to the meeting room, where Zach was already eating his lunch and, as usual, staring at his laptop screen. "Sit down guys, let's talk for a minute."

Ed sat next to me and said, "Zach and I wanted to talk to you about today's call with QCell..."

"Okay," I said, wondering what else had happened that would cause them to need a separate get-together for something that was already scheduled and had been discussed.

"See, Ethan," said Zach, turning his laptop towards me, "sometimes you think people are ignoring you, but instead they are showing you more attention than you ever wanted. Like in this case," he said, pointing to the attendee list for our upcoming call today. "I originally thought we would barely get their attention. I thought they weren't interested at all, right Ed?"

Ed nodded.

"But you know, I double checked," he said, waving his finger back over the list. "They've listed all of their board members and executives on this call and they have all accepted the invite. So, congratulations, Ethan, you're really in the spotlight now!"

"What Zach here is trying to say," said Ed, with a very serious expression, "is that for some reason it's not exactly shaping up the way we thought it would. And that's both good and bad at the same time. The good news is that they *are* interested in us, no matter what they say."

"What's the bad news?" I asked.

"We don't know why," interjected Zach, bursting into laughter.

"Of course it's important that during the call we are very careful with what we say," said Ed. "You will be doing most of the talking, Ethan. We need *you* to drive this puppy home. We want them to hear from the actual person that's driving organizational change here, rather than from us. We want it to be really authentic... and impressive. But at the same time, keep in mind that you are talking to an audience that will decide the fate of this deal, and we still have no clear idea what's on their mind."

"We thought we did," said Zach, still smiling, not prepared to bring closure to his last joke. "But it turns out that... you never know."

"Well, guys, I will certainly do my best, but it's hard to promise anything when there are so many variables in the equation..."

"We understand," said Ed. "All we are saying is that we have to listen first and listen carefully and then make every move with caution, that's it."

"My turn to be an interpreter," said Zach, smiling. "What Ed is trying to say is that in about three hours you will be crawling through a minefield. You will lead and we, your fearless friends, will be crawling right behind you," he said laughing. "There are two ways of spotting a mine. One is by taking precautions and carefully testing the ground ahead. The other one is by accidentally detonating it. We want you to stick to the first scenario..."

1:00 Program Risks

"At this point I would like us to go over those open issues that each team has identified and needs help with. We won't rest until we get rid of all of those program risks in your plans," said Sunil, pointing at the row of red stickies beneath the objectives. "The way we are going to achieve this is by 'roaming' the risks. 'R-O-A-M' is our magic acronym. Each letter is a classification category for risks. 'R' stands for 'Resolved'; we will put a sticky there if it turns out that there is no actual risk anymore. 'O' means 'Owned'; that is, when someone on the train has kindly offered their help driving it to conclusion with you. 'A' stands for 'Accepted' – these are the risks we can't do anything about and just have to live with. And finally, 'M' means 'Mitigated'; someone has a mitigation plan for the risk. And since there are no more questions, I'm going to get started here. The first team in the sequence is 'Server-side.'" Sunil approached their risk sheet and picked off one of the two stickies they had there. "Okay, let's see what our esteemed guests wrote here. I'm not sure it's written in English..."

The room laughed.

"No wonder we could never parse their APIs," someone shouted from the back of the room, triggering another wave of laughter.

"Let's be serious," said Sunil, barely able to keep his lips from a treacherous tremor. "So, if I'm right, it says 'Too much, too fast'. Bonnie, could you elaborate?"

"Sure, this is in respect to the overall issue of us being in a state of haste with all this work," she said. "We've never done anything like this before, and given that 'Server-side' and mobile applications development cycles used to be much longer than three weeks, we are concerned."

"But I thought you guys had stripped it all down to the required minimum functionality in order to be able to unblock the 'Arkenstone' teams..." said Sunil.

"Sunil," said Josh, jumping up from his seat, "we have the sibling-risk in our plan for that, too. It has nothing to do with planning per se. We operate under an assumption: that we will be able to execute in a new manner, frequently iterating as a whole. Bonnie's right; nobody here has done that before. So it would be unfair to speak with much confidence in this case. The risk is real; we don't have proven ways of working fast across programs. And, the impact is really significant. If Bonnie and these guys don't give it to us in time, there will be a negative ripple effect into a couple of critical features."

Ed raised his hand. "Hey guys, I have a crazy idea here. We may not have yet established patterns of implementing things fast across programs, but we are about to experience some goodness within one program, 'Arkenstone'. What if, for the duration of this PI, we just bring these guys over and have them work side-by-side with the 'Arkenstone' teams? That way everything will be developed and tested using *our* infrastructure, which should simplify it even further..."

The train began humming, "Yeah, bring them over! One more team!"

"I like the idea a lot," said Josh. "That will help us tremendously here."

Bonnie stood up and raised her hand, asking the group to calm down a little. "Guys, as much as we all like working with you–and make no mistake, we really enjoyed this today–I doubt that it is possible. We are tightly bound to a couple of ongoing things in our home program."

"Nope," said Zach. "Not any more, you're not. I will take care of it. We're gonna talk to your bosses soon anyway, Ed and I. Consider it done - we need you guys on this train. Hey, Sunil, put my name on that sticky as an owner, please..."

Sunil did as suggested and then placed the sticky into the consolidated risk sheet for the entire program, into quadrant 'O'.

"Oh, Sunil," Zach added, "let's assign those guys a fancy name, too. ASAP. I can't stand it when we diverge so wildly from the genre... Guys," he turned back to the teams, "a quick round of brainstorming?"

"Yeah! Let's do it! Brainstorming!" shouted out the teams.

"How 'bout we call them the 'Undead'?" offered Josh.

"Be nice!" said Zach, continuing and turning to Ed: "Hey Ed, do we need to keep him or can we just find ourselves someone a little less smart and a little more polite?"

"Not in this PI, Zach," said Ed with a serious expression.

"How about 'Lorien'?" someone in the back shouted. "That's where the elves came from to save the men in the battle at 'Helm's Deep'."

"Yeah! That sounds relevant," said someone at another table.

"I like that," said Zach. "Now we're talking... 'Lorien' it is."

"Okay, 'Lorien' has one more sticky on their risk sheet," said Sunil. "Let's see..." he picked up the sticky and suddenly rolled his eyes: "What?! Seriously? Guys, check this out: 'poor supply of doughnuts in our home program'?"

The group exploded in laughter and Bonnie immediately blushed.

"You are now part of 'Arkenstone', guys," said Zach, "Sunil, please put that sticky in the 'R' quadrant."

The laughter went on while Sunil went over and put it under 'R'. "Alright guys, calm down... enough, enough. Next team will be..."

He moved to 'Rohan' and then to 'Erebor' and so on until the consolidated set of objectives had no more red stickies underneath it. In the meantime, all the stickies ended up in one of the four R-O-A-M quadrants.

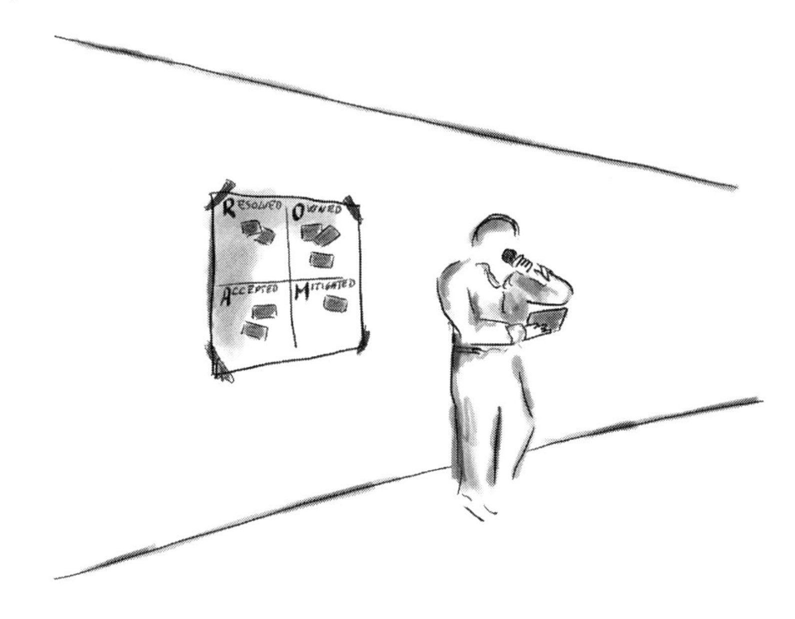

2:00 Confidence Vote

"The primary goal of the PI planing," said Sunil, "is to align to a common understanding of what will be built in the next PI and how it will be built. This means that both the business owners and the teams have to agree that this is an actionable, meaningful plan," he said, pointing at the teams' PI objective sheets, lined up next to each other. "Well, the business owners have done their part of the handshake: they have accepted all of the plans. Now it's your turn guys," he said to the teams. "What we are going to do now is conduct a vote of confidence. We can't call it a plan until all the people that will be implementing it confirm that it's truly feasible and that they feel comfortable committing to it. But before we take the confidence vote itself, I would like to talk for a second about the subject of our commitment here.

"When we say we commit to the PI plan, we assume two things. One, we commit to deliver on the PI objectives above the dotted line–which are for obvious reasons called 'Committed Objectives'–and that we do our best with respect to the ones that are below the line, which are known as stretch objectives. So, that's the first part of our commitment. Reality, however, sometimes sets in differently - not always optimally and often far from predictable. Things may go wrong or just evolve significantly different from what we had planned. Therefore, the second part of our commitment is to ensure that as soon as we find a serious divergence from the plan on the wall–something that essentially alters the PI objectives–we are going to bring this up with the business owners immediately, seeking optimum resolution together. The vote is just a fist-of-five, with one being extremely low confidence in the plan and five representing an extremely high level of confidence. As long as the average vote is above three, we are good to go.

"Okay, let's get started. Team 'Erebor': ready, set, go!"

The members of 'Erebor' raised their hands indicating their votes and Sunil started counting: "Five, four, four, four, five, four, five. Okay, that is definitely above three. Thank you 'Erebor'. Guys, give them a hand."

The train applauded and Sunil moved to the next team - 'Rohan'. That team also voted at quite a high level. He went team by team and all of them ended up with a decent confidence vote.

"Now, we also have to take into account that we are not just a bunch of isolated teams. There are dependencies that we need to address during the execution and that, overall, we will be delivering value in a collaborative manner. Therefore I am asking you now to vote altogether as a train. Ready? Go!"

The entire group raised their hands. "Please h-o-l-d, h-o-l-d, I need to get an idea of where we are," said Sunil, carefully examining the group's show of hands. "Alright, I think the vote is lower than the first time, but still above three and a half as far as I can tell from a rough estimate."

In the meantime, Adi stood up, approached Sunil, and shared something with him very quietly.

"Guys," said Sunil, "Adi has made a great suggestion here. It would help if we hear from the people that voted the lowest. And I remember there were a couple of 'two's'. Guys that so voted, could you please speak up."

One of the observers brought the second microphone over and handed it to a person from 'Ice Bay' that had voted low.

"I am concerned that we built the plan assuming that a new way of operating would be in place. I know that we have some buffers in the plan, but we also haven't experienced much in the way of dependency management. I'm wondering what happens if the assumptions we built upon start showing systemic error..."

"We had pretty much the same concern here," shouted another person that had also voted with a 'two'.

Adi raised her hand and Sunil gave her the microphone.

"I am really happy that you guys think that way. A plan is just a plan. There are certain assumptions built into it, you are absolutely right. I would like you guys to always see it that way and never become complacent. That's a good trait I wish was the general case across our industry. Now, your question still needs to be addressed. And with Sunil's permission, I would like to address it after we do the retrospective for this planning event..."

Sunil took over the mic and moved to the last agenda item.

2:20 Planning Retrospective & Moving Forward

Sunil rolled in a clean whiteboard, split it into three columns and labeled them 'What Went Well', 'What Didn't' and 'What We Would Do Differently Next Time'. Then he simply opened it for discussion and began capturing key points where they belonged on the board.

"Sunil, thanks for your great facilitation," said Ed and the whole group exploded in applause. Ed is right of course, Sunil absolutely deserved it. He had quickly dropped a few bad habits and had proved to be a really good RTE. Adi was really happy with him, too. Sunil approached the board and very carefully quoted Ed's whole phrase, writing as if it was a calligraphy contest, adding some extra emphasis where he saw fit: 'Sunil, thanks for your G-R-E-A-T facilitation.' That made everybody laugh and Sunil turned back to the group and said with a straight face: "Good start guys, keep going."

"I liked how we identified and managed dependencies," someone offered.

"... And the risks we identified, too. We've never done that before." Sunil added those items.

"I would like to add one negative item, if I may," said Olga, the product manager. "Or maybe it's something for the third column... I think my organization needs to do a better prep and engage teams' Product Owners earlier and to a greater extent. We will do that at the next PI boundary for sure."

Sunil captured that, too.

"And I have a positive item, too," continued Olga. "I think if it wasn't for the teams, the plan would have been complete bullshit!"

The group went insane. People applauded and it seemed it would never end. Well, there you go – Olga with her sometimes brutal honesty, had hit it right on the money.

"I think it was a great decision to bring over the 'Server-side' guys and give them their true name," said Josh. "Without them in the room, this plan would have been just one big bubble."

"Guys," said a tester from 'Erebor', raising his hand, "I may only be speaking for my team here, or perhaps other teams in the room had the same impression, but for us, this is the first time we have had any confidence at all in our plan..."

"Yay! Same here! Yay!" seconded various teams throughout the room.

Sunil added that last item and proceeded to the next step. "Adi, the stage is yours."

Adi talked for around fifteen minutes about what would happen next and how the train was going to address uncertainty, as well as possible problems to be expected throughout the PI execution. She answered a couple of good questions, but my brain was at this point unable to process any of that. Plus, I badly needed to preserve any remaining mental energy for the upcoming call with QCell.

I noticed that Sunil had taken the stage again. He talked for a while, and then asked Zach to say a few closing words. The next thing I noticed was that almost everybody had left the room.

I walked upstairs and into the conference room. I couldn't help but stare out of the window, waiting for Zach and Ed to show up. What a busy day... two days, actually. A whole new dynamic had been created. There is truly some magic to this planning thing – the magic of addressing complexity with the most powerful weaponry there is: face-to-face communication. Adi was right back then at the conference. I don't know why we had all capitulated so early by defining small teams and limiting direct interaction pretty much to the people on one such team. Now it just seems... stupid.

It was obviously getting colder outside: the window glass was quite refreshing to my fingertips, sending a different frequency signal to my brain. And it should have been even colder already at this point, given our proximity to the mountains. The big cloud that I had seen on the far side of the valley in the morning appeared to have finally reached town, against all odds. The whole sky was now covered in a milky foam, lighter than a feather and stuck for good under the dome. This one will be brewing until it's done.

I soon noticed how a tiny, miniscule white dot had hit the glass on the other side at a very steep angle, accelerated by the wind that had begun to show some real passion. The flake stuck to the glass and slowly melted. Then came another tiny flake and another, and in a minute or two the wind was blowing and curling and hauling insanely accelerated bits of the milky cloud, smashing them against the window without the slightest sign of remorse.

"Please enter your conference code number," said a voice that seemed to have been carved into my brain over the last couple years. I hadn't even noticed Zach and Ed enter the room, or put their laptops on the table, or connect to the big screen. They had probably been talking all this time, maybe even to me, but clearly to little effect.

"Ethan," said Zach in a very official tone, handing me a cup of coffee, "Ed and I just learned today that the best way for the two of us to be servant leaders is to just *serve* our employees more coffee..."

"The only way, I would say!" said Ed, while entering the code.

"Drink the coffee," said Zach pointing at my cup, "or you'll miss your own show!"

In the meantime, Ed succeeded with the code and the voice on the other side said, "QCell on the line, this is John. I have sixteen people here in the room, and we are all eager to see what you guys have got for us..."

"Into the fray, gentlemen," said Zach, unmuting the 'claw.'

ETHAN'S DIARY

- *Business owners and teams must spend lots of time together during the planning. The best way to ensure ample time is to programmatically walk around and attend every team, while assigning business value to the PI objectives. Many inconsistencies will surface and real alignment will occur as a result.*

- *Managing dependencies can be a tricky business. The guys came up with a great idea: consolidate all dependencies onto a single board – that helped a lot. It created a unique systems perspective on the entire ART's plan for the PI.*

- *In the case where significant dependencies on another program exist, having representatives of that program join the planning session turned out to be priceless. If that didn't happen, there would be no chance to build an achievable PI plan.*

- *No matter what, overloading a train is always a horrible idea. If it seems that the train is overloaded—or there are bottlenecks in the plan that require miraculous execution precision—you are in trouble and your plan will not work! De-scope...*

- *PI planning must result in a 'handshake' between business owners and teams. Business owners must accept the plan, while teams have to express their confidence level in delivering the plan. Nobody can commit the teams to a certain amount of work. Only the teams themselves can commit to specific scope outcomes.*

- *Teams can figure out a lot on their own as a result of cross-team collaboration. Sometimes, however, such collaboration needs to be facilitated, to provide the initial momentum.*

CHAPTER 9

The Pitfalls of Execution

"They can't see it, because what they are looking for is what they are looking with."

-RACHEL

ON THE BIG DAY, THE conference room that could comfortably hold about 25 people was filled to the brim. It felt like something exciting was going to happen – and how else would it feel? I hadn't spent too much time with Sunil, but it looked like he'd gotten it all covered. There was no telling where things really stood though, because everyone was so freaking busy now. I had barely had time for a single meaningful conversation with Sunil, or the Scrum Masters, or anybody else about the iteration status during the last few days. And all the bits of information that I was receiving were the usual 'we are getting there' kind of things. And I hadn't had much spare time to dig into much detail either: somehow, after the ART launch for 'Arkenstone', I had suddenly become a very busy and important guy, spending more time with Zach, Ed and Nerissa and various other big dudes and gals in our organization. I think

I was starting to enjoy it, too. Hopefully not because of its essentially flattering nature, but rather because I was learning how these people operate; how they think, what matters to them the most, and how I could help my organization move forward in the most effective manner by working directly with the executives and VPs.

"We need to think about taking the rollout a couple of steps further," said Ed, shortly after the PI planning. "I can envision more value for everyone by doing that. Especially now that we know how to launch a train."

And I couldn't agree more. Yes, we should take further steps. I think now that we have 'Arkenstone' up and running, we may just launch a couple more trains. Although as Adi told us, there are a few pitfalls to be careful about. And I'm not going to ignore her recommendations anymore, as I did with the leadership training back in the day. That one I payed for tenfold. And it was memorable enough that I wouldn't make that mistake ever again. Being careful however, is one thing and procrastinating is quite another. The latter we cannot afford. And it's also unfair. Now that we have a better method, it is unfair to keep other groups stuck with what they have - we need to take advantage of the momentum.

The important thing for that day however, was the first serious checkpoint for 'Arkenstone' - the System Demo. System Demos, as Adi explained to us, are the heartbeat of an Agile Release Train. If you are not doing them, you are essentially 'waterfalling' the PI, no matter what Lean and Agile jargon you use in the meantime to flatter yourself. "You can do whatever you want of course, but every two weeks there needs to be a fully integrated demo of the system increment," she said. And yes, she knows how to emphasize things, so we listened carefully.

Now that we had addressed the QCell problem, the importance of this PI became much, much greater. The call with QCell had a surprising outcome. The person we had feared the most; the lady that had just joined the QCell Board of Directors, Marsha–unexpectedly turned out to be our greatest ally in the conversation. And the fact that there were so many important people in the room on their side, actually played out quite well in the end: at least we didn't have to go around later, convincing different people individually. Marsha was the one who was blocking the deal in the first place. She suggested that QCell shouldn't sign with a company like ours because we are unable to reliably deliver our releases. But it turned out that she wasn't the only sceptic there. She was just further stirring a pond that was already full of murky water. Quite a few of the other QCell people, as it turned out, had the same concern, which they gladly articulated on that call.

"We called you guys because we, as a company, are refusing to accept our current way of working," Zach said, starting the call with a very philosophical speech. "We are investing heavily in changing our delivery capability. Redefining it, in fact... And I'm not talking about some highly localized attempt to do a little bit of disjointed improvement here and there. I'm talking about a comprehensive solution that our CEO is personally involved in, and that we are all taking very, very seriously." And Zach was telling the truth – just that morning he had spoken with the CEO about the method. What Zach failed to tell the people on the phone was that his conversation with the CEO had been largely about putting on hold any further lay-offs. Retaining our workforce would allow us at least to be able to deliver something... But isn't that a level of detail that just creates unnecessary ambiguity? Zach knew that it was. "Now I would like to introduce my colleague, Ethan," he continued. "He is the Head of our Transformation Team, and I would like him to talk more about exactly what we are doing here as part of the transformation."

And so I pretty much took over the rest of the call... I told their folks that on that same day, we had just finished our big planning event. I also told them how we trained our teams and how we worked with our leadership to prepare for the launch. I circled back to the PI planning itself, and described in more detail how the process looked, how important it is to establish alignment, perform fair capacity planning, and how critical it is to have everyone in the same room. And that's when I was interrupted...

"Excuse me, this is Marsha speaking," a voice on the other end broke in. "Ethan, what you are describing is ringing some bells for me, actually. The method you guys are applying, what is it called exactly?"

"SAFe..." I replied automatically. "Or Scaled Agile Framework..."

"Ok, VeraComm guys, hold on please," Marsha said as the whole group on the other side went on mute. I've never seen Zach so anxious as he was during that pause. And it was a really long pause, lasting for three or four minutes. A sense of uncertainty was creeping into my mind as well, readily offering various explanations, very few of them suggesting a happy path for us. Ed put us on mute also. "This is taking too long," he said, wiping his forehead with a napkin. "I would give a lot to hear what the heck are they talking about over there."

"Me too," said Zach. "I have to tell you people, this is not good. Right now I'm aging like a year every minute."

"Well, that's like..." Ed stared in the window for a quick second, "five hundred thousand times faster than usual, Zach," he said, smiling.

"Don't be a smart-ass–"

A sharp click and then background noise from the other side of the call interrupted our highly intellectual exchange of niceties.

"Okay, we're back guys – sorry for taking so long," said a man's voice that we thought was John, the organizer of the call and the person who had reached out to Zach initially to notify him of the problem. "Marsha here shared her experiences with SAFe from other large enterprises she's worked with. And based on what she's saying, we feel excited about the change on your end. Marsha said that the method primarily solves delivery issues, amongst other things, and we like that. She obviously likes what you guys are doing and that matters a lot, because *she* was the one who caused all the trouble in the first place..." he said as the group at QCell broke into laughter. "She's signaling me though," continued John, "that she has something to say to you guys. Marsha?"

"Thanks John. Guys, I like where you are headed with the new method..."

When she said that, Zach performed a little dance in his chair, waving his arms in the air in a very peculiar way. Meanwhile, Marsha continued...

"But I need to ask you all something. What I liked about SAFe was its very straightforward governance method... Or, said another way: it allows you to see where you are and how to proceed further very, very easily. Your PI will end in a quarter, is that right, Ethan?"

"That is correct..."

"I would like to be in on that demo."

Zach suddenly looked troubled and turned to look at me with a big question mark in his eyes.

"Marsha, consider yourself invited," I said automatically. "We will be glad to have you as part of that important event."

And that was it. As unbelievable as it sounds, the rest of the conversation focused on the additional steps necessary to make the deal happen. The actual deal would close a little later, in fact by a funny coincidence, shortly after our next PI boundary. But the feeling in the room was overwhelmingly awesome. We had done it! Zach and Ed were very pleased with my decisiveness during the call. And of course I was happy with the outcome, too. Later that night, despite my exhaustion, I was restless as I described every detail of the call to Rachel.

Adi stayed with us for one more day after the PI planning, to meet with the business owners, Scrum Masters, Product Owners and some other stakeholders, and to orient them on how to best support the execution of the PI. Adi has a busy schedule and is booked to the brim, so right after the workshop, she took off. The earliest we would be able to get her back was in about two months, and that was okay with everyone because it aligned well with our target timeframe to begin spreading the method across the rest of the organization. We weren't too worried about Adi's constrained availablity. In fact, rather than relying completely upon a consultant, it was time for us to develop an internal capability to problem-solve and really begin thinking Agile and Lean. We needed to learn how to effectively execute in this model on our own.

So that's how we all ended up in a demo room packed with people, waiting for the final preparations to be completed – we were all very anxious to see what our first iteration had produced. We could have gotten a bigger room but, as Sunil pointed out, it wasn't until the last minute that more people had decided to attend. Every team had sent their PO and SM to represent them. Some teams had also sent a developer or a tester. Olga was sitting up front, with Ed and Nathan. And since this was our first system demo, we also had a couple of guys from the Transformation Team as observers. It was important to start exposing as many of our change agents as we could to such events; some of them might become RTEs for other trains in the organization, or perhaps just operate as coaches for programs and teams. Zach showed up a little later (but still on time), and patted me on the shoulder as he proceeded all the way to the front where he sat down next to Ed. Then Sunil raised his hand giving everyone the signal that we should get started.

"We will have each team representative demonstrate their part of this iteration's scope," said Sunil following a short introduction to the event itself. "Each team will have about five minutes or so. At the end, we will see if there are any adjustments that need to be made to the rest of the PI, based on what we observe today. Teams, good luck!"

First up was 'Rivendell'. They had their developer and their PO on the stage and demonstrated current progress on Picture-in-Picture functionality. They showed it quite quickly, mostly focusing on a few key scenarios. They openly admitted that the application didn't provide any controls for PIP yet, and that they were still assessing the overall UX impact of this feature. And even though PIP wasn't complete, I could see that Olga and Zach were really pleased with what they saw.

"Good job!" said Sunil. He then invited the next team, 'Erebor', to present. Their Scrum Master took the stage and briefly recapped what they had worked on in this iteration. At the same time, the 'Erebor' test engineer that had come to present at the demo, was reloading the client application on the demo tablet, which was connected to the projector.

"Why are they doing that?" I whispered to Sunil as he sat down next to me to catch a breath between the team presentations.

"Doing what?" asked Sunil, sotto voce.

"Reinstalling the app through TestFlight again..."

"I don't know. To make sure that 'Rivendell' didn't mess up the settings during their demonstration maybe? I really don't know..."

In the meantime, the team successfully demonstrated their functionality and addressed Olga's questions.

"Next team, please," said Sunil after the group applauded 'Erebor's' presentation. "'Ice Bay', you're up."

The presenter from 'Ice Bay' followed the same procedure as the previous two by reloading the client app prior to starting their demonstration.

"They did it again," I said to Sunil.

This time Sunil didn't say anything, but was beginning to look a little puzzled as he continued watching and listening to the presentation. In the meantime, 'Ice Bay's' presenter, their PO, had demonstrated the first cut on hooking up a third-party PowerPoint presentation viewer, and was ready to move to the next piece.

"Wait!" whispered Sunil so sharply that people in the front row turned around. He bent forward a little bit and continued more quietly, looking askance at me: "It's actually a different app!"

"A different app?"

He whispered back: "Yeah, I think so" while looking around. "Is this a different app?" he finally said out loud as he stood up and walked towards the projector screen. "Is it really a different app? I noticed some slight divergencies on the UI from what 'Erebor' had just used when demonstrating their functionality."

The next couple of seconds passed in awkward silence.

"Yeah, we noticed that you guys were reloading the app through TestFlight every time," he continued. "So we were curious why would you reload the same app over and over again. But it turns out that these are different apps..."

Zach, Ed and the rest of the stakeholders in the first row turned around to look at Sunil.

"Are you saying there is a problem?" asked Zach.

"I don't know," said Sunil. "That's why I'm asking the team representatives, to find out."

Zach turned back to the presenter and raised his eyebrows: "So, what say you?"

"Well, they are not different apps really..." said the PO of 'Ice Bay'. "Rather they are different versions of the same app."

Sunil shook his head and by the silent movement of his lips, it was obvious that he had something on his mind he didn't want others to hear.

Zach stared at the screen for a while and said: "I'm not sure I follow–"

"Oh, don't you see what's happening?" said Ed, jumping in. "They are demonstrating separate branches." He turned back to the rest of the group: "Everybody here seems to have brought a nice little code branch of their own. Just like the good old days, eh? This is staggering. This is *not* what we said we would do..." He glanced at Sunil and then continued: "All those talks about integration and then this...? I thought we all agreed that we would do it right. This is really embarrassing – we're right back at square one!"

"Guys, I thought we were all onboard about integrating work from different teams. All of you were in on the discussions about integration. And now all of that is down the drain? Why? Why didn't you just follow the plan of attack we agreed to?" Sunil was definitely exerting effort to keep from showing the whole depth of his frustration.

Nobody said anything in response.

"Guys?" asked Sunil, looking around. "Come on, this is serious, we need to talk about this. Where is my last hope – 'Gondor'? Josh? Are you here?"

"Yes..."

"Did you guys do the same thing as everybody else?"

"Sunil, I don't want to sound like a smart-ass, but it's pretty much clear as day: if all the other teams branched out, whatever we were left with is by defintion a branch, don't you think?" Josh had just the slightest smirk on his face.

"Oh, so you think this is funny?" said Sunil, who was becoming increasingly frustrated.

"No, it's not funny. We tried to integrate," continued Josh. "Didn't we, guys?" he asked, looking around the room as multiple people nodded in response to his question.

"And...?" Sunil asked.

"We tried a couple of times and it just didn't happen," someone else added from the back of the room.

"We came to realize that if we kept trying, we would screw up the iteration," said Josh.

Sunil closed his eyes and sighed. After a few seconds of trying to escape reality, he looked back at everyone, pointed at the screen and said in a surprisingly calm voice: "I hate to disappoint you guys, but *this is* what we call a screw-up. This means that as a program we have no idea what has been delivered in this iteration, because what works at the branch level, as we all know from our less than glorious past, never works when put together." He stood still and calm for a few more seconds and then continued. "So, what I am going to tell you should not be taken personally, because it's not intended that way. It's just a fact. What you are showing here is by definition zero credit for this iteration. It's not a fraction of the whole. It is zero. And that's not an exaggeration..."

"Great start," said Zach to Ed, as he stood up and left the room. It wasn't too hard to guess where his thinking was at that moment. If we kept producing 'zero increments' at every iteration boundary, by the time Marsha came to visit us, this would be a deeply pathetic scene. Pathetic and memorable. It really would be the end of everything, I think: the end of SAFe for us, the end of our efforts to make this organization a better place, the end of my career...

Ed ran after Zach, and seconds later, Nathan and Olga stood up and left.

"We just blew it," said Sunil, looking at me. "Our chances of succeeding in this game were just shattered into a bunch of tiny, worthless branches..."

• • •

I noticed that the days were becoming noticeably shorter since we had begun the rollout. And despite the fact that many people don't enjoy such changes, I actually do like it. It seems to be better for sleeping. When it's dark outside, there's almost no need for Melatonin – your body simply knows how to rest better. But even that couldn't help me fall asleep last night. I just couldn't stop thinking about what had happened at the system demo and how quickly we had managed to fail at what seemed to be a great breakthrough that had offered so much hope.

"How are you?" asked Raymond. I was in the kitchen making coffee when he came in.

"So I guess you heard about it, huh?" I asked, already knowing the answer to my question.

"I did. And I feel bad for you, my friend."

"Thanks."

"...And for me."

"I'm sorry? What does this whole thing have to do with you?"

"Well, a lot actually. It doesn't take a genius to figure out that if QCell sees that we've screwed-up at the end of the quarter, VeraComm will be back in the business of laying-off their... whatcha call it... knowledge workers?"

He's right, of course – I hadn't thought about that. But none of this matters, really, because any way you look at it, we have no choice but to fix this problem.

"What else do you know, Raymond?"

"Well, I have heard some people saying that this whole transformation was probably doomed from the very start. And that it will just end up hurting the company even more."

"That's not news. What else you got?"

"Tough conversations are happening up there," he said in a quieter voice, pointing to the floors above us. "I don't know too many details, but I know it's too political for our paygrade."

"Stop talking in riddles, Raymond. You are not helping. Tell me what you know and you will do us both a big favor!"

Raymond shook his head and continued, "There's not much else to say. What I do know is that there was a tough discussion among Zach and several other executives; the CTO in particular."

"The CTO?" That is really surprising. From the beginning the CTO had pretty much paid no attention to this whole thing whatsoever. And now, just when we run into our very first hurdle, it turns out that everyone was actually watching carefully? Just a bunch of latent voyeurists, in my opinion. But what do I care? We have bigger fish to fry and the voyeurists will not be very helpful on that fishing expedition. And speaking of the CTO specifically, if it weren't for his direct reports, especially people like Ed, I doubt we would have made it this far at all.

It's people like Ed whose opinions I am really concerned with at the moment.

But what's really bugging me right now is how on earth Raymond knows all this? I thought I had gotten closer to this company's executives during the last couple of weeks, but he never ceases to surprise me with how informed he is; he's always one step ahead.

"Thanks Raymond," I said as I headed out of the kitchen.

"Sure. It makes me feel like I'm really helping... Cures my wounded self-esteem."

"Whatever Raymond..."

Now I need to go find the guys. Sunil was supposed to organize a debriefing. We invited some technical folks from the teams as well as the Scrum Masters. This *must* be a solvable problem, so we need to start working the solution. 'Silver Arrow' solved it, so why shouldn't we be able to do the same?

When I reached the meeting room, everybody was already engaged in a heated discussion. There was hardly any room left on the white-board. The whole board was filled with squiggly squiggles in different marker color.

"...And I'm telling you that we are much better off if we don't inter-rupt each other's flow of work," said Josh, drawing a circle around a bunch of squiggles. "Think of the ultimate outcome, Sunil. We are not trying to apply this practice or apply that practice... The end result we are looking for is to be more efficient. And, to be at least a little bit efficient, we need to have some isolated intervals of time where we can just work on our functionality, instead of thinking about how to integrate or whatever else we need to do..."

A nice little speech... Very enticing. Only I'm not buying into that stuff anymore. For now, I'm going to stick to what I know: integrat-ing frequently *is* possible. I witnessed it myself, period, end of story. Everything else is just a bunch of excuses. Adi shared a great insight with me once in a private conversation, something that has stuck with me.

Back then she said that engineers apply their intellectual capabilities in a very uneven way: in some areas they effectively address highly complex challenges; in other areas, they do even the simplest things absolutely wrong. And behind all of that stands our number one suspect–Mr. Mindset: the hidden cause of almost every systemic problem in a modern enterprise. When something looks weird or things don't add up, look behind the curtain for a belief system that is creating bias. If nothing else, at least I had learned that much during the last couple of months.

"Hey guys," I said, jumping into the conversation, "I have all respect in the world for your engineering skills. And, having been a developer myself, I know first-hand just how it is to be in the trenches. You are my peeps! But what has happened here is just not cool at all. And do you know why? It's not just that we failed the iteration - that is potentially recoverable. The problem is much, much bigger than that: we have lost faith in our own ability to learn. We are like that music box with the figurines that come out of one side and go back into the other in an endless loop. No matter what, we tend to fall back into our old habits, performing the same circle over and over again. We can even pretend, at least a little bit at the planning session, that we are gonna do things differently. But when the rubber hits the road - voila, here we are, just like those figurines: we enter into another round of our vicious cycle."

The guys had gone quiet. Sunil, however, seemed to be a little more relaxed now that I had joined them.

"How did we come to lose our courage so fast?" I continued. I was trying not to go too far, refraining from saying everything that was on my mind. "Guys, I have to tell you a little story and then you can do whatever the heck you please with it."

Sunil raised his eyebrows. Well hey - he's not the only one with emotions; we're all human beings here.

"I have a smudge on my record that I'm not particularly proud of. There was an incident, a long time ago, when I had a chance to step up, face some hard facts and head towards a better reality for me and the people that depended on me. But I chickened out and gave in to the conventional crap-thinking that totally possessed my mind at the time... I very clearly remember how I felt deep down inside; how I knew that I was making the wrong choice, and yet I let fear take over. Not only did I fail myself, but I also failed other people I cared about, and to me that makes it a chapter of shame. I would give anything to go back in time and have just one more chance... one more chance to look that fear in the eye again. And this time I know that I would, without hesitation, put my job, my dignity... everyting I have on the line, just to do what's right. But of course there is no way I can go back in time and do that. And now *you* are standing in front of a choice like that. You have two options: you can continue to justify your fears. And then, one day you will realize that when you had your great chance, you simply chickened out, just like me. Or, you can pluck up your courage and lead, because you are the only people who can do that in this case... But hey, it's your choice. Personally I'm done talking and worrying about it at this point," I said, as I walked out and closed the door behind me.

I had never told anybody that story, not even Rachel. You never know why things are the way they are; why memories work this way. They sit deep inside, like a snake in a bag, until the time comes that they spring out with incredible power and attack with precision. Perhaps at times we experience failures in our lives in order to fulfill the higher mission of being an inspiration to others. Or perhaps I'm just trying to reassure myself in this instance. But the most important thing to keep in mind, is that my job is not really about me at all – it's about them. I think now I am ready to do what it takes; to be of service to my organization and to these great people, who have nevertheless failed to unleash their potential again. And yes, I may have gone too far with this, but I think they deserve to know certain things. My dad would often say: "People you care about deserve honesty, not manipulation." He wasn't just saying that, he lived by that rule. I notice that every time I'm facing a tough dilemma or am experiencing uncertainty of any kind, his words suddenly appear in my mind, throwing me a lifebuoy in the middle of the raging waves that hiss and roar around me.

"What's up? Were you kicked out of your meeting?" asked Raymond as I entered the kitchen. I needed to refill my coffee and catch my breath for a few minutes.

"No, I'm just finished with my part of that meeting. Long meetings suck anyway," I answered automatically. "The real question is what are *you* still doing here?"

"Oh, I'm sitting here thinking about how to make my organization more efficient, you know..."

"Yup, I totally know. And you can also ingest more info and spread more rumors, while you're at it."

Raymond stared at me for a while with a bewildered expression. "Well, that just wasn't nice, Ethan. I thought we were friends. I've always tried to help you by telling you what I know."

"You're right, my friend, I'm sorry. I'm really sorry, you are the..."

I didn't get to finish the sentence because Sunil walked into the kitchen, his face beaming with pride.

"Boss, I don't know what kind of voodoo magic you worked in there, but after you left, the whole conversation shifted. Josh got really emotional about the whole thing."

"In what way?" I asked.

"In a good way. Oh yeah! Of course there still were skeptics, but Josh actually took the lead and pulled off something that none of us could probably have accomplished."

"What did he do?"

"He switched the topic of the whole meeting entirely. At first I wondered what the heck he was doing when he began telling everyone how he had gotten stuck in this iteration because of the video stream buffering issue. He told in detail how he debugged it and finally found the problem just where he would have least expected to. And then

Vivek from 'Erebor' said that he had had a similar issue before. Only in his case the issue wasn't in the screen sharing functionality. Instead, it manifested itself in downloading application settings from the server. The client application would mysteriously drop the connection and there was no earthly means to get to the root of the problem. About two days later he had an epiphany, and it turned out to be... Well, I don't really remember what he said it was, but something completely unrelated, as usual. So they all sat around a while longer, telling each other about their astonishing findings, until our tricky friend Josh interrupted the party by revealing his winning hand. You know that guy is really something, I have to tell you."

"Yes, do tell."

"So he asked the group: 'If we are able to do all this real rocket science stuff–debug the impossible, and build really smart, elaborate algorithms–then how come we can't master a simple-stupid technique like frequent integration?' He told everyone that he didn't want to remain shortsighted, that he had had enough of being un-teachable and not being able to step up to the opportunities around him. He said that it was time for everyone to do a full 'factory reset' of their brains, because over the years their 'garbage collector' had failed to recycle a staggering amount of junk; the kind of junk that happens to drive their thinking and dominate the decision-making process. I guess that analogy nailed it for those guys..."

"Gosh, you engineering peeps are real freaks," said Raymond. "I better go back to my much healthier IT-fellowship," he said as he made his way out of the kitchen.

"So they said they have to give it another shot," continued Sunil. "Or as many shots as it takes until they get it right. They said they would like to meet and discuss a further course of action. Additionally, the Scrum Masters would like to know what to do with the iteration planning that needs to happen today and has already been delayed a couple hours."

All of that is good news. Great news, actually! I know that there's always a chance of success when you approach things with the highest level of respect for people that create value; no matter how hard it seems sometimes because of the disagreements involved.

"Okay, here's what we'll do, Sunil. We will work up a full root cause analysis on this problem, so we need all of those engineers that were in the room back together: the eight or ten people that you had. And tell the Scrum Masters that until we resolve this situation and formulate a clear course of action, there is no iteration planning. I don't want to hear a word about efficiency or any of that from anyone! Enough of that crap. We are talking about a fundamental capability here, without which we cannot succeed. So, tell them to hold tight for a bit and that we will get back to them shortly."

• • •

Sunil gathered everyone together in no time. And it wasn't too hard, especially since the guys, who had been ignited by Josh's fervent speech, were restless.

"We're supposed to legitimately use the problem-solving workshop at the end of this PI," I said, wiping the whiteboard. "But we have a big problem *now* that requires solving, so we are going to break the rules and be proud of it. Is there anyone unwilling to break the rules in this room?"

"No!" they all shouted out.

"That's what I thought. Good. So... I got to observe this problem-solving process up close a while ago when Adi took me with her on a trip to 'Silver Arrow', one of her client's key programs. I was amazed by the simplicity and effectiveness of the method."

The guys were ready to take on anything that would help, it seemed. So I continued.

"Our first goal here is simple. We are going to work together to understand the most significant root cause of the problem. But let's state the problem statement first. Anyone?"

"We failed the iteration," someone suggested.

"I think we can be a lot more specific and transparent than that, guys," said Josh, jumping in. "How about 'We failed to frequently integrate across the board and therefore produced no system increment in this iteration'?"

"I like that," said someone else. "We know clearly what our problem is."

I gave Josh the marker and he wrote down the problem in the box that I had drawn on the board. When he was done, I filled in the rest of the drawing to complete the initial fish bone diagram with the standard big bones: 'People', 'Program', 'Process', 'Environment' and 'Tools'.

"Now, why do you think that problem occurred? Could any of these five areas contain the answer?"

"Yeah," said Josh with some reluctance in his voice. "The 'People' section definitely contains some potential root causes."

"Okay," I said, inviting him to proceed. "So what exactly would that look like? Can you draw another bone coming out of 'People' and label it appropriately?"

"Yeah, I think it's just that we approached integration the wrong way. The new method requires a different sort of thinking. We were thinking in our old way while attempting to apply a fundamentally new technique. It doesn't work that way." He drew another line and labeled it: 'new method, old thinking'. "Right guys?" he asked, turning to the rest of the group. His fellow developers nodded in agreement.

"Good. Now why do you think that's the case though?" I continued.

"Because we were too attached to legacy thinking, which has never proven to be effective," said another developer.

Josh drew another line, forking out of the previous one, and labeled it accordingly – 'too attached to legacy thinking'.

"And why is that happening?" I continued, asking the most exciting question in the world.

Nobody said anything for a while. Josh was staring at the white-board, rolling the marker back and forth between his palms. The room was incredibly quiet. During moments like this, it seemed like you could hear their brains boiling inside their skulls.

"We never really look for evidence," someone suggested. "I'll bet you it's been that way with many things, not only with integration. We simply happen to strongly believe that certain things are true, while never even attempting to validate them in practice."

Josh, who by now had completely adopted the role of the writer of other's ideas, drew another line and labeled it: 'we are not validating our assumptions'. "Are you going to ask us 'why that is', too?" he said with the typical smirk he wore when he had figured something out.

"Yep. Consider it asked."

"Well, it's actually very interesting indeed," said Josh: "why don't we look for any objective evidence in support of our assumptions...?"

"I know why," said the same guy. "For things like integration," he continued, "we just do it so infrequently that there is no way to validate any assumption. And that's because the length of time between things being coded and then actually validated is so freaking long that we just can't connect the dots."

"He's right," said Josh. "We integrate so infrequently that we can't learn anything from it." He reflected that finding on the board in the form of a new bone: 'validation is so delayed that it prevents us from learning'. "I think that's the root cause here. We've got it."

"It still doesn't tell us everything though," said the same guy. "Yes, this is great knowledge, but I still don't see how we can switch to integrating it more frequently."

"Okay guys," I said, jumping in, "that's just one potential root cause. We have to keep digging. We should feel free to build another path from the main bones and see where that rabbit hole may lead us."

A couple of quiet seconds ended with a developer from 'Rivendell' chuckling.

"What's so funny?" asked Josh.

"Nothing. No, nothing really."

"Oh, come on, tell us," Josh pressed on, "this is a brainstorming session and you are welcome to say whatever you like... as long as it's on topic. But tell you what: I sense that you are thinking something there, so now you must say it! I command you," he said in a funny low voice.

"Okay, okay," said the developer. "It's not really a root cause, but I just remembered how our integration attempt happened in this iteration and it made me laugh... a little..."

"Yes?" said Josh, "I'm all ears."

"So, when we tried to integrate, stuff just didn't work together, right? And now it seems to me that one couldn't *intentionally* make as many divergencies as we made in this iteration. No disrespect guys—I realize I'm a part of it too—but it's just hilarious to me, for some reason. I'm laughing because if you think about it, it's hard to be that wrong, even on purpose," he said, still chuckling.

Josh stared at him for a while and then turned back to the board: "But you bring up an interesting point," he said, drawing a line from the 'Process' bone and labeling it 'too many divergencies'. "Okay guys, from now on I will play the role of Ethan and I will be asking questions," he said with a frown, continuing the theatrics. "So, why do we think we had so many inconsistencies?" He glanced around then continued, saying: "Coincidentally, I happen to know the answer to that. The answer is... because we started too late in the iteration—"

"Yeah, but to be honest, there was nothing to integrate earlier," said the developer.

"Ethan, this is against the rules," said Josh, smiling at me and pointing at the developer. "This irresponsible person found a next order cause without me asking the 'why'. It's unacceptable!" He then added another line and the words: 'nothing to integrate earlier'.

He looked around the quiet room, "Come on, don't be shy, break the rules again... I know you want to do it more than anything..."

"I think I know why we had nothing to integrate early," said a lady from 'Rohan'. "I think it's because we're stupid..."

"That's freaking ingenious," said Josh with a very serious expression. "I doubt that any one of us would have figured that out on their own. Thank you! Thank you, for enlightening us, Elizabeth."

"No, hear me out," she continued. "I meant to say that the way we approached the whole problem of frequent integration was wrong from the beginning. It's like having a chronic stomachache and instead of going on a diet, you start eating everything in sight."

"Elizabeth, that sounds... potentially useful, but like in English, what would it mean?"

"Well, currently we do not build for early integration. We develop initial functionality while absolutely ignoring the fact that it needs to be built in a compatible manner."

Josh shook his head: "Please explain... I don't get it."

"Look guys, ask yourself a simple question: what broke the build when we tried to integrate?"

"Many things..."

"Pick one."

"Well, for example, plenty of incompatible method calls... Overall it was the interfaces between classes that ended up completely misaligned..."

"Yup. That's what I'm talking about! The interfaces are misaligned because those interfaces evolve independently, which is kind of insane if you think about it. We build our functionality first and that determines our interfaces with other classes and components. That is a guaranteed way to obtain divergencies everywhere possible." She turned to look at the developer who had found the matter funny earlier and continued: "No wonder it seemed to you as if those inconsistencies were created on purpose. We just build things in isolation from one another and then try to make it all come together and work, which it certainly will never do. It will never work because it's not supposed to. If we want it to integrate, we need to start building *every bit of it* with integration in mind!"

Josh squinted but kept quiet. In fact, everybody was quiet. Finally, Josh broke the silence: "I am willing to admit that you are right. It *was* stupid. Very thoughtful, Elizabeth. Ethan, I think we have found our most powerful root cause. And, I think we know what to do now..."

• • •

"Ethan, tell me that we have a chance at pulling this off. Or tell me something, at least," said Ed when I met with him sometime later upon his request. "You know, Zach will cook us both alive if we don't figure something out. Coming out of that demo, he was really mad at me and everyone else, you included."

"Well, we have a plan," I said.

"That's great. But I would like to understand this plan first, because just knowing that you've got something–and please don't get me wrong–isn't comforting enough. So... what you got for me?"

"Three things. First of all, we are going to produce a system demo in two days. The teams decided that letting it slip to the next iteration is unacceptable and will reinforce bad habits."

"In two days? So, I can invite Zach, right?"

"That is correct."

"Awesome! But this time around Ethan, I would like someone to show me the demo beforehand. You know, just so I can sleep better..."

"Not a problem. We will make that happen."

"Okay, what are the other two things?"

"Secondly, we have found a fundamental flaw in our integration process and we have corrective action to take. We will use a different approach now."

"Good, good! And the last one?"

"And finally, iteration 2 must be de-scoped. We will aim at a subset of the functionality due to the fact that this iteration will be two days shorter. As I said before, we are going to sacrifice a couple of days to pay off the integration debt from the previous iteration. When we're done with iteration 2, we will have to meet with Zach and Olga to carefully revise the remaining PI plan. There most likely will be some adjustments."

"And by that you mean you will be de-scoping the PI, don't you?"

"Yes, but it's for the better. That de-scoping will allow us to deliver reliably at the end of the PI."

"Well, I would be careful about using 'reliably' in a sentence if I was you, Ethan."

"Ed, right now I need your support like never before. I need you to trust us and I need you to back us with your bosses. Can you do that for me?"

"Oh gosh, it's just so tough to be a leader like me," said Ed, smiling. "A true servant leader... Sometimes I fascinate even myself. I will help, don't worry about that. Just worry about your part instead. Because if something doesn't work out, you and I will have to start updating our LinkedIn profiles."

"Understood. You can trust me, Ed. We'll make it. You'll see. And one more question, if I may."

"Yes?"

"I've heard about some kind of turf war going on between Zach and the CTO's office," I said. I noticed that Ed's smile suddenly evaporated. "Anything for me to worry about there? I mean, I don't care what it is as long as it's not going to create any distractions for anybody in 'Arkenstone'. And if you don't mind me asking, is this little skirmish something that could lead to changes that may affect the teams?"

"Yes."

"Yes what?"

"Yes, I mind you asking. Focus on *your* stuff, Ethan, while I cover your flank. Anything beyond that doesn't concern you. Go!"

• • •

The fields were completely covered with snow as I was driving to work. Technically, it's not winter yet, but the Front Range is the Front Range – it has its own temperament and its own ways. The long streams of cars in front of me seem to somehow violate the otherwise perfect calm of the hills that go up and down, revealing the mountains on the horizon and then hiding them again.

I spent some time thinking about what had happened during the last couple of days. Somehow the unrest in those engineer's creative heads caused them to reconsider many things. Prior to that they would have just been stuck with their bias, unsupported by any objective evidence. It took a little less than three days to integrate all of the individual team branches and produce a meaningful increment of value. But in order for that to have happened, two things needed to get done. One – everybody swarmed around that problem and that problem only, postponing all other activities until after the integration problem was resolved! No new functionality or anything else was added; every pair of hands was dedicated to resolving the existing inconsistencies and getting ever closer to the final goal – a real system demo of the iteration. Josh suggested that we just integrate to the best of our then current ability and not start experimenting with the new ideas that had resulted from the problem-solving workshop. And that was a good call, because in a very short time there simply was not enough room for that.

The second thing we had to do was reduce our appetite a little bit. The guys realized at some point, that the branches they had created in iteration 1 contained too many divergencies with respect to each other, and that to fully integrate everything would probably take at least a week. And that was a great finding on its own: you code it for two weeks in isolation and then it turns out that you need another week to integrate it all. What a living monument to our blindness. Very memorable! To make it work in a couple of days, we decided to simply pull out some functionality. And that proved to be our best decision

– a decision that allowed us to finish in three days and invite Ed to the preview, just as he had asked.

"Wow, so it's all in one app, isn't it?" he asked, his face beaming.

Sunil invited him to try it for himself, clicking whatever he liked. That same day there was a demo for Zach and Olga that also went really well. Both were pleased with what they saw and it looked like we were back in business.

The next thing to do was run iteration 2, the right way this time, integrating as we went along and trying to see if we could really execute what we had planned, as a whole train. It was a tough call because there were only seven business days left out of the initial ten. This was the time to apply the new techniques which were supposed to begin changing both the behavior and the outcomes. The only problem was, that although we had a general idea what was wrong and what to do overall, we had no specific, proven skill.

When I arrived at the office, Sunil was already waiting.

"We finished the re-planning session for this iteration," he said. Obviously we had to descope this iteration quite a bit. But what's left is actually achievable, the teams say." He added: "Josh proposed an interesting idea. He offered up that anyone who would like to discuss their current learnings in the realm of continuous integration, could meet at four o'clock in the big room."

"That's a great idea," I said and added a reminder to my calendar for 4 pm.

In the meantime, Sunil and I went through a list of various other things that were of importance during the execution. Yes, integration was our number one problem at the moment, but it wasn't the only thing to attend to. We called for a couple more guys from the Transformation Team and planned out our additional steps. One of those steps was the Scrum-of-Scrums that we wanted to make more efficient, even though the frequency of twice per week seemed totally fine. The other one was the PO Sync meeting. While the story behind the Scrum-of-Scrums was pretty straightforward–just an additional way to coordinate dependencies and escalate and remove tactical impediments during the iteration–PO Sync was supposed to solve a completely different set of problems. It turned out to be especially valuable at a time when we needed to de-scope our iterations, and yet produce meaningful increments of value. PO Sync is where 'content coordination' happens; it's where all of the POs make sure that the train is working on a consistent set of things at the time. For us it turned out to be invaluable.

The time passed so quickly that the next thing I knew the 4 pm meeting reminder had suddenly popped up in my calendar. Deep inside I was really looking forward to it; the promising moment of truth that should break the deadlock we had ended up in.

"Guys, thanks for coming," said Josh to an audience that looked bigger than I had initially expected. We had gotten about 25 people, maybe even more. Meanwhile, Josh continued: "I have to confess it has been a tiring day, because the way I spent it involved a lot of brainstorming and debugging and discussing things with brothers-in-arms. I hope your day was equally exciting."

"Same here," a developer from 'Ice Bay' said, raising her hand.

"It's like some magic was out there helping us today. I mean communication, first of all," continued Josh. "And the greatest development is that today at around 3:40, we got a working build. That's unbelievable."

"But then we just messed it up again!" said the developer.

"Yeah, but that's okay," countered Josh. "I think it's totally fine, we don't have to be perfect."

Elizabeth stood up and went to the whiteboard. "Yes, making errors is fine, but not at the rate we are still doing it," she said, taking the marker. "Talking to other teams is great, but it matters what *kind* of talking is going on. Remember what we talked about at the problem solving workshop a few days ago?"

Josh shrugged.

"We talked about the fact that we build stuff and then have trouble making it work together."

"Oh yeah, that's right! We did..."

"Well, now our cycle is much shorter, but the problem didn't really go away. We are a bit better, but only because we are overdoing it on the communication side. What I'm saying is that so much walking and talking will not get us to a very high velocity either. We are overkilling it. I'm afraid there is a problem: this may not be a sustainable practice."

"I agree with Elizabeth," said another developer. "I don't think we will be able to sustain that rate of communication around it. We are totally overkilling it, yes!"

Josh looked around the room and said, "Well, okay, I can see how this may be a little too overloaded. What suggestions do you have to offer?" he asked Elizabeth.

"Oh, I've got something alright. My team, 'Rohan', tried this technique with 'Erebor'. I'm sure it can work out across multiple other teams, too. I think its real power will manifest when we *all* start practicing it. So, here's the deal," she said and started drawing. "The first thing we did was to avoid any extra logic being built. All we aimed for at first was just aligning the interfaces and interactions between our areas of code." She drew two squiggly areas connected to each other. "Well, we briefly talked to 'Erebor' but then immediately tried to integrate–"

"Integrate what?" asked Josh.

"Interfaces. For instance, you have a method on one end and you call it from the other."

"Yeah, but there's nothing behind the interfaces. They're like stuffed dolls, there's nothing real underneath. Am I right?"

"Josh, that's exactly the point," said Elizabeth's teammate, who had also come to the meeting.

"I don't get it," said Josh.

"Well, let me just continue and hopefully you will understand in a minute," Elizabeth interjected. "When my team tried to integrate with 'Erebor', we were surprised to find that it didn't work out. We were calling their methods, using incorrect method signatures. In other words, simply talking to each other didn't get anybody too far. To see the problem, we needed to integrate those interfaces, and only then did we spot an inconsistency. Integrating interfaces, even with nothing behind them, was more than enough for initial validation of each teams' course of action."

"Okay, and then what? Those things still weren't integrating, right?" said Josh.

"Well, then we got together with one of the 'Erebor' developers over skype for about five minutes and quickly resolved the issue. It turned out that the difference in signatures was totally understandable; it's just that we couldn't anticipate it all upfront. We fixed it and then integrated successfully. So, bear with me now; our 'stuffed dolls' only had interfaces defined and would return some simple hardcoded values instead of executing any meaningful logic. But at least we could have an initial 'handshake', with 'Erebor'."

"Alright, so you integrated hollow interfaces successfully, then what?" continued Josh.

"Then we decided to take on a small chunk of functionality that we wanted to synchronously develop across the two teams. Roughly an hour's worth of work - something that would actually be aligned on both sides. We then repeated the process and tried to integrate. Of course we failed again, but then briefly talked on skype, shared the screen, debugged together, and in eight minutes–I kid you not–we got it to integrate tip top!"

"Don't you see?" said her teammate, "we grew the functionality synchronously, step by step. We ran a total of four cycles, spending little-to-no time at each cycle to resolve inconsistencies, and then moved on to the next little increment. It worked like a charm."

In the meantime, Elizabeth finished the picture on the board, illustrating the entire flow that her colleague had just described.

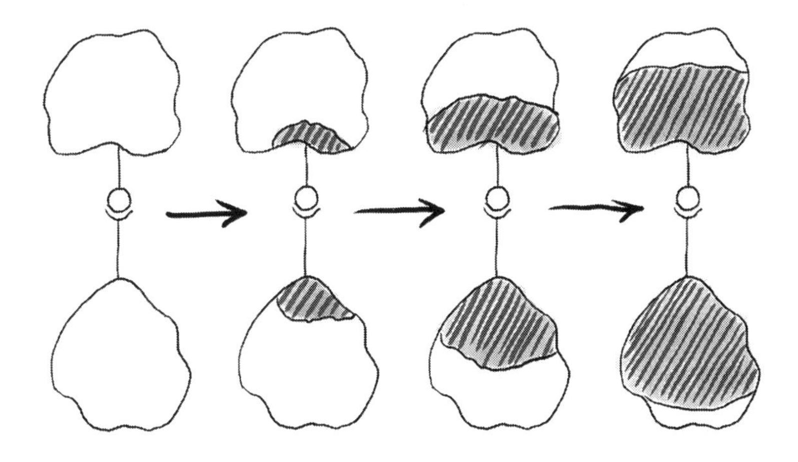

She turned back to everyone and said, "If we start by first ensuring that interfaces and interactions are going to work out correctly, and only *then* move to the actual logic, we are five times more efficient. It's just mind-blowing how awesome this is."

"With this simple approach we are unstoppable," said her teammate. "We can integrate our branches multiple times per day! I still can't believe it's true, but it is. With this technique, the lifetime of a local branch will amount to a few hours, maximum."

"And even if you haven't discussed what you are doing with the others yet," interjected Elizabeth, "no worries. Just don't get stuck building too much logic and then letting that determine the interactions and interfaces between classes and components in the code. If you do that and then try to integrate, it will have too much divergency already built in. Instead, reverse the sequence. Get those interfaces figured out first, integrate them into the mainline, and quickly fix anything that goes wrong during the integration. At that point changing hollow interfaces costs you nothing. Our problem is that we are trying to pull up weeds that are already deeply rooted, which costs us a lot of effort. Long story short, validate your assumptions by doing, before it's too late..."

. . .

Later that night, completely brain-dead, I was walking with Rachel down a path that was completely covered with snow. Our footsteps were making a funny trail that looked like a four-legged creature with shoes on all four paws. Rachel was telling me about her day, and I was grateful for the little bits and pieces that were reaching my mind, helping me switch the context a little bit, and give a tiny beam of hope to my almost entirely worn-out brain cells. And it worked perfectly fine... for about five minutes. Eventually the vicious loop of thoughts that I had carried home in the secret pocket of my subconsciousness took its toll.

"Hey Rachel," I said, unaware at this point whether I was interrupting something important or not. "I want to ask you something..."

"Yes?"

"Remember our conversation about trainings and mindsets and belief systems and so forth – the one with the 'Sleepytime' tea?"

"Sure, I remember," she said, smiling.

"It seems like no matter which direction you look in, there are always things that we do wrong, and obviously it's a mindset issue every time. I'm already getting tired of it. It's like this mindset thing is my nemesis. And it's absolutely everywhere, like a bad rumor. For example, the guys were trying to follow our new method, but the old mindset took over, leading to failure. It took them a lot of time and effort to figure it out. It also took some really emotional conversation to move the needle at all. So I guess I'm just wondering what kind of a curse this mindset thing really is. Why does it always take so much effort to point it out, and why is it so hard for them to see the problem in the first place?"

Rachel smiled again and stopped walking. "They can't see it, because what they are looking *for* is what they are looking *with*..."

"You mean, it's... It's stuck so deep inside..."

"Absolutely. They are not doing it on purpose or just to be difficult. I'll tell you something else: they don't even make deliberate errors, really. The errors are baked into their way of thinking, which in their eyes makes them completely error-free. From their point of view, it is totally logical, even though to an observer it may appear totally flawed. I'm not even talking about them fixing an error – just to be able to see it as such in the first place, their brain needs to be completely re-wired. And that's a very painful process, always requiring a strong impetus..."

My phone suddenly rang. It always rings when I least want it to. And of course, it was Ed.

"Hi Ethan. How are you doing there, buddy?"

"Fine, look, can I call you back in an hour?"

"Well, this won't take too long. One minute is all I need."

"Okay... what's up?"

"Hey, remember when you asked about what was going on between Zach and the CTO's office and all of the politics behind that?"

"Yes. And you told me to mind my own business..."

"Well, I think maybe it was a little premature for me to have said that. I actually do need your help there."

"Okay..."

"See, Ethan, it turns out that the CTO's office happened to communicate the plan for the next PI to the CEO. And given the importance of the big demo coming up in nine weeks, there's now quite a bit of attention from the CEO on this whole thing with 'Arkenstone'. Long story short, there are people that are trying to create some strong political momentum by holding us accountable to exactly what we said we would deliver in this PI. And that's why they put the CEO in the loop and presented the exact plan to him... to prevent us from having any elbow room in case we needed it. There are different factions in the CTO's org, you must understand. It's complicated..."

"Yeah but that–"

"That means that we cannot de-scope the PI. If we do, there will be problems. Serious problems. We must execute everything as committed."

"But we've already lost a significant amount of time! We won't make it!"

"Ethan, we have to make it. We just don't have any choice..."

"Ed, this is exactly what we were fighting against: overloading the teams. We can't go back to that way of doing things simply because of some 'game-of-thrones' stuff happening in our organization. That will kill everything we have built so far. It's not just back to square one, it's much worse than that! The teams will quickly lose faith in the new method. We will become total hypocrites in their eyes and then it will all collapse under its own weight!"

"Ethan, look, this is one of those times when you don't have a choice. And neither do I. We must do it in order for this whole initiative to survive. After this PI, if we do it right, things will be different. Completely different - I promise. But you have to help me with this. Help us all, yourself included..."

He hung up after he wished me a good night. Well, no question, I'm definitely going to have a great freaking night now.

"Is everything okay?" Rachel asked, looking worried. Her question was understandable given what I had just said on the phone and–perhaps even more troublesome–the tone in which I had said it.

"Yeah, everything is okay. Business as usual! You know, I think you're right. They can't see it, because what they're looking with, is in itself, deeply flawed. But I think this time around we are not going to treat the patient with some weak-ass OTC pills. We are going to perform a major surgery and whatever is left of this 'Frankenstein' will hopefully have a chance at a normal life."

ETHAN'S DIARY

- *As exciting as PI planning can be, it may be quite deceiving, especially for a group like 'Arkenstone' that has no instincts around synchronous execution of common scope. Planning is one thing, execution is quite another. Lesson learned: don't trust yourself too much, don't get too complacent as a result of successful planning of the PI. Executing the plan takes a whole bunch of new skills.*

- *It turns out there is a simple way to determine whether you are really delivering something or just blowing smoke: it's called the system demo. Performed at every iteration boundary, it serves as a metronome during PI execution, preventing the train from 'waterfalling' the PI.*

- *Our legacy mindset never ceases to surprise me: it always seems to find a way to reincarnate in a new form. Demonstrating a bunch of individual team branches at the system demo was a good example of the old mindset taking a new form, and I am really tired of this masquerade, to be honest. It seems that every time people face a challenge, they simply fall back into their old, default ways of thinking and operating. We are reminded once again that the only enemy we are fighting here is Mr. Mindset; not the people, not even the process...*

- *But it's not all that hopeless. Beliefs can change, and our engineers proved that by eventually coming up with a new technique allowing us to solve the problem. But in the early stages of transformation like this, people need close support from the change agent. Otherwise the old culture quickly takes over and continues to produce its poisonous fruit.*

- *If only engineers could apply their brilliance to all aspects of their work... Wouldn't that be heaven? Instead, something else is happening. In some conventional areas they are demonstrating incredible creativity and skill. In others—like process—all their ability to think rationally suddenly disappears. But there's a great opportunity here: a lot of things in this organization can be improved. We just need to start thinking and stop taking certain things for granted. They figured out that their integration flow was completely inverse to what it should have been, and that was the reason they struggled so much. Well, as I said, they are smart and capable and I have a lot of faith in them – they just need to start applying their brains to the correct set of problems.*

- *Rachel, as always, has a unique perspective on things. She's right; people that are driven by their old mindset store it so deeply in them that you can't even blame them for making mistakes. In their own view, that sort of thinking can't even be categorized as a mistake. They can't find the flaw in their thinking because that's the way they think. They wear lenses that distort reality, but they have no idea that they have them on. So how can you blame them? All you can do is appeal to their logic and senses, present facts, stay on target, remain persistent, and most importantly – be respectful and honest with them. Finally, it will leak into their brains.*

- *I guess I will never learn to completely switch off the phone when I'm hanging out with Rachel.*

CHAPTER 10
One Shot

"There will be no place to hide..."

–ZACH

"DO YOU WANT ME TO gather the Scrum Masters together so we can tell them about the change?" asked Sunil. I had just told him about my conversation with Ed the night before and about the whole deal with the pushback on de-scoping the PI.

"No."

"No?"

"No. That will not help us with anything. We are not going to accept the pushback. Don't you see, Sunil, that it will just reinforce the old mindset?"

"Yeah, but it seems like the stakes are pretty high up there," said Sunil, pointing up to the ceiling. "We all could easily get chewed up and spit out."

"True. But if we take too many precautions and compromise at every turn, we are gonna lose it, all the same. Can't you see, Sunil, that every time we adopt something new, the same story is repeated over and over again: we are allowed to play with the new toy until the moment it affects someone's way of working up at the top and then they simply pull the plug. But I'm not going to compromise this time. I've made quite a few futile attempts to improve the life of this organization. But this time, I am going to go the full distance, whether they like it up there or not."

"So what should the teams do in the meantime?"

"The exact same thing that we agreed to: follow the de-scoping scenario. Get the remaining PI scope reduced so that people can feel confident delivering it. And make sure we involve Olga to make prioritization decisions, as necessary..."

"And you're okay with that, even though it's in violation of your boss's direct order?"

"I don't particularly enjoy being disobedient, Sunil. Especially with Ed. He's a good guy, but there's nothing personal here: I have to do what I have to do..."

"Are you sure about this?" he asked, squinting.

"Hey! I've got this – don't worry about it. Go to the teams; I'm sure they need help. And that whole thing that happened yesterday... the spontaneous meeting at four o'clock, remember that?"

"Yes? What about it?"

"That's an example of a *community of practice*, forming right before our eyes. Let's help it shape up. That whole thing just feels... so right, so natural. We need to help them any way we can to sustain that momentum. Yesterday we witnessed collective intelligence crushing a big problem like it was nothing. And in doing so, they naturally shared important knowledge. *That's* our future, Sunil."

Sunil stood up and left the kitchen. Now it was time for me to go and start what I intended to accomplish. It would be great to talk to Raymond first – maybe he knows something about this whole thing going on between the execs, which I have no perspective on: who's fighting whom and what exactly it is they are trying to achieve. But, as it happens sometimes, he's not there when he's needed most. Or maybe I'm refusing to accept the fact that it's actually best that he's not around. Indeed, why would I want to get any of that political junk stuck in my head, except out of pure curiosity, of course. Doesn't what I'm trying to achieve for my company exist at a level above all the politics? Screw the politics! That's only a distraction from the ultimate goal. It's only creating a maze of twisted pathways and imaginary roadblocks, when what's required sometimes is to just ram through. Yes, Sunil's right; I may pay for it dearly, but I don't think I care about or fear the consequences at this point. It is amazing what a human being is capable of when trying to achieve something for others. If it were strictly for my own sake, or for the sake of my career, I don't think I would have the guts to pull it off. I would sit on it, speculate, second-guess it, until the call to action slowly drowned in the viscous depths of the status quo. Just exactly how our brains work is a great mystery, but it seems that the moment one consciously chooses to put personal goals aside and focus on a higher mission, the cowardly, precarious ego can suddenly no longer stand in the way of success. If I learned anything from my dad, it would be exactly that. I can't even imagine how deeply ashamed he would be if he were still around to see me devolving into a pathetic creature, putting politics above my life's mission and chickening out at the very first real test of my determination. No, I feel serene like never before. It's strange, I know, but it's just the way it is...

. . .

"Are you out of your freaking mind?" asked Ed. "You absolutely cannot do that, Ethan. I'm telling you: No! Period. End of story..."

"Ed, I respect your concerns, but I am going to do it anyway. It has to be done. Things cannot continue the way they are going. I'm going to talk to Zach, whether you support me or not. My goal is not to confront you or to be disobedient. Unfortunately, it just so happens that in order to help this organization take advantage of this opportunity to change things for the better, I have to go against what you are saying. I don't feel great about it, Ed, but make no mistake: I'm going to do what's right."

"And how do you know what's right? Is it now solely up to your judgement for us to determine whether something is right or wrong in this organization?"

"It's simple, Ed – there's not too much to figure out. I'm willing to do everything I can to help my company, the teams and even those people that have caused us all of this trouble. So, yes, from that perspective what I'm going to do is right and therefore I am going to do it."

"Ethan, listen, I understand that you probably have become a little too attached to the guys in 'Arkenstone', but you have to let go of this. You *cannot* go to Zach and even more importantly, under no circumstances can you ask him to organize a meeting with the CEO."

"It's not about getting attached to 'Arkenstone', Ed. It's not even about the fact that we condemn them to failure if we don't de-scope the PI. That would be freaking bad, but at least survivable. A much worse problem is that they would lose trust in the new method and that would be the end of everything. I'm not letting it happen, Ed, I'm just not. I'm sorry," I said, standing up and walking toward the exit.

"Ethan, if you take this action, you will be making a huge mistake. I won't be there for you if you throw it in my face like this. You'll only have yourself to blame..."

And that was the last thing I heard on my way out. Not the most encouraging thing to hear, but a job is not always about having fun. It's not about making yourself a cup of fancy cappuccino from a sophisticated machine every day, or having a nice conversation with someone about how good it would be if we had even more snacks, and if those snacks included gluten free, organic options. No, there are also moments like this, when everything is at stake.

I walked down to the lobby, looking out at the skies painted with beautiful silver clouds, stretching like gauze from one edge of the sky to the other. These clouds were incredibly high in the atmosphere, above even aircraft cruising altitude. Beautiful, but unreachable, as is often the case in life. In the meantime, far to the west, a completely different action was about to unfold. A large, thick cloud was crawling over the peaks on its way to spread across the blue sky. It was shamelessly dictating its own set of rules to the flicky winds that had begun to sense danger and were looking for paths of retreat. Slowly but steadily, getting bigger and bolder, the cloud began its descent into the valley, hiding the peaks entirely from view. It's belly was becoming darker as it began to lose patience, blowing air in all directions, throwing birds off course and making trees bend their heads in frustration.

"Ethan? What's up?" asked Zach as I entered his office. He greeted me in his typical manner, not even looking in my direction, fully consumed by his huge monitor, like his life depended on it.

"I want you to help me arrange a meeting with our CEO. I want to talk to him. We can't do what they are requiring of us. We know how to help VeraComm win big, but to pull that off we need to follow a few simple laws of physics in product development. We can't allow this intervention to happen and destroy everything we've built so far. We can't let them prevent 'Arkenstone' from de-scoping their PI. I'm sure I will be able to articulate the importance of the right course of action to the CEO..."

Zach, who clearly wasn't prepared for such a drastic shift, abandoned his monitor and stared at me – he looked like he'd seen a ghost. He kept staring at me and it seemed like his mind was racing all over the map, his entire face reflecting various combinations of astonishment, stupor and distress.

"You're not kidding, are you?" was the first question out of his mouth. "Do you understand what will follow immediately after?"

"I do."

"No, I don't think you do! Gosh! Did Ed talk to you?... Did you talk to Ed?" he asked, rolling his eyes. "Well, of course you talked to Ed, and since he's not here, you... proceeded on your own, so to speak," he said, chuckling. But the very next moment he became completely serious. "You've got a lot of nerve to come here like this, you know? Ed was right about you. You are a quiet boy until it's war time," he laughed. "He speaks very highly of you, by the way, so don't disappoint him like this. And, as per your request... the answer is *no*!"

I couldn't resist just laughing.

"What? Why are you laughing, Ethan?"

"Because I know why you had to respond that way. And I knew you would."

"If you knew that I would, why did you come then?" Zach was beginning to lose his temper.

"Because we are all stuck in our old patterns of thinking. All of us! You, me,... Ed. And I hate it. I hate it in me, and in others. I don't know what it will take for us to break through this thick brick wall, but one day it will happen. And once we are on the other side, we will look back at all of this and laugh at how wrong we all were... Zach, I hate to say this, but nobody can save us but ourselves. We can hire ten more people as bright and as expensive as Adi and we will still fail. Because we are willing to change processes, even willing to pay a lot of money for it, we can do a lot of things, except for one–the most important one–*changing the way we think*. Even if we happen to magically succeed with this demo in nine weeks, it will not change anything. Oh sure, it will briefly take the edge off and possibly the market may even respond positively at first, and we may all start to think that this is it, we've made it! But in fact, it will not change anything fundamental at all and we will run into an even tougher problem very soon. And that problem will be much worse than anything we've seen before. Because the best we can do on this course is to sqeeze the heck out of our own people and hope that they will deliver something. But all they will end up doing is creating a bunch of exceptionally crappy code under that pressure, and each additional step of the way will be harder and harder to take; not to mention the impact it will have on team morale. QCell's new Board member Marsha, who in her past career has experienced how SAFe enterprises operate, will spot the fake soon enough, make no mistake about it. It will be obvious to her because there is a huge difference in how real Lean-Agile enterprises develop software compared to our current reality. I saw an excellent example of a real Lean-Agile enterprise myself when Adi took me on a trip to visit her customer a couple of months ago. I witnessed how their engineers act and think and I've seen how their management operates, too. She said that they had been through some tough times and had to fight a lot of demons of their own before they got any reasonable results. But, unlike us, they got tired of fleeing their own fears and faced them instead. They made their choice and now they are really successful. Zach, this is it. At this point, I pretty much have nowhere else to go. Trust me; I'm not a complete psycho – I understand what's at stake here. I can't run into the CEO's office and do what I need to do unless you arrange the meeting and provide the correct context. If you help me arrange this, then we have a chance. If not, all of us will end up with a big zero. Zach, it's *your* call at this point and I need you to lead as never before to enable me to do my job. And if you think that I don't realize how dangerous all of this is, you're mistaken. I do know. And I'm already in trouble with my boss, as you might have figured out. But the opportunity before us is worth much more than that."

Zach turned his chair towards the window and stayed like that for a while. He stared out through the glass as it caught a couple of early drops. It was impossible to say whether those were raindrops or maybe a couple of snowflakes, flying at high spead and crashing over the warmer surface of the glass. Zach was clearly deep in thought and the best I could do at that point was just wait. I didn't know what else to say... I felt I had said all that needed to be said. If this didn't work, I'd have to think of something else, but could anything else even save us in this case? If I had a bunch of alternative scenarios, I probably wouldn't be ramming my head into the wall like this. Am I being desperate? Maybe. But who cares at this point.

Suddenly a loud ringtone came from Zach's computer – clearly his phone was hooked up to it and both devices ringing together created quite a turmoil. Zach turned in his chair, looked at the monitor, smiled and picked up the phone.

"Yes?"

The person on the other end was carefully explaining something. I couldn't understand what was being said exactly – all I heard was a lengthy monologue.

"He's here actually," responded Zach, squinting at me and after listening for another ten seonds, said: "yes, that's what I told him."

The voice on the other end kept going for a while longer until sharply interrupted by Zach:

"What?! Have you lost your mind too?"

Zach made a very disappointed face that gradually, as he listened to additional explanation from the other side, morphed back into his normal calm expression.

"Once the dust settles, I'll hang both of you," he said into the phone, adding: "well, I know I may regret this, but what the heck!... Let's do it."

He hung up, putting his phone on the table and clapping his hands: "Guess who that was? Well, I'm gonna tell you anyways. It was Ed, asking me to support your request..." Zach said, making big surprised eyes as if talking to a five-year-old.

Wow, this is indeed a surprise. But I don't mind surprises like this one where it suddenly turns out that I may have a good opportunity to succeed in my mission. Actually, maybe it's not so surprising in the end. I know that Ed cares deeply about this company's fate and is capable of turning around really complex situations. He's already proven that many times. I think he re-evaluated his initial reaction. And I'm sure glad he did – it would have been the worst thing ever for us to have an ongoing grudge. I'm glad we managed to avoid it.

"I'll arange the meeting, but you better know what to tell the man," said Zach, interrupting my train of thought. "Otherwise, when the fat hits the fire we'll all be in trouble and there will be no place to hide... I'll send you a meeting invite. And now, if you would excuse me, I would like to attend to some other things..." he said, smiling as a matter of politeness rather than anything else.

Later, as emotions calmed, I began thinking hard about what I would tell the CEO, especially knowing nothing about the nature of the political maneuver the CTO's office was undertaking. Why was it so important to them to make sure that the head of this organization personally insisted on the 'Arkenstone's' initial scope commitment? What seemed to be an irrelevant detail a couple of hours ago had suddenly begun to create some reservations. Now, as I cleared my way to the last step, I began to realize what was really at stake. But, it's all gonna be fine. I just need to find Ed and ask for his help in making sense out of this mess. I'm hoping he can help me understand the motivations of the parties involved. I need to know what is happening in the bigger political picture. I'm beginning to realize that I really can't run into this situation completely blind and unprepared...

ETHAN'S DIARY

- *Being a change agent doesn't leave you too much time for deep existential thoughts. It's a tough job for sure; but never in my life was my existence so overflown with meaning. Every step of the way, I was fighting through everyone's skepticism about adopting the method, trying to lure people into the leadership training, and trying to get them to approve and actively participate in the ART launch. And while doing this I see the same thing over and over: the harder it gets, the stronger the feeling is that I'm doing the right thing in my life. I know, maybe reading these lines five years from now I will find them to be a little naïve and unreasonably optimistic. However, I don't think you stand a chance against the rough reality of an enterprise deeply stuck in it's legacy thinking, unless you believe that you can do the impossible.*

- *I guess I haven't been completely accurate: sometimes I do let existential thoughts sneak in through the little cracks in my insanely dense schedule. And in moments like that I find myself wondering why it feels like all my life, all my prior career, I was just preparing myself to be a change agent? I had a chance to work as an engineer and then a development manager... Would I call either one of those a strict prerequisite to becoming a change agent? No, but all things being equal, I can say I have benefited from that background immensely, because I know what I'm talking about when the topic is development... And gosh, when isn't it about development? Additionally, my background in the PMO organization turned out to be very helpful, as I was able to acquire essential visibility into many of the dark corners of my organization. All of this background kept me from developing a strong bias based on one or two local successes. The reality is much more diverse and complex, requiring far more open-mindedness and soft eyes to spot subtleties in each particular aspect of organizational context.*

- *Sometimes it feels like I'm fighting this battle alone against an armada, but that's not true at all. I am very lucky that I have my Transformation Team. While I'm out banging my head against the thick walls which protect the precious legacy mindset of this organiztion, there are people that are working hard to support our first train in its first PI. They are busily laying the foundation for future steps in the transformation. In fact it would have been very hard—no, simply impossible—for me to attend all aspects of the rollout at the same time.*

- *Goodness, don't I get angry and lose faith in my bosses sometimes? Well, I'm not going to answer my own rhetorical questions here, that's for sure. But I guess I underestimate them sometimes. Yes, they are people too, so they make mistakes or give in to old habits sometimes. But then, don't they have glorious comebacks, like Ed had? And if he hadn't, would I have stood a chance?*

CHAPTER 11

The Way Out

"These guys have very big roadmaps and very little patience..."

–ED

"YOU PROBABLY WANT TO ADJUST that," said Ed, pointing to the rear suspension of the bicycle he had kindly offered to loan me for our little winter adventure. "When you're riding on snow and ice, you want them firm, or even locked. Otherwise it only amplifies the side momentum and the next thing you know you are on the ground. With a locked suspension, of course, things may get a bit shaky on the packed snow, especially at high speed, but at least it's safe."

"Hey, thanks for bringing a bicycle for me," I said while adjusting both the rear and front shocks.

"No problem," Ed said, removing his bike from the rack. "Julie and I have six bicycles in our garage."

"Why didn't she come with us?"

Ed shook his head. "Well, guess what? She was cycling with me in the snow last weekend and got sick as a result. A very bad cold. She was sick all week and she's still coughing terribly. Can you imagine that?" he said, adjusting the height of his saddle.

"So why didn't you stay home with your wife?"

"She said my presence is not gonna cure her cold anyway so... why not?" he said, heading towards the trail.

A couple of moments later we were riding on the trail, going up and down and sometimes making unexpected turns over the steep banks of frozen creeks, being lured deeper into the woods. Ed was using his smartphone for navigation: our plan was to make it to Twin Lakes, or 'Twin Puddles' as Ed likes to call them, and that was quite a test of my riding skills. Riding downhill is always fun, but going uphill, especially on these forest pathways which are barely recognizable under a thick layer of snow, was a true challenge. You have to push hard but keep it steady, otherwise the 2.3-inch tires start to slip and slow you down, eventually leading to a halt – the most annoying thing that can happen on ascent. Starting over again from a dead stop is more of an art than a science and consumes a lot of energy, but I definitely learned some new tricks.

I really needed this ride. The calm of winter around us brought a peaceful sensation that I guess I had needed very badly for quite a while. We were in the middle of our second PI for 'Arkenstone' and we had a lot of new work ahead of us, especially on the change management side. After PI 1 was finished, the Transformation Team's backlog went through the roof. But that's good news, because we survived our big test with QCell. Marsha attended the demo with six other people from her organization and they were incredibly pleased with the PI results. And why wouldn't they be? 'Arkenstone' produced an excellent, super-stable demo. And, after a certain point, having shown Marsha and her colleagues different user scenarios, we just handed her the demo tablet and invited her to do whatever she liked with it. And that's where the real fun began. She got a big kick out of the whiteboard drawing feature, which turned out to be a very effective and super-intuitive tool. Marsha was also impressed by the screen sharing functionality

– she obviously was quite aware of the challenges that phones and tablets have in this regard, as compared to desktop computers. She tried opening all of the possible document formats that were available to her on that tablet, and they were rendered nicely on the computer that was on the receiving end of the sharing. Long story short, it was a killer demo. In fact, Sunil and I had a lot of confidence in 'Arkenstone's' ability to produce a good demo by the end of that PI. The teams had learned a very hard lesson after failing iteration 1. On the second attempt to demo the system increment three days later it was successful. And from then on, every single iteration in that PI had a system demo – a critical routine was therefore established. We realized while working on it that successful system demos at iteration boundaries are a good predictor of the PI outcomes.

But something had happened before that; something without which that PI would have been a complete mess. Zach had kept his word and organized a meeting with the CEO. The CEO was quite reluctant to allow us to change our plan, but together Zach and I managed to convince him that it was for the better. Interestingly, I noticed during that conversation that the CEO was repeating certain answers multiple times, as if someone had put them in his brain and all his mouth knew how to do was stick to the script. And I could clearly see that he was quite uncomfortable with the whole thing, so he might have compromised just to get Zach and me off of his back. Zach congratulated him on the wisdom of his decision and so we departed, feeling good about our chances for success. Having been able to de-scope the functionality allowed us to focus on the right stuff at the right time and succeed with the quest.

And then one morning shortly after the PI demo, Raymond surprised me again.

"So... now you must feel like quite the big guy..."

"What do you mean?" I asked, cleaning out the coffee machine and loading a new batch of grounds.

"Oh, come on, Ethan. Now that your boss has been anointed, you are definitely looking at a quantum leap yourself. Well, I guess some people deserve to have multiple promotions in a short period of time, while other servant leaders like me just have to be content with the scraps," he said glumly, making a pathetic expression and wiping imaginary tears from his eyes.

"What are you talking about, Raymond? How is my boss anointed? Anointed to what?"

"Are you pretending now or you are truly clueless?" he said, looking at me suspiciously. "I see: you really don't know anything. Wow!... Very typical for you, I guess..."

"Raymond, for goodness sake, spare the riddles for your future grandchildren and get to the point! What exactly is it that I don't know?"

"That Ed is VeraComm's new CTO..."

"What?!"

"Yes. He's a big dude here now. Not that he was ever a joke, but now he's a legit senior executive. Gosh, I wish I could always be as clueless as you are. Then I would have surprises like this every once in a while. Wouldn't that be awesome?"

And it was great indeed. I was so deep in the weeds with 'Arkenstone' at that time, it's no wonder I didn't know anything. I hadn't been talking with Ed much and he had actually kind of disappeared for a while – he was probably busy taking the reins. As I found out some time later, both Zach and Marsha from QCell had heavily campaigned for his promotion. Our old CTO had left, which had passed almost unnoticed, at least for me. And I can't say that I regret his departure. I won't miss a CTO that doesn't show any interest in crucial transformations going on in his own organization. It seemed only to attract his attention when an opportunity to capitalize politically came up and then he would craft schemes, that often ended up damaging his own organization. His attempt to prevent us from de-scoping the PI is a good example. And why would he do something like that? Just because he and Zach were engaged in some kind of turf war...? Well, I'm actually happy that he's out. We took the risk and we showed true results in the end. And that not only warranted and sealed the partnership with QCell, but it also helped us establish solid, trusting relationships with their leadership team in a very short time. Of course our CEO had to respond to such a breakthrough and he did so by making the staff changes happen. And how does this all help me? I wouldn't have even dreamed about an opportunity like this. Now that I have the ear of the company's CTO, lots of things that would have been otherwise impossible as part of the rollout, will now be a piece of cake. Oh man, am I happy that this promotion happened. I already have a backlog of items to work through with Ed. And now that we are riding deep in the snowy woods together, I will certainly be reminding him about a whole bunch of things that my Transformation Team needs his support on.

"So what do you think?" Ed asked as we stopped to catch our breath. He poured dark, fragrant tea from his thermos into small plastic cups.

"This ride is awesome. Hard, especially going uphill, but totally awesome." I said, still gasping for air after our last ascent.

"We are a little less than half-way through. At this pace I think it will take us about ninety more minutes to get to the 'puddles'," Ed said, sipping his tea. "But that's not what I meant," he said, looking at me very seriously. "I want to talk about the next steps for VeraComm and where we're going next with the rollout. The reason I'm asking you this is because after working with QCell side-by-side for a few weeks, I've come to realize the depth of integration required between our portfolios. It's huge. We need to understand which direction we're moving in and how we want to propagate the method further. Plus, Marsha is cranking up the pressure cooker..."

"How exactly?"

"Well, do you think VeraComm was the only company with outdated processes and thinking?"

"I see. So, she wants to launch a SAFe rollout over at QCell, too?"

"No."

"No?"

"No. She wants VeraComm and QCell to both be part of one big rollout initiative."

Wow. That's something new... I noticed that it has started snowing. Under the tranquilizing effect of the slowly descending snowflakes, the trees seemed to plunge into an unnatural stillness: not the slightest rustle could be heard at the heart of the forest, which was preparing to disappear from the maps, just in time for its early afternoon nap.

Ed scanned around him slowly, as if looking for cues about how to express himself. Then he looked back at me and continued: "It's actually going to get pretty messy, Ethan. Marsha is not creating artificial pressure on us. The pressure is *real* and is coming from some of the QCell executives, who are very eager to start building stuff. And you can't blame them for having an appetite – that's why they jumped into this deal in the first place. As Marsha explained it to me, these guys have very big roadmaps and very little patience. After visiting our PI demo and seeing it with their own eyes, they basically expect us to launch trains everywhere in the remaining parts of the organization ASAP. And as soon as we're done with that, they want us to start working on numerous initiatives in their backlogs. She said that the pressure is huge and that certain activities on her side have already been launched in support of the partnership, many of which involve significant capital expense. It's game on Ethan, and these guys are not kidding. They are damn serious..."

"Ed, I don't know what you expect me to say exactly," I said, removing my gloves and taking a sip of Earl Grey. A cup of tea had never in my life tasted and smelled so incredibly rich and invigorating as it did that day. "But I immediately liked what you just said because that pressure will significantly elevate the importance of the transformation and will also give us all enough momentum to ram through any potential impediments on either side. I like it. I really do, Ed"

"Good! See, that's exactly how I feel too, but it's also bugging me a little bit. I'm not sure we necessarily know what steps we should take next and whether there is any conceptual difference when taking the new techniques we have just mastered to such an extreme scale. It's certainly possible to just go ahead and replicate what we did for 'Arkenstone' in all the other programs. But for some reason it feels a little scary to just blindly pursue that course," Ed said, removing his phone from its holder on the handle bars. "I need to look up the weather," he explained. "I don't remember any mention of precipitation in the forecast yesterday."

Meanwhile the snow had finished its ostentatious prelude and grew bolder, dumping down at will.

"Doesn't seem to be any connectivity out here," muttered Ed, standing up. "We should keep moving before the two of us turn into icicles."

The entire world seemed to become darker and less friendly, as an endless gray cloud stretched its arms out to embrace the entire sky. It seemed to be colder now too, or maybe that was just because we hadn't moved for quite a while.

"Crap!" exclaimed Ed, "I'm an idiot."

"What happened?"

"I can't fire up the freaking GPS again," he said, full of frustration. "I totally forgot about this stupid problem. Even though, in principle, the GPS should be able to receive a signal from the satellite without carrier coverage, the stupid app requires internet connectivity to get started. Crap! Now I can't even use the freaking thing."

I pulled out my phone to try as well, but had no success either.

"I should have listened to Julie when she suggested that I get myself a Garmin or something like it," Ed said, putting his helmet on. "Duh..."

"So this trail," I pointed forward, "isn't it where we want to go?"

"Well, I guess so," said Ed. "If we keep a good pace, we'll be back in three hours," he said, and slid his watch back under the sleeve.

We kept pedaling and pedaling, but the trail seemed to have no end. We became really frustrated; it seemed like the forest was deliberately hiding its precious 'puddles' and enticing us further into the deepening snow. The edge of the front fork of my bike was now brushing the white, cotton-like surface and only about half of the wheel remained visible above the level of the snow. I realized that I had forgotten the feeling of rolling downhill – the trail seemed to be taking us further and further up into the mountains.

"Hey Ed," I shouted, loud enough to wake a bear from hibernation. "Are you sure that the lakes are higher up than this?"

"I think so," replied Ed, loudly as well. He kept pedaling. "We are not in the Himalayas; the ascent has got to end soon, one way or the other."

...And it did. In about fifteen minutes we were rolling downhill again. Finally! Ed was shouting something, but I could only catch every other word. The downslope gradually became steeper and the wind, exaggerated by our ever-faster movement, was shamelessly stealing the meaning of his every phrase. My eyes were totally blinded by tears, which were then annoyingly pushed down my temples by the cold wind. I only had a vague sense that the trail had become even steeper as we moved downhill. Were we even on the trail anymore?

Suddenly I heard Ed again. I wasn't sure what it was at first, but it quickly turned into a plangent bawl. In the next second my hands plunged downward, following the handlebars and the wheel, which seemed to lose contact with any firm surface. I realized that I was no longer on the bicycle when my knee hit something hard and I found myself rolling helplessly downhill, spinning insanely fast like I was in one of those NASA centrifuges from a favorite childhood movie.

I realized the fall was over when my elbows, back and knees stopped slamming into unfriendly objects and I remained still. My helmet seemed to still be on and I realized that my head had hit something solid at least a couple of times during the fall. Where was Ed, I wondered? I pushed up a little to look around and spotted my bike about twenty yards back uphill. As I looked back up the 'hill', I realized that we had fallen, with our bicycles, from the top of a cliff of an unbelievable height. But where was Ed?!

He was sitting in the snow some fifty yards away. "Ed, are you alright?" I shouted, putting all my remaining strength into my cry. That seemed to rouse him from his stupor. He stood up and began slowly walking toward me.

"Where's your bike?" I asked, trying to stand up. Ed shrugged and grabbed my arm to help pull me to my feet. Standing, I realized that my knee was hurt really badly.

"Where's yours?" he asked.

I pointed towards a spot in the snow at the foot of the cliff. Five minutes later we found Ed's bicycle too, and then we realized that his phone was no longer in the holder.

"Crap. Now what?" he said.

"If it makes us feel any better, we don't have coverage here anyway."

"Eh... that's right. So who cares?" He looked at the cliff: "That was quite a jump from up there. I couldn't see a thing, and then suddenly realized that something was wrong, but only when it was too late." He smiled, "But look at us: one hurt knee and one bitten tongue?" He spit blood out onto the snow. "We are two lucky dudes; that's what we are. Let's get out of here..."

We decided that since we had lost any electronic means of navigation (my phone was not receiving any signal either) we needed to find a better vantage point. Climbing back up from where we had fallen didn't seem like an attractive idea, so we headed south toward a hill that had only a moderate incline and almost no trees.

"The freaking snow has already covered our trail," said Ed pointing back to the hill we had fallen from. "Can't see anything up there."

"What's that?" I said, pointing to about nine o'clock, where I thought I glimpsed a thin, dark streak, barely visible through the fuzzy veil of falling snow.

"Oh! That's..." Ed looked at his watch and turned around a couple times until he located what he thought was the brightest part of the cloud... "Southwest," he concluded, pointing at the streak. "Which means that that's the interstate and we have shifted about ten miles south from the 'puddles.'" He turned back from the highway, which had begun fading from view due to the strengthening blizzard. After staring for almost a minute into the wall of pouring snow, he finally tapped me on the shoulder. "See those hills there?" he asked, pointing between the no-longer-visible highway, and the cliff. I barely recognized the silhouette of some sort of elevation. "We had our tea-break behind that hill," he said. "If we keep pushing that direction we will quickly find the trail head, 'cause it's near the other side of the highway."

"Why not go by the highway then?" I asked.

"Two reasons," he said, getting back on his bike. "See those gullies between us and the highway? They are countless. It would take forever to cross all that, especially with your knee."

"And what's the second reason?" I asked, as Ed started rolling.

"The highway has no bike lane and the big trucks will be ramming through the blizzard. So let's keep that option in mind only as a last resort," he said, rushing forward in the direction of the hills.

• • •

Three long hours later we were sitting in Ed's Jeep, with the heat cranked to high. Ed drove in complete silence for quite a while. My knee was numb, but at least was not really bothering me anymore. I must have hit it pretty hard against a stone or a tree. Pedaling on the way back was a real penance, with every motion sending a thunderbolt of pain straight through to my brain.

"You know, this is what we are missing as part of our transformation," I said, finally deciding to break the silence.

"What? A cliff?" He said, smiling.

"No, not the cliff, but rather the thing that actually got us out of this trouble. *A bigger picture view*. I am amazed how quickly we managed to figure out the right direction once we acquired the right viewpoint. We evaluated the options and selected the right one. That's what we're missing when talking about the next steps."

"I'm intrigued: keep going," he said, switching to high beams as the road darkened ahead of us.

"I think our current success with 'Arkenstone', no matter how critical, has a tendency to sort of make us myopic."

"How so?" Ed asked, accelerating slightly on an uphill section of the road.

"Well, we launched one train and it's already showing amazing results. And now we have suddenly started to think about the whole transformation that way: we just go back to all the rest of our programs and do the same thing with each one. It feels like we are falling back again into the trap of local optimization."

"I'm not sure I understand," said Ed, "the problem we had was that our teams were too isolated from each other. Every program was pretty much a bunch of disjointed teams that didn't know how or even want to collaborate. That's why we launched 'Arkenstone', to allow us to take a bigger picture view on development in the 'Mobile Solutions' program. And now you're telling me that it was local optimization?" Ed shook his head. "How come?"

"Well, from an individual team perspective, it *is* a broader view, I would agree. But then, if you go one level up the ladder, the train launches get you to the same problem: emphasizing components over the whole; only this time around the components are bigger – the trains. In the end, if all we did was create the same isolated structures, only bigger in size, it wouldn't get us very far. Even if every train executes perfectly, our organization will still remain a disjointed set of trains, optimizing their individual train performance at the cost of enterprise outcomes."

Ed drove in complete silence for a short while. No emotion, as usual, just carefully watching the road which had become completely dark by now. Only snowflakes, sprayed by the thousands in front of us, performed a mysterious chaotic dance, lit up by the thick light from the Jeep.

"Yeah," he said finally. "You're right. It does sound like local optimization. So what do you suggest?"

"I suggest that we take an even higher-level view and carefully consider all the pathways in which value flows through the enterprise. I think that 'Mobile Solutions' (currently known as 'Arkenstone') was just an exception; a perfect example of a program that was organized around a tangible end-to-end solution. But I bet you anything that not every other program is like that. Some might only deliver a fraction of the solution at best. That's where we need to see a bigger picture, because if we just start blindly launching trains within the current program boundaries, we will apply the right process to the wrong structure, I'm afraid. I don't believe that it will work – we may just end up designing the wrong enterprise. Each program will perfectly follow the same process model as 'Arkenstone', but that will be irrelevant because, unlike 'Arkenstone', their system demo will not be a complete increment of value, because of how we structured those programs in the first place..."

"Sounds like this is something we should address immediately," murmured Ed, obviously still struggling to speak due to his bitten tongue. "Can we use Adi for this?" he asked, then paused for a few seconds. "Or do you want to do it yourself?"

"I wouldn't mind getting some external help," I said. "This is a very important exercise. If we determine the structure correctly, we will have a chance to improve so many things, I can't even list them all. But if we fail to build it right, we will condemn those teams to failure and it won't even be their fault..."

"Yeah," he nodded. "Who do you think we're gonna need for this exercise?"

"Good question. I think we'll need representatives from every program. That will provide the right context... And higher-level stakeholders, of course."

"I agree."

Soon a small cluster of lights emerged on the horizon – we were crossing into the city limits. And in a couple of minutes I would be in the best place possible after such an adventure: home, pretending like I'm watching TV, while my mind continues to replay the summersault from the cliff. The lights were getting ever closer, gliding past us and then quickly disappearing, to be replaced by brighter ones as we headed down the road. Finally, we were downtown and would be soon at my stop.

"You know," said Ed, pulling up to my building, "it is weird to admit, but we needed that cliff. It kind of makes me think: if we survived today's adventure, we will survive everything else, too. But don't tell anybody about the cliff and all that other stuff. I don't want Julie to find out from my colleagues about my 'gliding' exercise. She worries about me too much as it is already."

I nodded without replying. 'We are two lucky dudes': that phrase revolved over and over in my brain, until the rhythmic beeps of the elevator had counted the floors and the steel doors opened wide in front of me, patiently reminding me that I had arrived. Tired but happy, I limped to my apartment. The weekend had just started... And I wanted to enjoy every bit of it.

ETHAN'S DIARY

- *Thinking of the rollout as just a series of ART launches would be a grave mistake. We need to design a Lean-Agile enterprise, not just a bunch of disjointed trains. Otherwise we are creating the same problem of local optimization, only one level up. That may be quite dangerous.*

- *We are so used to harnessing the power of creative, highly intelligent people to solve problems with the systems we build. Well, the enterprise is also a system and it's equally, if not more complex, than the solutions we're building. So, it's probably time to acknowledge that fact and apply the right talent to organizational analysis and design.*

- *As we do that, we can effectively launch trains everywhere else in the organization.*

- *Despite the fact that I'm injured, cycling in the snow is freaking awesome. As soon as I recover, I will go straight to the bike shop. Apart from a new bike I'm getting myself a real, carrier-independent GPS navigation device. And, strictly because expensive things are usually fragile, I also need my good old paper maps and compass.*

CHAPTER 12

Following Pathways of Value

"This is one of those required things that will benefit you only if you do it voluntarily, so no pressure."

–ED

ADI WAS IMPRESSED WITH OUR desire to slow down and take a bigger picture view of the rollout before taking any further steps. She said she's proud of us for taking one of the SAFe principles–'Apply Systems Thinking'–very seriously and gradually making it a part of this organization's mindset. She reminded us again though, that prior to taking any further steps, we need to conduct leadership training for all those people that will be involved in the action.

She was right, of course. Ed and I certainly supported the idea and started making arrangements.

"Our leadership team is concerned," said Marsha in one of our catch-up meetings, "that instead of launching trains you guys came up with this 'bigger-picture-view' workshop and the leadership training as a prerequisite. That will just delay everything even further. Our guys are becoming really impatient with this situation." She also said that the role of the messenger between the two companies had begun to annoy her, but Ed and I decided to stay right on target, regardless of the cost. It would have been much better not to have a sword of Damocles dangling over our heads, but regardless of the circumstances, we weren't going to compromise on our agenda. Marsha reiterated: "Things are overheating and this is not helping our relationship... You should keep in mind that the sentiment that VeraComm is not able to deliver on promises is a recurrent topic here, often reanimated in our discussions by different people. And the more time it takes for you guys to start delivering on our roadmaps, the more toxic it's getting here. My advice: don't play with fire."

But we did. Ed and I decided we had to push the agenda no matter what, because the alternative was much worse and we both knew it. To find out much later that we had designed a 'Frankenstein's monster' that couldn't function and was falling apart in action didn't sound too attractive.

Eventually, and reluctantly, Marsha agreed to talk to the middle management at QCell responsible for the areas directly impacted by the partnership to see if they would attend our training. The leadership training was organized exceptionally quickly. This time around we actually designed it so that Sunil could co-teach with Adi. That proved to be very effective: Adi was speaking out of her vast experience with different organizations, while Sunil was a practitioner they could connect with on a completely different level. It was just one awesome duo, really.

Adi gladly agreed to help us with the workshop too, but with Ed and I expressing a fervent desire to get to the bottom of the question of what to organize the other trains around, Adi suggested that we facilitate the workshop ourselves. She said she would make herself available to offer suggestions, as necessary.

My knee had started to heal, but it was a slow process and I had to use cane for a while. I guess I looked a bit like some evil genius that way; only I was neither evil nor genius. I was just a happy guy that was eventually starting to see the results of his work–the first launched train–which was truly encouraging. All of the pressure we were under was incredibly annoying, not to mention that we were playing a dangerous game, testing QCell's limits. But deep inside I knew that we were on the right track. Nothing gives you quite as much confidence as an early win...

Then one day the 'Gondor' team invited me to lunch, just out of generosity, I guess. But I was very surprised to arrive at the restaurant and discover that these guys occupied half of the place. As it turned out, they had invited quite a few other folks: Bonnie and her guys from the 'Server-side', the entire 'Rivendell' team, and a few folks from various other teams. Later that day Josh, the developer from 'Gondor', told me: "Ethan, something feels very different about all of this. Different and yet somehow natural..."

"Different how?" I said, not sure exactly what he was talking about.

"I probably told you way at the beginning, when we had just launched 'Arkenstone', that things already felt different. Well, we have stopped thinking of ourselves as a team in the conventional sense," he said pointing at his teammates who were spread across three large tables: hungry engineers, leisurely enjoying each other's company. "Look at this - the 'Gondor' guys aren't even sitting with each other, but are lost somewhere in the crowd, talking with their new buddies from the other teams. I guess it has sublimed..."

"Sublimed? How do you mean that?" I asked patiently, knowing that it might be slightly difficult to follow the crude stream of consciousness of a near-genius software developer.

"The sense of team bond, the camaraderie... It all moved up from the team level to a bigger thing - the train. See, we only invited a few teams we had worked with side-by-side in this PI. Ideally we would have loved to have invited them all; there were plenty of other things we worked on with people from the rest of the train, too. It's unfortunate we weren't able to make this impromptu lunch a bit bigger. We probably would have needed to involve our RTE to facilitate the logistics," he said, bursting out in laughter. But then he became serious and added: "You know, I think all of that team ego we had before has evaporated... Or maybe it's just shifted toward something bigger and more meaningful - the Agile Release Train. I think most of us began to recognize the change as we started reliably producing integrated system increments every two weeks. I guess it opened a whole new world for us. It's something we are beginning to take pride in as a train, as we realize that our team alone can't accomplish all of that. You need other people and then you begin to take pride in every little victory... together. It feels awesome. It adds a whole new meaning..."

"Is that just your opinion, or do you know other people that are thinking the same way?" I asked.

"Hey guys! Guys! One second please! Guys...!" Josh shouted out to the crew, trying to be heard over the peculiar amalgam of conversation, laughter and gesticulations from a bunch of over-energized, badass knowledge workers. "Guys, I have a question for you," he said a little quieter, as the group began to calm down. "Ethan and I are wondering, how would you evaluate to this point all of us working in this new model and being part of the Agile Release Train? As a group, could you do a quick fist of five? The question is whether you would like to proceed down this path or go back to the previous ways of working?"

Everyone raised their hands with fives on them. Some whistled. Some banged on their tables. Bonnie, however, didn't vote.

"Bonnie, what's up?" asked Josh.

"I just... I'm thinking about the rest of the 'Server-side'. Knowing that the process there is still deeply broken and is relying on our old ways of doing things, I really feel for them. As much as I enjoy celebrating our success as part of 'Arkenstone', I hate to see them struggle and the happier it gets here, the sadder I feel about them."

"Bonnie, things are going to change soon," I said, noticing that the crowd had become really concerned with what Bonnie had just said. I guess people that work together and talk to each other face-to-face don't think of 'those other people' as remote, uniform, abstract 'things' anymore. I think direct interaction makes us better people, allowing for things like compassion, respect and sacrifice to kick in. It's truly amazing what a simple and yet powerful method of team building we've discovered here. "Bonnie, very soon we are going to launch trains in other areas of VeraComm and the 'Server-side' teams will not be an exception. I assure you that it will happen..."

I was honest about the intent. But I didn't know back then that achieving that goal would require a whole new set of skills and a different thought process. Every time a great theory meets practice, a lot of big 'gotchas' happen and our case wasn't in any way unique. One thing was clear to us all: we knew that we badly needed the workshop in order to be able to move forward.

Adi strongly suggested that from an organizational change management perspective, we capitalize on the momentum created by 'Arkenstone'. "Every rollout requires something to fuel it, otherwise people simply grow complacent and drop the ball or even become resistant to change," she said to me and Ed in one of our discussions. "The thing is, you have that fuel in abundance for a narrow window of time. You need to use it and use it fast, because as good as it is, it very quickly fades."

"What are you talking about?" asked Ed.

"I'm talking about something special that you have had as of late..."

"You mean, 'Arkenstone'?"

"Yes, but there's something specific about 'Arkenstone' that can inspire others," said Adi. "Wanna guess what that is?"

"Oh, well – I would guess their successful PI. The demo that impressed the business folks as well as our new partner, QCell. Is that what you mean?"

"Exactly!" said Adi and continued: "Guys, it's important to learn to use early successes to propagate the method. So, let's talk more specifically about this. I would like you to make a first step in that direction *before* the workshop. We want people that come to the workshop to be specifically aware of current successes. We want them all to be onboard, or at least as many as possible. Identifying the next steps in the transformation only *seems* to be an easy task, but in fact things can quickly turn tricky during those workshops, you can trust me on that. So what are you going to do to spread the awareness?"

We didn't need to be told twice. Two days later we had made a list of all the people we intended to eventually invite to the workshop, and we organized a short meeting for them. Sunil ran that meeting, which was essentially a compilation of the best recorded moments of the 'Arkenstone's' PI demo, highlighting the actual product. We also showed lots of photos from the PI planning, the system demos at the iteration boundaries that were held during the PI execution and so forth. The presentation ended with a slide that had a group photo of the entire train that we had taken at the end of the Inspect & Adapt session. That last photo was captioned: 'We know our current problems. We're gonna fix them!'

That brief meeting made quite an impression on everybody in the room. People asked questions for over thirty minutes after the presentation. At the top of the hour, Ed asked Sunil to disconnect his computer from the projector, saying: "I know you guys still have plenty of questions. But most of those cannot be answered in a setup like this. One important thing I learned during this first big step in our rollout is that the only true way of getting your questions answered is by doing, not by talking. So, I look forward to seeing you all at the workshop next week. This is one of those required things that will benefit you only if you do it voluntarily, so no pressure," he said laughing.

Following all of the preliminaries, we ended up with a group of people, 21 strong, from both sides, representing for the most part key program stakeholders from the majority of our programs. This included some of the higher-level stakeholders like Zach and Nerissa from our side, Marsha and a few of her colleagues from QCell, various folks from our product management and finally, a couple of architects, as Adi had strongly suggested. We were worried that a 21-person workshop would be problematic in terms of facilitation, but as it turned out, the problems came from a completely different, unexpected domain.

The big day arrived. The workshop had 100 percent attendance. We started early in the morning, but it took some time before we really hit our stride. We needed to crisply state the problem that Ed and I had been trying to solve all along, and we finally nailed it. The problem statement was written at the top of the whiteboard: 'Our programs are not generally organized around the flow of value. We need to look for a better organizational design to support value delivery.' That clarity helped a ton, getting us started on the right path. And then some unexpected discussions began...

"So, I understand that not all of our programs are really full value streams, like 'Arkenstone.' But can we at least start with those that are?" asked someone in the group.

"Yeah, that would be easy pickings," seconded someone else.

"Wait, wait," Zach said, looking around the room. "Not so fast guys. I don't think that 'Arkenstone' is as perfectly independent as you might think."

"Why not?" the same person asked.

"Well, those of us that were part of the launch probably remember that we brought in Bonnie and a couple of her guys to the PI planning and how helpful that was."

"You're right," said Ed. "Not just for the planning. We stole them for the whole PI and it helped tremendously. I also remember what triggered that whole transfer: we had decided to double check on the 'Server-side' delivery schedule, remember?"

"Oh yeah," said Zach. "That was quite a surprise, one that could have ruined the whole effort for 'Arkenstone', if left unattended. So we borrowed those guys for PI 1, but soon we'll have to give them back to their mother-program, by the way."

"Okay, so here's what we've got," said Ed, pulling the lid off of his marker. "This is 'Arkenstone', formerly 'Mobile Solutions', and this is 'Server-side'. Actually neither of the two programs is an independent value stream. A value stream that really delivers mobile functionality looks kinda like this: it fully subsumes 'Arkenstone' and bites a little bit off the 'Server-side' program."

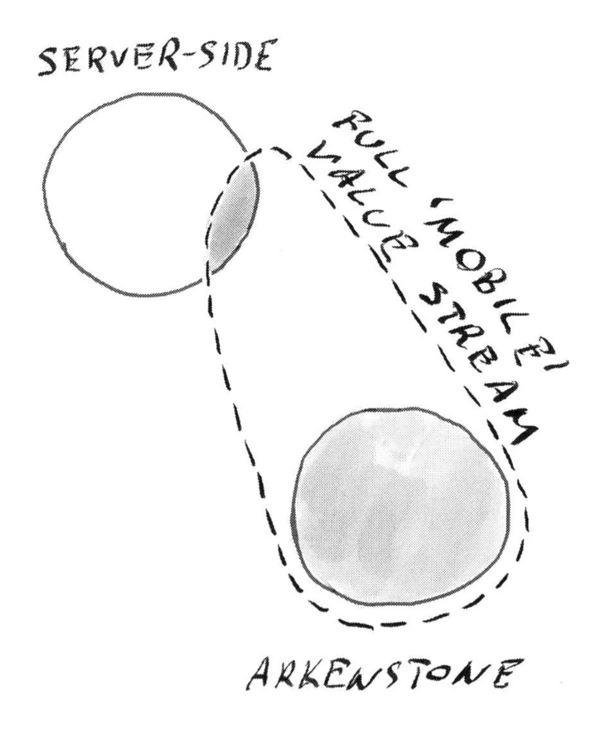

The picture was a simple, but extremely helpful illustration of our structural problems. I automatically jumped in: "Well, here's an interesting question then: why are we organized into the programs that way and not the way the value flows?"

"Whoa, whoa," said Eugene, 'Server-side's' program manager. "There are specific reasons why we are organized that way."

"Like what?" asked Ed sharply.

"Like the expertise that needs to evolve in a community of like-minded people, working on the same type of tasks; like architecture that needs to be robust across the entire server-side functionality, and so forth..."

Ed smiled without saying anything. It was very nice of him not to force his people into accepting his point of view, but I'm not sure that this is going to be helpful here. Of course Eugene is going to have a hundred reasons to justify the existing structure, otherwise he's gonna lose control and influence over his people. Something tells me that this is not going to be an easy conversation.

"But you see the picture, right Eugene?" interjected Zach. "You see that the value flows differently...? And despite all of that, you suggest that we should stay the way we are?"

"I do," said Eugene, his face gradually turning red. "Consistency is important! I can't support a structure that is going to destroy the underlying systems."

Well, this guy's not gonna give up easily. Obviously he's got nerve, too, I'll give him that. Standing here in front of VeraComm execs as well as QCell people and being able to defend his position no matter what – that's tough and I respect that. It's a pity he's defending the wrong side, but still, very impressive.

"I don't think you understand, Eugene," continued Zach. "We have empirical evidence that the decision to move some of your people over to 'Arkenstone' for the duration of a PI was extremely helpful."

"I don't know why we are relying on a single data point to make serious organizational decisions..." said Eugene, his face now glowing with frustration that he nevertheless managed to keep under wraps.

"Oh, you are wondering why? Because we don't have the luxury of five years to run a research project to give you extensive scientific proof,

Eugene," said Zach, now himself becoming a little cranky. "This is not a PhD thesis we are working on here. Sometimes we have to trust our senses and make decisions based on incomplete information. Also, I'm a little confused here about how adamant we've suddenly become in terms of requiring comprehensive proof before taking further steps. I don't remember anyone asking for scientific proof years ago when we created the current 'Server-side' program. Furthermore, you agreed to lead it when we offered you the program manager position. I don't remember you asking for more data points, just to be sure that the structure was right..."

Somebody chuckled in the back of the room, but the overall atmosphere was becoming very tense. Who would have thought that we would have hit such a big roadblock right at the beginning. This is obviously getting out of control.

"My program wasn't exactly structured the way it is today," countered Eugene, not prepared to give up. "It grew from–"

"Hey guys!" Adi suddenly jumped in, raising her hand. "I apologize for interrupting the conversation, but with your permission I would like to take a few minutes and describe a broader perspective on the organizational design."

Zach nodded to acknowledge Adi, while Eugene remained standing quietly with an unhappy expression on his face, probably failing to realize that this interruption might have saved him from entering into a progressively more heated discussion with one of the company's key executives.

"I'm very happy that you guys have learned one important thing: launching Agile Release Trains is essential to success. Trains are the key delivery vehicle in SAFe. And I can totally see and understand both sides of this conversation. Needless to say, organizational design is quite a tricky business. However, there's also something we can leverage here that we already know from our initial experiences with the ART construct. But first, let's recap some basics. Let me ask you guys, how would you define the Agile Release Train?"

"...A self-organized team of Agile Teams," said Sunil automatically, then adding: "that delivers value in a synchronized and incremental manner."

Well, that's good because the RTE should be ready to answer questions like that. I'm not sure where Adi is headed with all this, though.

"You're right of course, Sunil; good answer," said Adi. "And could you just expand a little bit in terms of what it really takes to 'deliver value in a synchronized and incremental manner'?"

"Sure. I would say that the most important things are the following: they plan the PI, which means that everybody on the train participates in that event. They execute iterations in a synchronous manner, producing system demo every iteration. And finally, they review the results of the PI together, as part of the Inspect & Adapt."

"Excellent," said Adi, writing three bullet points on the board:

- Plan together
- Execute synchronously
- Review the results together

"So, guys, look carefully at that simple list," continued Adi, "when we say we need people to be on the train, that's really about all we are asking for. We are not necessarily asking for a big-bang redesign of the organizational structure. Let me be clear: all we are asking here is for those people on the same train to plan together, execute synchronously and review the results together, period, end of story."

I noticed that Eugene's expression had begun to change from unhappy to puzzled to curious. His brain had already started to receive a comforting signal, but was still processing it and not sure what to expect next.

"So, Adi, you are basically suggesting that we are not actually changing the structure of the organizational units... We are not altering budget ownership or reporting structure or anything like that. We are only asking permission from the 'Server-side' program management to have their people participate in the key events for the 'Arkenstone' train, is that correct?" Zach asked, immediately realizing what Adi was trying to achieve here.

"Absolutely," said Adi. "I only want to add one thing to that," she said, drawing an arrow connecting the 'Server-side' and 'Arkenstone' blobs on the board. "It is always desirable to collocate people whenever possible. While it has no implication on the formal org structure, it nevertheless helps those teams tremendously in establishing strong collaboration patterns."

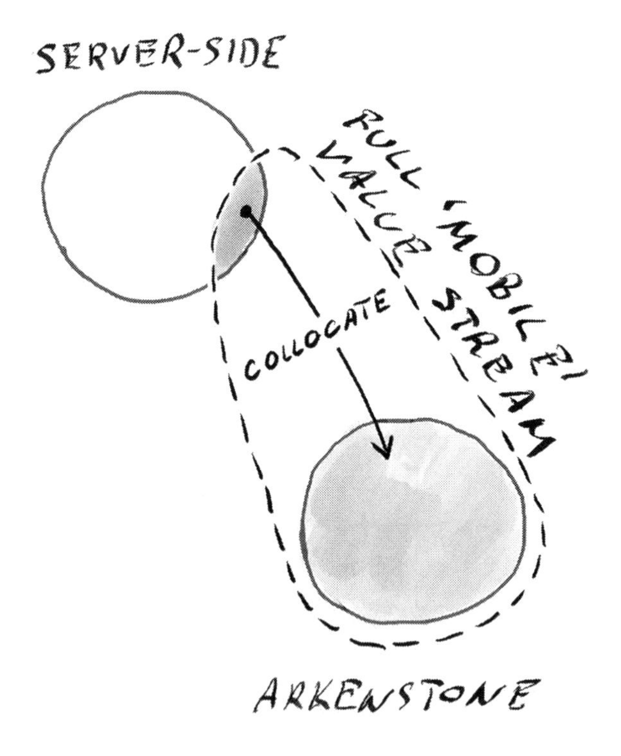

A brilliant turn! Wow... Eugene looked much more relaxed. He nodded, saying: "I'm actually fine with that. I see how collocation might be helpful. I think we're good as far as I'm concerned..."

Of course we are. I guess this will save us a lot of distress with the other programs, too. We've only gotten started, but have already found an example where a value stream cuts across multiple existing program boundaries.

The rest of the discussion was even more intriguing. We moved to the next area in our organization – 'Desktop Solutions.' The 'Desktop Solutions' program had a similar problem to 'Arkenstone's': the group itself contained about 110 people working on the web front-end and desktop client applications, which were using 'Server-side' functionality quite extensively. And just like with 'Arkenstone,' the dependencies were substantial, which meant that 'Desktop Solutions' wouldn't be able to deliver much value independently. Zach looked at Eugene again, saying: "I think we need your people on that train, too."

"That's pretty much everyone there is, after we move a bunch of guys to 'Arkenstone,' isn't it?" asked Eugene cautiously, his face once again signaling the beginnings of frustration.

"Is it?" asked Zach, looking at Ed.

Ed nodded. "Yeah, I think it is."

Eugene remained quiet for a while, squinting at Zach and by his posture indicating that he was not welcoming this development.

"Hey guys," Ed said, breaking the silence, "I think we all need a break. Let's say, thirty minutes. I'm sure you guys have a long tail of new emails to attend to by now. Also, that's what the duration of a decent coffee break should be, if you ask me."

And while people headed out in different directions, generously contributing to the increasing chaos, Ed grabbed Zach, Adi and me and we all went to his office.

"Hey guys, I'm sorry but I needed to stop the argument. It was quite a pathetic view seeing one of my best guys–Eugene–in such a position," said Ed.

"Please continue," said Zach.

"Don't you see? He's not thinking. I mean, he is thinking, but about the wrong thing. He's not able to be helpful, because instead of thinking about the best organizational design, his mind is occupied by fears and worries about job security. I bet that he's not the only one in that room with the same kind of problem – we just haven't tackled enough examples yet to 'threaten' others," Ed said. He continued, turning to Adi: "Great job with the idea of leaving the structure in place, and instead just asking the program management's permission to have their people participate with others in the common events. It got us fairly smoothly through the first speed bump – the 'Arkenstone' case. The second one–'Desktop Solutions'–was just too much to handle, though."

"You think?" asked Zach.

"Yes, I do," said Ed.

"But isn't it also weird that the flow of value in this organization is kind of... orthogonal to the structure of our programs? No wonder we couldn't deliver anything," countered Zach. "Also, we are playing by the new rules here: you are the CTO now. You don't need anyone's approval for things like that. Just go ahead and restructure your organization the way it best serves our customer and let's be done with it."

"Look, Zach. What you're saying is right and I agree at some level, but I can't just do it by decimating my guys."

"Yeah, but I don't think we have a choice, Ed. This is definitely for the better," maintained Zach.

"Oh yeah? And so it basically means the end of Eugene's career, doesn't it? Here's the thing: Eugene is a really sharp guy and I simply don't want to lose him. Also, he didn't design the program the way it is – we did. So, it's *our* responsibility to take care of our own people. I don't want to use SAFe as an oppressive mechanism with respect to any individual in my organization. I guess, we've learned one thing so far: if you want to be really successful with something, ground all you do in trust. That's the only way I can envision a successful enterprise-wide rollout of SAFe. But I don't see how dumping a talented, capable person is going to help us establish that trust."

"Ed, I hear you," said Zach, "but I'm gonna play devil's advocate a little longer, if you don't mind." He said, laughing: "Or even if you do..."

Ed shrugged his shoulders, ready to face whatever was coming his way.

Zach continued: "So, imagine, my almost-best-friend Ed–just imagine–that instead of having this problem with the management of each program we suddenly don't have the problem... because they all miraculously disappear, okay? Just poof! And nobody's home. If that magically happened, wouldn't it solve all these problems we are talking about here?"

"No, no," Ed said, shaking his head. "Zach, we are completely missing the point here... Those program leaders are not an artificial construct. Gosh, I read an article on this website recently... what's its name... I forget. Well, that doesn't matter. The article was basically suggesting that in order to succeed with Agile, you need to create an absolutely flat structure, removing all levels and letting all the engineering management go. That threw me off immediately. I'm not a professional consultant or methodologist or anything like that, but just being a practitioner with my moderate exposure to Lean and Agile, I understand how deeply flawed that idea is."

"How so?" asked Zach. "Maybe it's just what we have needed all this time? No engineering or program management, just RTEs everywhere and that's it."

"Zach, are you kidding?! Who will hire people, help with skill set development? Who will take care of training programs and all of the other people management aspects? Who will manage compensation, benefits, promotions? Who will protect the programs from people like you and me when we start slipping off the new course and fall back into our old ways? Who will help the teams operate with external vendors and other third parties? Who will bring virtually any SME on board, when necessary? Who will support the interaction with other parts of the enterprise that are not involved in development?"

"Okay, okay, that's enough," said Zach, "you win, okay? So now what? I guess nobody here appreciates our current org structure, but it looks like we're gonna keep it because we don't want to disappoint Eugene and the other program managers whose programs are at the intersection of different value streams..."

"That's not necessarily an accurate picture," said Ed. "We can do both at the same time, actually."

"How?"

"Well, let's start drawing, because my brain is going to explode if I don't get my thoughts out of my head and up on the board," said Ed, grabbing a marker. "So, what we have is three programs: 'Arkenstone', 'Desktop Solutions' and 'Server-side', which is managed by Eugene. I'm still looking to split 'Server-side' and have those parts join other programs, so that we would end up with only two, each one being a full value stream."

"Okay," said Zach nodding. "In which case Eugene gets whacked..."

"No, he doesn't," continued Ed. "Let's run some numbers here. Initially, 'Arkenstone' was 96 people, 'Desktop Solutions' 110 and 'Server-side' also a little over a hundred, as far as I remember."

"118 actually," I said, knowing that number from my recent conversation with Sunil.

"Ok, great, 118 it is. Now let's play the migration game," said Ed, adding numbers to the picture. "Let's say that Bonnie and her team of nine people move permanently to 'Arkenstone', just as they did in PI 1. That leaves us with 109 people in 'Server-side', all of whom we'll move over to 'Desktop Solutions'. That makes 'Arkenstone' 105 people total while 'Desktop Solutions' becomes 219. Hey Adi, this is too big for a single train, correct?"

"Absolutely. Try and think of 219 people planning together, for instance. Imagine the room, the logistics, all the communication overhead. Imagine that just going over each team's plan would take more than two hours..."

"Yeah, I totally agree. So what do you typically do in such cases?"

"Well, when a value stream is bigger than the optimum train size, roughly 50 to 125 people, you simply split that value stream into more than one train. We do need to be careful about *what* we organize those trains around, because that may have significant performance implications."

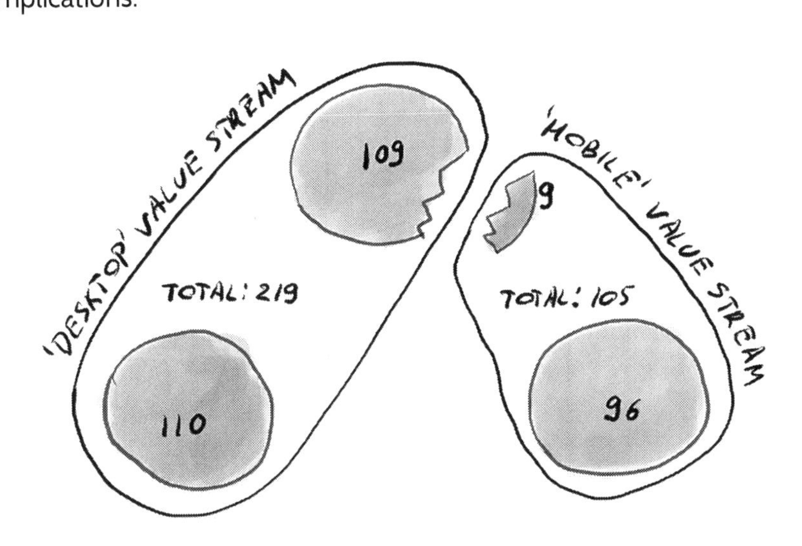

"Bingo!" said Ed. "Here's what we're gonna do. We split Eugene's current program as this picture suggests," he pointed at his own drawing. "But then 'Desktop Solutions' value stream will actually consist of two Agile Release Trains and regardless of what we organize them around, Eugene will support one of them. Problem solved!"

Zach stared at the drawing as if trying to find an error in it, but then, after a few moments of silent observation, said: "Okay. I'm good with this. I guess if executed as intended, this is going to unblock us in terms of the rest of the programs, too. And I would like this to be resolved ASAP, because that would demonstrate to the QCell people that we are not stuck in a maze of decision-making, but rather are able to progress quickly toward the ultimate goal."

"Yep," said Ed. "I'm gonna talk to Eugene one-on-one when we're done here, and if he's okay with this change, which I'm sure he will be, we will just announce the change to the group."

And so he did. A few minutes later when we had all gotten back to the main room, Ed announced the modification. Everybody understood the motivation behind it and noticed that Eugene was now fully relaxed and happy to take over his new responsibilities. Everybody was prepared to proceed with the next steps.

And one immediate such step was to determine how exactly to split 'Desktop Solutions' value stream into two trains. Adi took the stage...

"Guys, our goal here is to build those trains in such a way as to satisfy two major objectives," she said, approaching the board. "One is to minimize hand-offs. As we already know, they slow down development and make things highly unpredictable," she said, writing it on the board. "And two: ensure sustainable velocity over time..."

"Okay, this is good," said Ed. "Guys, ideas? I would like to invite *everyone* to participate in brainstorming, not just the few of us already standing here."

"What if you just leave them as is?" suggested someone.

"What do you mean, 'as is'?" asked Ed.

"Well, I mean, whatever you move over from the 'Server-side' to 'Desktop Solutions' - make that a train."

"Yup, sounds good," confirmed someone else in the room.

Ed stared at the picture for a while without saying anything.

"What if we try it, Ed?" asked the same person.

"I don't think so, guys," Ed said finally. "Look, if we did that, even though formally it would be one value stream, the trains would be organized the same dysfunctional way as our programs were before - basically back to the same silos. Anything meaningful this value stream plans to build automatically requires a handoff between the two trains in such a case," he said pointing at the drawing. "That's a step back - we can't do that."

"It almost looks like we need to pivot 90 degrees here," said Zach.

"Yup," said Ed. "I hate to say this, but you seem to be right, Zach," he added, causing a wave of chuckling across the room. "Any ideas? Anyone?" he asked, looking around.

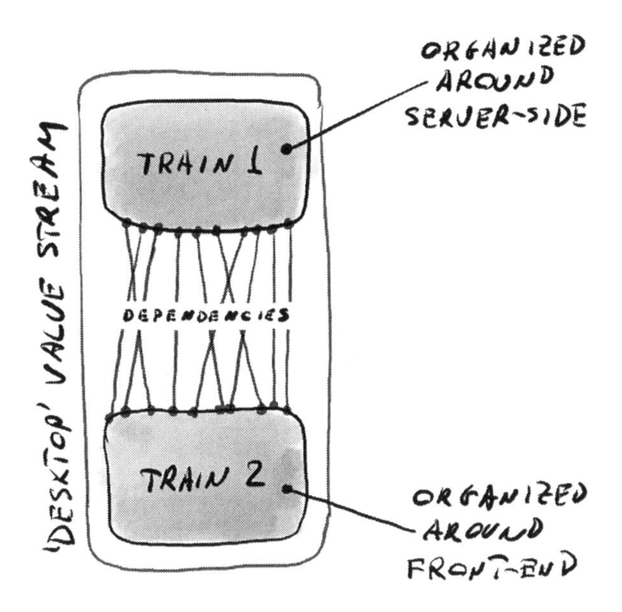

But there weren't any suggestions. The room had gone quiet except for a couple of guys whispering to each other and pointing at the whiteboard.

"Hey guys," said Eugene, "what if we just follow the value?"

"Follow the value?" asked Zach. "That sounds great! But would you be so kind as to explain what you actually mean by that?"

"So, I was thinking, if we're building one of these end-to-end pieces of value..." started Eugene and then looked around, as if begging someone to continue. "By the way, what do you call them?"

"Features?" suggested Sunil.

"Well, trains already use features as their main 'currency'," I interjected. "Let's avoid unnecessary confusion here. We need a different term for value stream level, otherwise we'll have a mess."

"Okay, so what else should we call it?" continued Eugene. "I need a noun." He turned back to Zach, saying: "We need a noun, senator!"

"I don't know... why are you asking me? Nerissa, what word do you use when explaining to the customer that our solution has something new in it. A new what?"

"...Capability?" said Nerissa, shrugging her shoulders.

"Yeah, I like that. I really do," said Zach. "So, my answer to you, Eugene, is 'Capability'," he said, smiling.

"Thanks," said Eugene. "I actually like that term too." He pointed back at the whiteboard and continued, saying: "So what if we just built those trains around distinct types of capabilities? That way the trains, by definition, will be able to build something end-to-end and will have minimum hand-offs altogether."

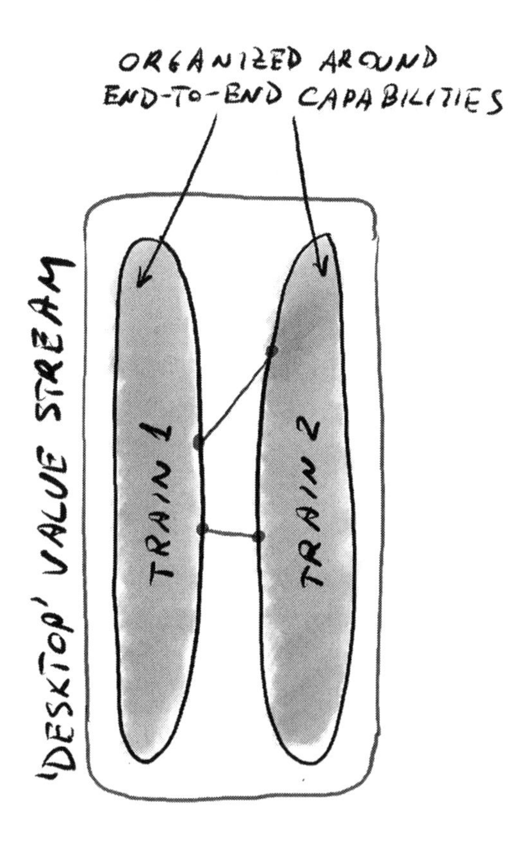

"Hmm... I like where you're headed with this, Eugene," said Ed. "Guys, I need some help here. Let's think about the key capabilities that we offer in 'Desktop Solutions' and try to separate them into two buckets, then see if we could organize the trains around each of those buckets. So, what constitutes 'Desktop Solutions'? Come on..."

"That's easy," said Zach. "Even *I* know that. One important capability is actually joining a conference call. That's what hundreds of thousands of our users do on a daily basis."

"Very good," said Ed, posting the capability on the whiteboard.

"Another one is initiating and managing the call," said Eugene, adding, "and of course, sharing the screen..."

Ed added two more capabilities to the list. "Any more?"

"Recording video and audio," suggested someone else.

"Chatting, posting questions, raising your hand," said Sunil. "These all could go together as one, I guess."

"Scheduling a call," suggested someone from the back.

"That's covered already as part of 'Initiating and managing the call'," replied Ed, continuing: "Okay, any other ideas? This looks to me like a pretty comprehensive list. I think we will keep it open and add stuff if we spot anything else later, but this is a good start. Now, let's see how to best group these capabilities, so we can end up with just two buckets, one for each train. Any thoughts?"

"What if we merge two of them," said Eugene, "namely 'Joining a call' and 'Initiating and Managing the call'? That could be one bucket. I think we can just call it 'Calling' for short. Everything else will fall into another bucket."

"That makes it 'Screen sharing', 'Recording' and 'Chatting, et cetera...'," summarized Ed. "What do you guys think?"

"I like it," said someone. "I think those are like-sized buckets, roughly speaking. And that's a good thing, I suppose."

"Agreed," said the next person. "Looks good."

"I'm not sure if it's good or not," said Anand, one of the system architects invited to the workshop. "See, if you split it this way, it would imply that every train will be touching on every significant subsystem or layer. And to me that is quite concerning. I would like to go back to Adi's two objectives. On the one hand we want to achieve fast flow, on the other hand we also want the flow to be sustainable. I see how we are achieving the former, but I'm really worried about the latter."

"I don't get it," said Ed. "Explain. What subsystems or layers are you talking about? What impact does it have on sustainability?"

Anand approached the whiteboard, saying: "Let's assume that these are our trains, okay?" he pointed at the two buckets. "Each one will be touching the server-side functionality, website front-end and the desktop application. And I'm seriously worried that in that case, given that the trains will have different reasons for changing the functionality in those layers, the system will gradually deteriorate and the whole construct which we call a value stream will grind to a halt. That's because adding every new piece of end-to-end functionality will be more and more painful."

Ed squinted at the picture, but remained silent. Anand had made a good point. Indeed, such danger existed. In fact, I could think of a number of cases where system architecture would decay under even less pressure. I had witnessed a lot of that first-hand, when I worked for VeraComm as a development manager. He's right – the problem is actually very serious. Especially because by the time you notice something like that about your system, it's usually too late and the system design is already terribly disfigured. Then adding any new functionality will cost you a tremendous amount of time. What's worse is that reversing from such a state is incredibly difficult. It's a very real danger.

"Anand, I think this is one of those cases when the problem is also the solution," said Eugene.

"What do you mean?" asked Anand.

"Well, you have raised a legitimate problem, no question," continued Eugene, "but I think *you* are also best suited to help us solve it. I think we simply need some cross-train architecture governance and for that we need someone like you."

"I like the idea," said Ed. "Yep. Solve it right at the foundation of the problem. I would say we need to ensure that it is the right type of governance, because I don't think we have generally been very successful with architectural process at this company so far. I like the idea, Eugene, but for now I would treat it merely as an assumption that needs validation."

"I know how to validate this very quickly," I said, pulling my phone out. "Let me call somebody..."

Three minutes later, Josh, breathing heavily, appeared in front of the group.

"That was fast," said Ed. "Hi Josh, how's life?"

"You tell me," he said, smiling and still trying to catch his breath.

After listening to our explanation of the idea of architectural governance across the two trains in his sister value stream, Josh said: "I understand. And yes, good point; architecture can deteriorate fast if different parties independently change those layers. But I can tell you right now what kind of governance will *not* work and what you guys should be striving for instead. As a developer and a person that talks to other developers on a daily basis, I have learned one important thing..."

"What is that?" asked Ed.

"If you want people to inherently and naturally follow certain rules, simply stating those rules or announcing them won't get you there. People won't be able to respond the way you need them to because that information will remain *superficial* in their mind. What you want instead is to have them deeply care about those constraints, architectural requirements and nonfunctional considerations. It has to reside deep in their minds, not just live on paper. When I'm coding, I'm thinking, right? So if I don't think in terms of higher-level architectural implications, I will just keep contributing to the overall system decay."

"And...?" said Ed, encouraging Josh to go on.

"So, in order to encourage developers to care about higher-level architecture on a day-to-day basis, you can't make decisions for them. Instead, you have to make them part of the decision-making process. If they have contributed to those architectural assumptions, they will be sure to follow them and keep them in mind at all times. And I can totally understand how some of those may come solely from you Anand, but people need to be involved in the process in order to validate, to reason about it, to offer certain adjustments and so on."

"So how do you envision that happening?" asked Ed.

"Well, in a number of ways. Certainly, one big part of it is PI planning. That's where architects and developers have quite a bit of time together to discuss such things. But the process needs to go beyond just the PI planning, otherwise it will be the same superficial crap that never works. It's simple: to make something a part of a regular thought process, it needs to be continuously reiterated. I would say that operating during the PI, adjusting the architectural view as you go as well as prepping architectural assumptions for the next PI, is the best way to be proactive about this. Also, it's the best way to avoid the telephone game..."

"What telephone game?"

"Well, you have two trains there, correct?"

"Yes..."

"They will be planning the PI separately, with the only glue between them being the architects. That means that the developers from the two trains will not be talking to each other during the planning. That's the telephone game. What I'm suggesting is direct collaboration across the trains prior to the PI planning. We have actually applied a great mechanism for things like that before and it's working perfectly fine for us in various aspects of architecture and engineering practices. I'm talking about our Community of Practice. In the same way that it works across multiple teams in our case, so it might work across those two trains in your example. That may actually fuel the alignment across the board and allow you guys to avoid the biggest problem with architecture: often things are one way on paper, but operate a completely different way in reality. You need to have a full communication triangle," he said, drawing a couple of squiggles on the board.

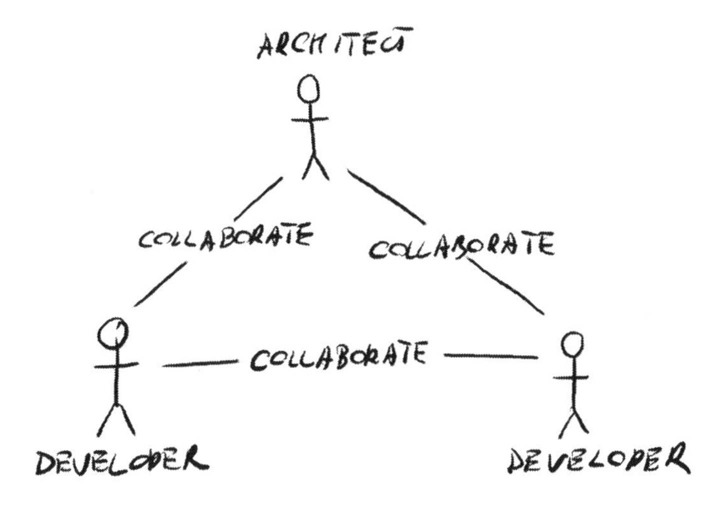

That was very solid and helpful insight from Josh. The group decided to follow his advice as well as the initial plan: organize the trains around capability areas, but provide effective, highly collaborative architectural governance and guidance across the trains. It was also decided that Eugene would take care of the train building the core 'calling' capabilities. This would allow us to get two value streams finalized.

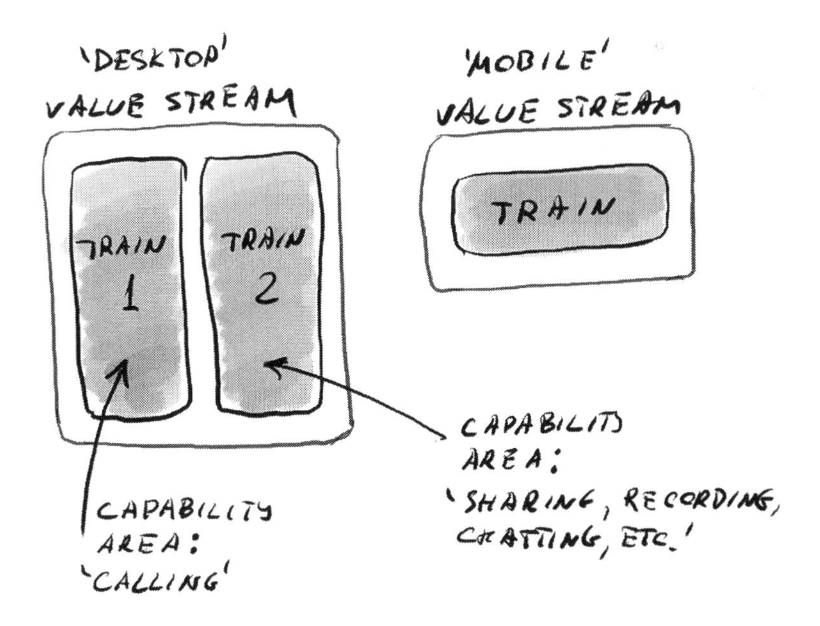

By the time all of that was finalized, it was already lunch time. Everybody badly needed a good break; we were basically brain-dead after a morning of long discussion. Following lunch, it was decided to delay any decisions with respect to 'Integrated Solutions' - the group involving software, firmware and hardware teams. In fact, the hardware and firmware guys needed more guidance anyway. Plus, traditionally in our organization, hardware folks are not too open to adopting anything that comes from 'software people'. And because the method was being tried out first in 'Arkenstone', which is pure software, they had a 'legitimate' excuse to throw a fit. Adi suggested that we give them a time out and address those value streams somewhat later, keeping the focus today on the software portion only. This is quite ironic however, given that Lean product development as such, originated in the world of real and tangible things, not exactly software. I guess history has a twisted sense of humor. But nobody is going to give up on the idea of operating in an aligned manner as a whole enterprise, rather than just a couple of trains here and there. The end goal is not negotiable and we are way past the point of no return. We will have to attend to our hardware and firmware guys at a later date.

In the remaining time we moved on to the next software case and basically became stuck. It was the 'Enterprise Customer Management' program that gave us a serious headache this time.

"...Wait a second," said Anand, "I don't really understand this. The two value streams we explored today–'Desktop' and 'Mobile'–weren't like this. In fact, if you ask me, those are *true* value streams, each one delivering valuable software to our customer. But 'Enterprise Customer Management' doesn't deliver any software products to anyone. It's just something intangible... some 'foo', that's it..."

"Intangible? Are you kidding me?" said Zach, laughing out loud. "Just so you know, out of these three examples, your paycheck is supported only by 'Enterprise Customer Management', because that's the only one where customers are paying actual money. Both 'Desktop' and 'Mobile', while they deliver software to the end user, don't generate a single dime in revenue."

"He's right," said Nerissa. "'Enterprise Customer Management' is where customer enrollment happens, among other things. That's where they pay for the licenses."

"I understand that guys," said Anand, "and I didn't mean to be arrogant. But something still feels completely different about this case, compared to those other two value streams."

"I think I understand what you're saying," said Eugene. "Like the other two value streams, this one involves software, but in a slightly different way. I guess those subtle differences can be really important," he said, grabbing a marker. "Let's pick 'Mobile', for example. That value stream clearly delivers software to the customer," he said, illustrating his point on the whiteboard.

"As part of this value delivery process, we define, develop and deliver value – that's what this value stream is doing, agreed?"

Anand and the others nodded.

"In the case of 'Enterprise Customer Management' however, we actually have completely different steps in the flow. This time the sequence is not 'Define', 'Develop', and 'Deploy', but rather 'Register a new customer', 'Select the correct licensing model', 'Process the payment', 'Adjust product and cloud settings', 'Provision the products' and 'Set the support level'. And for these steps to actually work – the software has to kick in," he said, completing his drawing.

"There are multiple systems supporting these steps," said Eugene.

"It seems like these are just two different types of value streams," said Ed. "In the previous case it's mostly development, while in this case it is simply an operational workflow, if you will."

"I like that," said Eugene. "Let's just call them that. So, 'Desktop Solutions' is a *development value stream* and 'Enterprise Customer Management' is an *operational value stream*. It's a very good way to disambiguate them."

"You know what's interesting?" continued Ed. "'Enterprise Customer Management' actually also has a development value stream that is associated with it – it's the people that develop the systems supporting it. And for us, that is the value stream of interest."

"Agreed," said Eugene. "We need to do the same thing that was done with those other value streams: figure out who is involved in development. And, if the group is small enough, make it one ART; or alternatively – split it into multiple Agile Release Trains. So how many people are there?"

"It's not too big," said Ed. "Those are dispersed teams but I think it's around 60 to 70 people, max."

"So, one train then...?" confirmed Eugene.

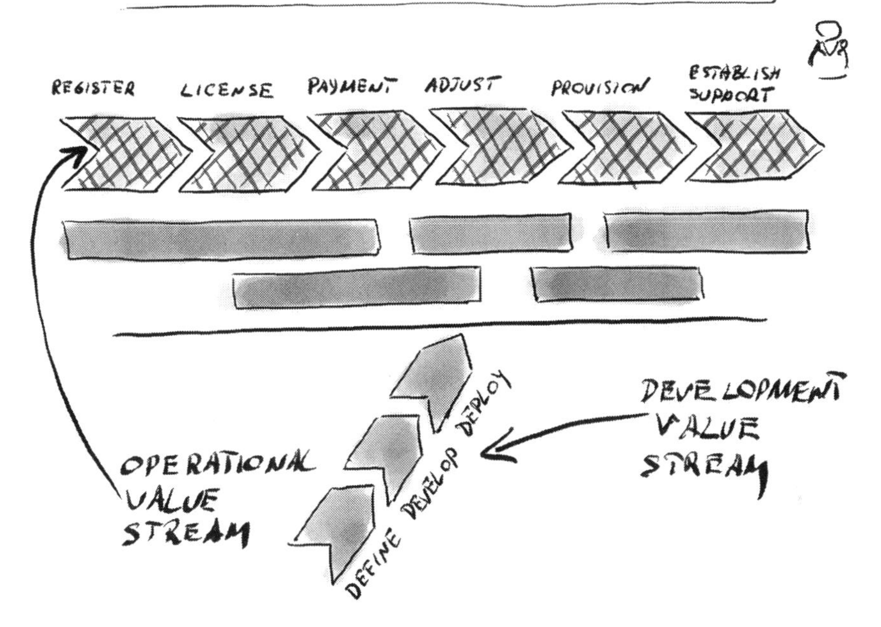

"Guys, hold on," said Marsha, approaching the board. "Your 'Enterprise Customer Management' value stream is actually our significant integration point across the two enterprises."

"You're right, Marsha," said Ed, "I completely forgot about that. We want to have a single sign-on across the two security domains."

"Not just that," continued Marsha, "but we would also like certain tighter scenarios of interaction and data exchange between our systems: both on the front-end and the back-end."

"So, how many people do you guys have as part of your workflow?" asked Ed.

"It's not that big on our side either. Around 50 folks, I think."

"Interesting... So, we actually have a value stream that cuts across organizational boundaries, it seems... We probably just want to split it into two smaller trains: one on your side and one on ours."

"Ed, I would like to offer a more radical idea, if I may," interjected Eugene. "What if we have just one train instead?"

"But that train would cross organizational boundaries, wouldn't it?"

"That's the point."

"I don't understand..."

"It's simple," said Eugene. "If we launch it as a single train, there will be a natural forcing function in place, directing the teams on both sides to collaborate."

"But they can't be a single train," countered Ed. "Our teams are in Colorado and theirs – in California. How the heck do you think they are going to plan the PI together, have you thought of that?"

"It's actually worse than that," said Marsha. "The California office only has a bunch of stakeholders for this area of concern, while all the teams are actually in Bangalore. They are not even part of QCell."

"Not part of QCell?" asked Ed.

"It's a vendor. We outsource development to a couple of vendors."

"Well, that's just great. Eugene, any more ideas?" Ed said, staring at him. "I'm telling you guys, the ART construct is not going to work in this case."

Eugene didn't have anything to say.

"Hey, Marsha?" said Ed, "out of all the anticipated integration points between our companies, how many involve outsourced teams?"

Marsha walked across the room, stood at the window for a few moments, quietly counting in her head and then said, "I'm afraid, it's all of them."

"Great..." said Ed, shaking his head. "That's just freaking great..."

"Hey guys, I don't think it is all that bad necessarily," said Sunil, jumping in. So far he had been mostly just listening. "I think we might have initially approached this problem from the wrong angle."

"Sure," said Ed. "Enlighten us."

"I am an RTE that's in his second PI, so I think I've had a chance to experience the Agile Release Train operating model first-hand, actively participating in the fate of my train. So what I'm going to tell you simply stems from my experience with this notion."

"Yeah, yeah, go ahead," said Ed, waving Sunil on, inviting him to continue.

"So I would like to offer a distinct perspective on what I think Agile Release Train is. For just a second I would like us to go beyond the ceremonies and practices of the Agile Release Train and stay rather, at the goal level. What kind of benefits are we trying to achieve with this concept? Let me offer an example. We do PI planning because we need alignment like we need oxygen. We need to understand what we are building, why we are building it and how we are gonna build it. That's why we brought all of these people into the same big room. And now, just because we can't get everyone in the same room, we are going to conclude that the concept of ART is not applicable? Please let me rephrase what that implies in terms of the benefits: we are basically saying *no* to alignment across the teams and stakeholders. And that means inevitably going back to our old ways... Another example: system demo. The reason we do it is because we want to measure the real progress, not a bunch of disjointed branches of code."

"I still don't understand what you are saying, Sunil," said Ed.

"I'm saying that if we strongly believe in the benefits we have begun to see, we will find a way to adjust the means of achieving those benefits in a geographically distributed case. We just have to show a little bit of faith, that's all. So, back to our examples... PI planning. Let's say we fly those few stakeholders from California to either Colorado or Bangalore–it doesn't matter where right now–to simply reduce everything to just two locations. And then we pick a date and ensure as much overlap between the two locations as possible, and just plan the freaking PI. Yes, they will be in different time zones, but we are not in the 19th century here. So let's at least pretend that we can establish viable communication between the sites to enable collaboration and alignment at a sufficient level." Sunil paused for a bit, but then resumed, his face shining: "My parents still live in Pune. I talk to them every Saturday on skype. And guess what? It's possible. We have communication cadence, if you will. And here, having so much at stake, we can't establish quarterly cadence for distributed planning? Why? Because it's too much rocket science for us...?"

Ed had been pacing during Sunil's speech but suddenly stopped. "Well, ladies and gentlemen, I think Sunil has a point. We may have capitulated prematurely. I would like to give this thing a shot.

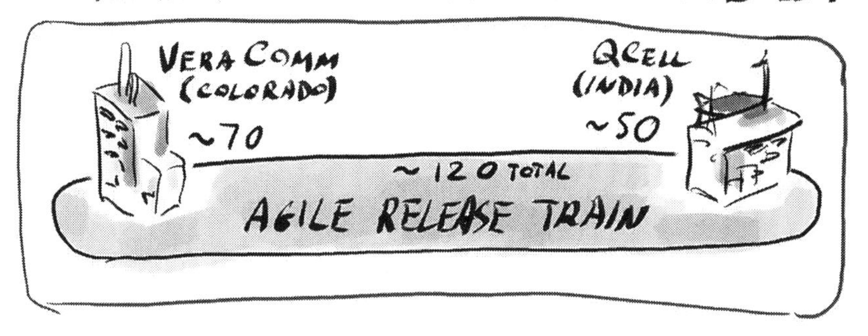

But I will need actual process expertise on the remote end, otherwise I'm not approving this. So here's the question: who's going to India to support the distributed ART launch?"

• • •

Later that day, once the workshop was over and we had tackled all of the value streams we could and defined all of the ARTs within them, I was surprised to discover that the temperature had dropped significantly. Outside, the cold air was shamelessly scratching my face, embracing my neck with its long cold fingers, trying to find a way underneath my coat by any means. All the snow that had been soft and squishy earlier in the day, had frozen into a disfigured icy surface, creating too much work for me with my cane. I automatically looked up as a small gaggle of geese fluttered overhead, crying for the lost summer in their primordial tongue. I thought they had all departed already, seeking better fate in warmer regions. It must be that one of those lakes doesn't freeze till the last moment, giving them hope beyond hope but finally betraying them, closing the last gap in the otherwise perfectly flat surface of ice, sealing the precious water and forcing the beautiful creatures to spread their wings in search of a better home.

"Ethan!"

I turned around to see Marsha walking in my direction, carefully navigating the rough ice.

"Ethan, hold on one sec, please," she said, while approaching me in the parking lot. "I wanted to thank you for this workshop. I understand now why you and Ed were so insistent about it. I'm glad we did it and I'm sorry if I appeared to be a little unsupportive earlier."

"No worries, Marsha," I said, knowing that one way or the other, out of all QCell people, she's the one that's truly on our side.

"Also, regardless what we talk about here, it doesn't change the fact that my company will be pushing their extensive roadmaps into these trains with all the power at their disposal. I will help you as much as I can, but you can't imagine... you just can't imagine what you are gonna have to deal with. Anyway, great job today and let's talk soon," she said, jumping in her rental car and carefully navigating the icy parking lot.

I looked back up at the sky and was barely able to spot a small moving dot - my geese. They were well on their route despite the cold wind that had stretched the clouds into a peculiar, long mane, weaving towards the south-east where the dot eventually disappeared from my sight.

ETHAN'S DIARY

- *Train the people that you plan to invite to your value stream analysis workshop. Also, demonstrate early wins to them whenever possible, prior to the workshop.*

- *You may be surprised how misaligned your actual org structure and the flow of value can really be*

- *There are two types of value streams: development and operational. Development value streams deliver software to the customer, while operational value streams offer a certain type of service. Every operational value stream has a development value stream associated with it: the teams that develop the software systems in support of the operational workflow.*

- *The key objective of value stream analysis workshop is to identify value streams and ARTs that realize them*

- *50–125 people is an optimum ART size. If a value stream is bigger than that, it should be split into multiple trains. Trains can be organized around subsystems or capabilities. Organizing around subsystems can lead to too many hand-offs, though. Capabilities may offer a better organizational paradigm, but may lead to deterioration of the system design over time. Architectural coordination may be needed in such cases.*

- *Value streams may not only cross different departments within an organization, but also cut across multiple organizations per se. Trains that realize such value streams can also cut across organizations. Having a train across geographic locations creates a unique opportunity to establish coordination where it's lacking the most.*

CHAPTER 13

The Overflow

"I guess bad decisions make good stories."

-ED

SPRING BURST INTO MY CONSCIOUSNESS like a meteor, exploding into a myriad of fireworks, touching every inch of the frozen land and letting all of the winter hostages escape safely into the long-awaited warmth. The remaining islands of snow, hiding in the shadows and shivering wildly with fever, wrapped themselves into the blankets of dust, hoping against hope to be saved from the inevitable finale. And then the biggest orchestra in the world arrived, occupying the highest and most prominent stages: the branches of the still naked trees and endless strings of electric wire. The whole of nature seemed to delve into a deep, metallic symphony, dissolving into an enormous number of tiny tweets and then growing once again into a single powerful blast. Overflown with emotions, they can't notice how day to day they play more and more overtime, forcing the boundaries of the night to shrink, letting more music and light into the day.

This year I hadn't even noticed when or how the transfiguration had started. By the time it had begun, it was already too late: winter had been wrestled to the ground and tamed. Tapping out and crawling away–back to its lair–it intended to spend the next couple of months licking its wounds and resenting the entire world, which had betrayed it once again.

It was becoming progressively hotter, both in the air and in our heads. VeraComm and QCell had executed their first PI together and the results were... confusing, to put it mildly. I don't know exactly how it happened, but that PI did not make anybody happy. It failed to satisfy the engineers that had just recently learned how to gain a real victory, but were now tasting the sourness of defeat again. It also failed to create more trust with the stakeholders, whose take-away was that a lot less had been pulled into the PI than should have been. And even the stuff that *was* planned had been radically de-scoped during the execution, leaving much less in the delivery pipeline than they had initially hoped. The quality of the PI demos across the trains was well below the bar: most of the stuff being heavily scaffold'ed, falling apart with a minimum pressure. And then the rumors began...

Nobody was really able to say where the whisperings originated from or what to expect next, but everyone's favorite topic (both at VeraComm and QCell) had become how we had failed our third PI. Conclusions were made, suggestions offered, and assumptions extended that perhaps VeraComm was simply incapable of scaling the success of 'Arkenstone' to the whole enterprise. Things began to spin out of control with too much talk, a widespread lack of faith and what's worse - very little action. Finally, Ed and I were kindly invited to a meeting with the company's CEO. He explained to us in very crisp terms that this is exactly how people lose trust, and that earning it back takes ten times more effort. He said that he was very concerned about the volatile nature of our approach, and while there had been some early successes, he had to admit that if things didn't improve in the near future, he would have to reach out for external help to 'sort out the mess we'd created'.

"That's just wonderful!" said Ed on our way out of the CEO's office.

"What is?" I asked, too tired to think about the possible consequences.

"What he just said. Do you know what that means?"

I shook my head, unable to compute.

"It means that he's going to reach out to his old buddies from some consulting firm that specializes in a bunch of... nineteenth century methods. They will deploy a dozen knuckle-heads in suits that will wave their hands and unleash all the rigor of a highly documented, phase-gate utopia upon our already miserable fannies. And then they will look carefully into QCell's huge roadmaps and conclude–to the great satisfaction of the management–that they have a way to implement it *as is* and meet all the milestones, if we all just try real hard. They will do a full inventory of all the capacity reserves across the board to ensure that everyone is loaded 100 percent, which will be a disaster, as we perfectly well know. However, due to the flawed nature of their process model, the earliest QCell will notice that we are hopelessly lagging behind will be in about nine months or so. Then it will be time for the 'Olympic Blame-Game'. Those 'trusted consultants', perfected beyond human limits, will suggest as usual that the teams and their management have made a number of mistakes, due to their low process maturity, which will trigger weeks and weeks of assessments. And after that they will offer a generous selection of 'watermelon' metrics, suggesting that this is the organization's last chance to prove whether they are capable of pulling it off or not–"

"How do you know all this, Ed?"

"Because it has happened with our hardware folks in the past. You may not know this because you have never overlapped with them, but I know these guys. It will be the same... people, flashing their badges around, acting annoyingly polite but ready to screw you over at the drop of a hat. Gosh, I hate those suits!" Ed grabbed a bottle of sparkling water from the vending machine that he had finally convinced to ingest his five-dollar bill.

"What's a 'watermelon metric'?" I asked.

"It's just the B.S. they will offer," he said, picking up his change. "All kinds of measures that aren't worth a hoot."

"I don't understand the watermelon reference, I'm sorry..."

"Oh, that's because they're green on the outside and red on the inside," he said, chuckling and opening his bottle that in one quick second inevitably sprayed the perfect amount of liquid on his shirt. "And I hate when this happens," he said glumly, pointing at the machine. "Who on earth engineered it that way? Vending machines shouldn't shake up bottles while dispensing them. Gosh..."

"No, they shouldn't, Ed."

"...Hey, Ethan. In all seriousness, we need to get to the bottom of this mess. I don't know how it all happened, but I actually agree with our CEO in one regard: as we moved to a broader scale, we simply failed, and that's scary as hell..." Ed said, running towards his office still shouting as he went: "Figure it out, Ethan. I'm going to work with our QCell friends to soothe their burn a little bit. Meanwhile, you've got to figure it out..."

Easier said than done. Yes, some things are known problems; like the fact that Marsha didn't manage to get the key QCell stakeholders into the leadership training. And as weak as it sounds, I'm not sure that's the only thing that was responsible for the unsuccessful PI outcomes. I have to admit that with the number of value streams and trains that we launched, I also lost visibility into the process. And I doubt that anybody else was able to accurately say in what direction the whole elephant was moving. It looks like we were really lacking some essential piece of the puzzle.

I ran up to the next floor to talk to the Transformation Team – I needed to see what my guys had to say. One positive development is that now I can run all I want; the knee problem is a distant memory. In fact, Ed and I undertook another attempt to get to the 'puddles', and this time we were successful. The snow had started to melt, making our travel a lot more difficult as we cut through the muddy, slimy substance. But this time we prepared well, and despite a few unpleasant surprises – we made it. It needed to be done. We just couldn't let it slip and go on the record as a 'fail'. One morning I realized that I now have three bikes in my garage. The top-notch carbon-fiber-frame mountain bike, with its amazingly designed split, adjustable suspension, is still densely covered in a thick layer of dirt from our ride. And we are buying a forth bike, one for Rachel this time.

When I entered the room, my guys were in the middle of a discussion with Sunil, drawing something on the board.

"Hey boss," said Sunil. "How is the day going so far?"

I was glad to tell them them how was my day unfolding. I even calmly described my less-than-adorable conversation with the CEO, at least the disclosable part of it. I noticed that they all moved away from the whiteboard and closer to me, quickly forgetting about their drawings.

We talked about the PI problem for a while, and then decided to organize a meeting with the representatives from all the trains to make sure that we weren't speculating too much – it's important to stay connected with reality. One thing we had firmly learned was that the Transformation Team can only be as good as its interactions with the rest of the organization. So we decided to double down the beaten path.

"I can tell you what happened in our value stream – 'Desktop Solutions'," said Eugene as we explained to all of the meeting participants what we were trying to achieve. "It was our first PI..."

"Yeah, but 'Arkenstone' rocked *their* first PI, remember?" I said.

"Sure, I remember. But our problem was multiplied by the fact that we actually... we got..." Eugene waved his hands trying to pick the right words out of the air, but they just wouldn't come.

"We simply got overloaded," said his colleague. "We took on too much stuff in our last PI."

"But how is that possible? Didn't you guys have teams to do estimation and planning?" I asked, failing to compute what they had just said.

"Yes..."

"But then how did it happen? I don't understand. The whole point of the PI planning is to prevent things like that from happening."

"It's just not that simple," said Eugene.

"Okay, I have nothing but time... why don't you explain it to me?"

"You see the teams didn't have enough time to fully explore the scope."

"Two days wasn't enough; is that what you're saying?"

Eugene didn't reply, but instead gave me a guilty look.

"The two days of planning didn't matter," jumped in Eugene's colleague. "PI planning couldn't have saved us. There was no prep at all. At the PI planning, the teams saw the scope for the first time. All that stuff that came in from QCell was a huge unknown. The teams did their best, but there was not much they could do under the circumstances."

This is ridiculous, I thought. "Did anyone else have this problem?"

All of the programs except 'Arkenstone' raised their hands.

"But how did the teams manage to do their confidence votes then?" I asked, totally staggered.

"Well, the teams understood that there was not much they could do about the problem. They came to realize that if they voted low, it would put a halt to the whole thing and cause a lot of trouble."

I really can't believe what I'm hearing; I hope I'm dreaming. I stopped having nightmares a long time ago, but now it looks like they're back. Goodness, I wish this was one of them, because if this is reality then it is too bad for all of us. "So, just for protocol, Eugene, what you guys did has caused a lot of trouble for everyone. If, instead of encouraging the teams to make false commitments, you had stopped that bullshit, you would have done the right thing. You guys simply betrayed your teams!"

"But we thought it would be better to..."

I didn't even listen to the rest of the sentence. I hate myself when I think up excuses and I equally despise hearing them from other people. How can we scale anything if our mindset is so corrupted? It seems we can't be honest with ourselves. Each time we agree upon a rule we immediately find a way to twist it. Even the smallest impediments make us immediately compromise our own ruleset. No courage, no trust, no transparency... Here's one thing though: I'm not going to keep banging on their door, hoping that they will become so conscientious about it that they drastically alter their behavior. I've learned not to trust such 'miracles'. The action I'm gonna take is going to be a lot more effective.

I was walking down the hall to Ed's office, noticing our state-of-the-art interior decor; fancy pictures on the walls and different kinds of decorations, like little and big modern art sculptures... What ironic evidence of how shallow and superficial we have become, embellished beyond perfection on the outside, miserable inside. My father used to say something I didn't care much about as a young man, but that I have certainly come to appreciate now: 'if you perform poorly on the battlefield, you're gonna get killed; if you perform poorly in the enterprise, but use the right words to describe it - you're gonna get promoted'. Well, I'm gonna bring them a freaking battle - enough games.

"I want all of those cowards out, Ed! Absolutely all of them. If not, we don't stand a chance here," I said, after explaining to him what had happened.

"Let's not rush to conclusions prematurely, okay? Those are smart guys we're talking about–"

"I don't care if they are freaking Nobel Prize nominees. They have poisoned the well. They spit on the very foundation of what we are trying to build here. By basically forcing the teams to make unrealistic commitments they drove the miserable failure of the PI. They are a disease and I'm gonna cure my organization of it, I swear. We keep wondering why the old mindset makes a comeback every time? Well, it's because of them... Or worse, actually – it's because of us... Because *we* are allowing it to happen. Maybe we should call it a crisis of leadership, Ed."

"Whoa, Ethan, hold your horses now. Trust me, I am on your side in this."

"Well, then let's take what Zach said the other day seriously: imagine that they all disappeared along with the numerous problems they're creating. Let's stop fantasizing and make it a reality. Ed, you must take action."

"I will Ethan, as soon as you calm down, I will..."

And he did. Fifteen minutes later he and I were sitting in a big meeting room, watching all of the program and development management quickly come together on short notice. Ed said that he would do the job, but that he'd be doing all the talking. So, I guess I'm just gonna post-up here like a scarecrow and watch things happen around me. It will certainly take a great deal of self-discipline to stick to my part of the bargain and not intervene.

"Guys, I requested your presence at this impromptu meeting because of the problem that this company ran into during the last PI," Ed said in quiet, comforting voice. But I think everybody knew perfectly well why they had been invited and his visibly calm approach only made the atmosphere more tense. "Now, what I'm gonna tell you next might come as a surprise, but so be it; surprises are becoming our normal modus operandi." He paused, taking a sip from his cup with big red letters suggesting: 'Please don't confuse your Google search with my engineering degree.' "We are lacking some processes in place at the higher, portfolio level and that, I think has contributed to the problem." He continued: "Well, that's on me. But that's not exactly why I feel so disgusted with myself."

The people in the room looked perplexed, to say the least. It was annoyingly quiet, too.

"Do you know why I feel that way?" asked Ed, looking around for any response. Failing to find any, he continued: "It's because I failed at my most important mission – to build a strong community of leaders that, above all else, seek to enable their people to do the best job in the world. And what did I build instead? An organization with leaders that failed to protect their own programs from total overload, and instead forced the teams to commit to impossible outcomes, despite obvious problems in their plans. Instead of solving the engineers' problems and making their lives easier, the opposite has been done: their leaders' problems were imposed on them. Do you know what I'm talking about? Well, let me explain it then. You have been played and QCell played you. They snuck lots of scope in at the last moment, while in fact you were responsible for making sure that the prep of all the content happens ahead of time. You just sat there watching the problem progress, until it was too late. And then, during the PI planning, you simply screwed the teams over, basically committing them to a highly improbable course of action. I have one last question to ask before I tell you what I'm gonna do about all this 'glorious' leadership style. So here is my question: how did you expect them to succeed with it? What was your 'secret sauce' that was supposed to make it all work? What am I missing in this outrageously ingenious plan?"

Ed had obviously perfected the skill of asking rhetorical questions after becoming the CTO. Not that he was ever bad at it, but probably given the newer and broader set of responsibilities, the questions had obviously become spicier.

"Well?" he said, looking around with a visibly disappointed expression. "I don't have an answer to that question either, so let me get to the most important part of our conversation: what's gonna happen next. I want to be very clear about this, and want to make sure that everybody in the room understands it. I am strongly convinced that development management is absolutely critical at scale. And now that we are adopting Lean and Agile across the enterprise, it's become clearer than ever

– teams need strong support and enablement – in fact it's absolutely vital to their success. We are looking at a unique opportunity to unleash all of their creative power and their talent in building absolutely amazing things, meanwhile kicking the hoo out of our competition... proving to the entire world that we're still open for business."

He stopped for a few seconds letting those words sink in and rolling the cup in his hands. Then he continued:

"Here's a huge... I might say–devastating–change. Come tomorrow, I will only have one type of leader in my organization: people who lead with honor, courage and deep respect for their teams. Just to be clear: there will be no other type of leader here, as of tomorrow. All leadership will be proactive, transparent, and busy enabling the knowledge workers that, by the way, work their fannies off for this organization. If you, per chance do not envision yourself in such a role, I expect your immediate resignation." Ed stood up and walked towards the doorway then suddenly stopped, as if he had forgotten something in the room. "Have a nice day," he said with a dry, formal smile on his face as he disappeared.

. . .

As usual Adi left shortly after the value stream analysis workshop. I don't know how many organizations she's working with, but I have never considered her constrained availability to be a problem. It's rather the opposite; I couldn't be happier because should she start spending too much time with us, I think our organization would have fewer real opportunities for learning. Learning works in mysterious ways: it seems only to work if you struggle through it. Otherwise it's just some junk information that comes in one ear and goes immediately out the other, leaving nothing behind in our brains. We were looking for such an opportunity for learning this time and gosh, weren't we struggling already? Every day was bringing only more uncertainty and challenge. Our problem was big. It was big in terms of the scale, but also big in terms of the impact it would have, should we fail to solve it. Adi knew about the problem, but it was one of those times when she surprised us by not having much to add. The problem was that we didn't have a way of planning and executing reliably at the highest–portfolio–level of the organization. Yes, we got all of the value streams and trains identified and that was good. We even made some rough intervention into the leadership practices in Ed's organization, so ultimately we could hope for some improvement there. But we didn't have a consistent method of operating at the portfolio level. Well, that's not entirely true - we had a home-grown method that was horrible and in the past had gotten us into trouble more often than not. Every year we would spend 2-3 weeks on intense annual planning. None of the quarters would ever be executed as expected, but we kept doing it and nobody knows why. With Ed's promotion and Zach's complete support, it wouldn't be too hard to drop the old way entirely and switch to a newer and better method. There was only one problem: we had no such method...

Our problem was further complicated by the fact that we had completely lost control over the intake process due to a total invasion of QCell people who were bringing more and more work in every day, it seemed. Yes, it was part of the deal, but we were obviously suffocating under all that uncontrolled load and there seemed to be no end to it.

I needed to talk to Sunil to see if he had any ideas about how we might survive this mess. He was meeting with the architects in one of the conference rooms on the third floor. I figured his meeting was just about to finish, so I decided to go grab him before he escaped somewhere else. Sunil was developing into an amazing RTE, but that also implied that his schedule was getting way too busy lately.

"Hey Ethan, I'm basically done here," said Sunil as I entered the room. "Would you like to go to your office?"

"What is that?" I asked, totally distracted by the whiteboard that was completely covered with various kinds of bizarre arrows, lines and stickies.

"That's a state machine," Anand, one of the architects, proudly said. "That's what we decided to use to track how we build our architectural runway. Are you familiar with state machines, Ethan?"

"I am – it's basically an entity that has certain transition rules between different states and offers a mechanism to determine which step you are on at any time."

"That's correct," said Anand, smiling. "Except that we are cheating a little bit here. This is more like a bunch of state machines running in parallel. See those stickies there?"

"Yes?"

"Each sticky can independently move through the steps, left-to-right."

"What info is on a sticky?"

"Each sticky represents some architectural work; some sort of enablement our systems need. Like this one, for example, is 'Automatic, recoverable socket connection'," he said, pointing at a sticky.

"And what are the states a sticky goes through?"

"It all starts with what we call the 'Funnel'," he said, glancing at the rest of the architects in the room, who were suddenly chuckling at an inside joke that I absolutely didn't want to be in on. "This is where all of the new stuff enters the system, so to speak. Then, if a sticky seems to make sense we move it over to 'Review', where we take a closer look at it. And if it still makes sense to us at that point, it moves further, into 'Analysis'. That's where we actually unleash all of the power of modeling, prototyping and what have you. We make sure that we really understand what we are dealing with and what the architectural implications are across our systems. Once it's finished in 'Analysis', we move it to 'Implementing' – that's it. Simple."

"Lovely," I said, having my curiosity fully satisfied and beckoning Sunil to follow me.

"State machine? Gosh... seriously?" I said to Sunil as we walked down to the lobby.

"Yeah, these guys are geeks at the purest level. Very smart guys though. Also, what they do is incredibly helpful to the teams."

"I don't doubt that, Sunil. It's just that calling something a state machine... Well, the good news is that they developed that board exclusively for their own use, so the problem is contained."

Sunil chuckled.

"But imagine Olga or Zach being told that what they are looking at is a state machine," I continued, realizing that I couldn't get rid of this rich, juicy topic so easily. "Can you imagine the look on their faces?"

Sunil was holding his belly with both hands and snorting, trying to get some air into his lungs, but it looked like his imagination was his biggest enemy. After another minute of laughing he finally calmed down and I promised not to bring up that topic again, which caused him to crack up for a couple more seconds. Finally, we were able to turn serious and for good reason: we had to do something about our big challenge.

"So, let's just take a moment and try to identify what exactly is causing us all of these problems," I said as soon as Sunil and I got to the whiteboard.

Sunil looked at the clean board for a while. "You mean excluding the fact that our own development and program managers totally failed their mission?"

"Yes, that's correct. And just between you and me, quite a few of them have already reached out to the Transformation Team, requesting some sort of follow-up to help them better navigate through their new responsibilities in context of Agile and Lean. The conversation that Ed had with them actually performed its function. You can tell when Ed is not kidding..."

"Yes, indeed. So, back to our problem then," continued Sunil. "In fact, I think there were a couple of them..."

"Okay, go ahead."

"One problem is that we don't have a way of standardizing the intake."

"What do you mean exactly, Sunil?"

"Well, here's the thing: every train operates with features, right? We decided during the value stream analysis workshop that if a value stream involves more than one train, we're gonna call the backlog items *capabilities* at the value stream level. But what we are dealing with here is way different. What we are seeing are much bigger initiatives that sometimes cut across even multiple value streams, creating impacts of epic proportions. We don't even have the terminology for that kind of thing."

"...Of epic proportions? I like that," I said. "Maybe that's what we should call it - an epic."

"Epics?" Sunil looked at me, smiling. "Well, at least it conveys the message. I'm fine with that - let's call them epics. It's actually somewhat funny and scary at the same time."

"So what do we know about epics? Let's try to define them."

"Well, we know that they are big."

"Thank you for the obvious but less than helpful input, Sunil. Look, to a team of seven people, a feature is also considered big. Bigger than a user story, at least. Everything is relative. We need to be more specific."

"Well, an epic may cut across multiple value streams, as I said. I think it may also actually span multiple PIs. I guess failure to understand that epics can take more than one PI to develop was one of our problems."

"Very good..."

"And you know," continued Sunil, "I think the real problem was that everything was out of sync; almost as if it were done on purpose. Our value streams started working on some epics, but later it turned out that some of those epics contained work for other value streams too, which was not initially anticipated. Some of those discoveries were made only at the end of the PI, which is outrageous. But it's hard to blame the people in those value streams because they had limited visibility into the bigger picture. Plus of course, everything was overcomplicated by the fact that QCell people were trying to push those epics down our throats at every opportunity. There was essentially no collaboration between them and our high-level stakeholders, other than general inspirational talks and the endless mutual praise. As I said, all of the parties involved in this PI were absolutely desynchronized."

"Interesting..."

"What's interesting? Have you got an idea?" asked Sunil.

"Well, just thinking out loud here. What comes to mind is Principle #9 of SAFe – 'Decentralize decision-making'..."

"What? Are you crazy? How can you decentralize it even further?" asked Sunil, staring at me as if I had told him something deeply offensive. "It's anarchy already. What do you want to decentralize?"

"I don't quite..."

"I'm confused. I thought you just said that you did?"

"No, I said that Principle #9 came to mind. And if you remember what it actually suggests is a fine balance between *centralized* and *decentralized* decision-making."

Sunil kept staring at me, still with an unhappy expression.

"I think what we failed to understand in this case is where that boundary dividing centralized and decentralized decision-making is, in terms of scope of work. I think, having realized that we are dealing with large, cross-cutting initiatives, we need to centralize all key decisions regarding those initiatives, otherwise the 'anarchy', as you called it, will continue and we will struggle even more."

Sunil nodded. "I see what you're saying. So, I guess that's where the boundary is: with epics, use centralized decision making; everything smaller than that – decentralized."

"Yup."

"It's funny, but I think that is, in a sense, the whole point of epics; to be able to make centralized decisions in a largely decentralized environment."

"I'm not sure I follow, Sunil."

"Well, remember, when you asked me to define epics and I said that they are backlog items that may cut across multiple value streams and may span multiple PIs?"

"Yes..."

"So, that's a weird definition. It may cross multiple value streams, but it may not. It may span multiple PIs, or may not. It's a crappy definition."

"So, you have a better one?"

"I do," said Sunil, with a victorious smirk on his face. "An epic is any significant initiative that requires additional analysis and approval from portfolio people. Period, end of story."

He's right, it makes total sense. I think we've come to a significant breakthrough here.

"Sunil, I think we should get this going. It seems what we learned is that we are dealing with a new type of backlog item, and that we need a joint portfolio team that could collaboratively make those decisions."

"Yeah," said Sunil, "if we have backlog items, we also need a backlog, don't you think?"

"Yup."

Later that day we described our concept to Ed, who was incredibly happy to hear that we had at least some idea of how to address this problem. We decided that our next step would be to organize a portfolio team meeting, invite people from QCell and just build the backlog. Everything should be pretty simple...

Goodness, was I wrong. The meeting turned into sheer hell. First, when we tried to put it all into one backlog, we quickly realized that there were literally hundreds of epics. And then Sunil came up with the 'ingenious' idea that we should just prioritize the backlog. He even offered a method that he knew worked well at the program level – Weighted Shortest Job First. Unfortunately, in this case, it completely failed us: the epics were so big and fuzzy and there were so many of them, that we got stuck in endless arguments almost immediately.

The fuzziness of the epics, and the total lack of facts in support of our countless assumptions, turned the workshop in an endless battle of opinions. Finally, completely frustrated, Ed called it a day and promised all of the portfolio stakeholders that we would come up with a better plan of action, and wished them a fine evening.

Interestingly enough, I don't remember Ed ever telling me that he was unhappy with me or the way I was doing things. He didn't say anything this time either. But the brief look he gave me after that meeting told me a crisp and convincing story without a word having been spoken. And just precisely because he never explicitly criticized me, I feel crappy about letting him down.

"Have a good one," said Anand, who I ran into in the lobby just before leaving the office. I noticed that he wore a black t-shirt with a tag line that only the chosen could understand: 'There's no place like 127.0.0.1'. That entertained me, but gosh, what a geek, I thought.

Later that night, while watching our next movie of choice, Rachel couldn't help but notice that my mind was surfing other worlds, clearly light years away from our living room.

"Is everything okay at work?" she finally asked, adding: "And I really expect a meaningful answer, Ethan, not your typical 'everything is fine' B.S. So...?"

"Yeah, well, we have some challenges taking our methods to a higher scale," I said, trying my best to keep staring at the TV set.

"Okay, let me translate that for everyone," she said, clearing her throat for the imaginary audience, sitting in their imaginary seats and eager to delve into the details of her narrative. "What Ethan is trying to say is that he's obviously having a serious problem with his management again – those big dudes and girls that can fire him and his entire team with the single stroke of a pen. As Ethan has pointed out, he is racing against the clock as always, and as it usually happens – he is already late. Ethan also wanted me to let you know that the reason he is not with us today–even though he pretends he is–is because he doesn't have a solution yet. Maybe he has even tried some things out, but so far nothing has worked... or perhaps it seemed to work, but eventually made things even worse. What Ethan is trying to tell us folks, is that we shouldn't worry though, because this is the absolute bottom, there's nowhere further to fall. Thank you. Thank you. What a great audience..."

I couldn't stare at the stupid TV any more. I noticed Rachel had a slight smirk on her face, which makes her incredibly beautiful. I'm hopelessly attracted to her wits and at moments like this, I realize how grateful I am to have Rachel in my life. I tried to kiss her but she dodged me, smiling and saying: "Nope. You must admit that what I said is completely true."

"Yes, it's true."

"Not to me – to them," she pointed towards the wall next to her, where her imaginary audience was patiently waiting for the culmination of this evening's performance.

I turned to the wall, still cracking up, and said again "Yes, what the beautiful lady said is completely true."

"Oh, you're laughing," she said, "you're not being so serious..." And then she lost it too. We laughed together for about a minute and then, totally red-faced, began to calm down.

"I'm very proud of you," she said, barely touching my lips, "even though you are totally incorrigible. Or maybe *because* you are incorrigible."

She told me about her job, too. Things were going well at her work. Her recent article had been accepted into one of Europe's most prominent science magazines. That's truly amazing, even though it was beyond my comprehension why she would want to submit an article to a European magazine while she lived and worked in the United States. But I prefer to leave some things a mystery.

"I will have to travel to London then, at some point," she said, "to present at a local conference. Will you come with me? Please...?"

I stared back at the TV, pretending like I was following the movie that had long since passed the point of no return for me.

"You can't even take a vacation, can you?" she asked, looking at me, her expression very serious.

"I'll see what I can do."

"...Which means that when the time comes to book the tickets you will say 'no' and the reason will be just as I indicated... right?"

Of course she's right. Gosh, am I really doing this? How did I entrap myself so hopelessly into all of this? I really can't even take a week of vacation and spend it with the dearest person in my life...? In London...? Ethan, really, what the...?

"Okay, I'm sorry. You're right. But tell you what, I will go with you. No matter what happens at work, I'll go. One thing though... I probably will have to work evenings during our trip. That's..."

"...the time overlap with your one and only true love - the Transformation Team," she said bursting into laughter. She hugged me, saying "Okay, okay. You will be allowed to work your evenings while I will be eating... Fish & Chips," she said, doing her best with an authentic British pronunciation of it. "Having you there with me, Ethan, will make me feel almost at home..."

'Nothing like 127.0.0.1' - automatically flashed in my mind, making me laugh.

"What's so funny?" asked Rachel.

I told her how I had run into Anand in the lobby and what was written on his t-shirt. I explained that in computer networks, 127.0.0.1 is used as a reserved IP-address for your own computer, also known as 'home' and how these guys are funny overall.

"But they are good-funny, right?" she asked.

"Yes, they are good-funny," I said, trying hard not to think about those examples when they aren't, really... "There was another funny one with Anand recently, too," I continued. And I told her the whole story about the state machine and how Sunil and I were completely cracking up, imagining the expression on Zach's face or Olga's face, if they had been told what they are seeing is a state machine.

"That's funny," she said. "We actually had a similar situation in my department. Back in the day I had a colleague – Liz. Wicked smart lady, but with the same problem. Her field of study was cognitive psychology and she seemed to be advancing in an interesting direction. She even published her results in a couple of the world's top scientific magazines. I think she was onto something really, really deep there. It turns out she actually developed her own theory of cognitive psychology – very substantial work that nonetheless was never recognized simply because her theory was too difficult to understand. It was way too 'geeky'–just like that state machine in the case of your colleague. Quite a few people initially tried to follow her thread, but had to eventually give up after finding it too hard to comprehend. I think that's just the way her brain worked, though. I don't think she did it on purpose."

"So, what happened?"

"Nothing. Despite the great potential to be applied in many other domains, those 'state machines' here and there in her method almost certainly prevented that from happening."

"Other domains? Like what?"

"Oh, are you kidding? If her theory was just a bit simpler and more concise, people would definitely have started using it in real-life applications, like decision-making, learning, problem-solving, treating attention disorders, etc. – all solid, real stuff."

And suddenly it struck me right in the head. This is it. This is what we are missing. Sometimes funny things are, in the end, not so funny.

"Ethan? Are you with me?"

"I... I need to make a call... real quick," I said, jumping up off the sofa and reaching out for my phone.

• • •

During that PI, Sunil and I did the seemingly impossible: we really managed to establish a fine-working governance mechanism at the portfolio level. My conversation with Rachel had triggered a thought about the funny state machine that Anand and his friends invented to track the progression of architectural work. Maybe it could be perfectly applied to managing portfolio epics and avoiding the nightmare of our long, unusable backlog filled with fuzzy, unattractive chunks of work. This time, however, we decided to experiment with the process ourselves first, showing it only to a select set of people.

In our first round we tried simply applying Anand's 'state machine' to epics. The only change we had made was adding 'Backlog' and 'Done' as two additional states:

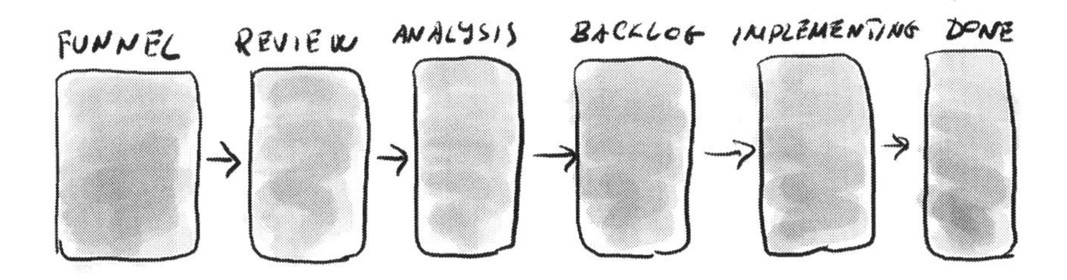

The system looked very promising because it would ideally allow us to keep a shorter backlog. The idea was simple and we had no qualms about shamelessly stealing it from Anand: epics would be progressively elaborated as they moved left-to-right in the state machine. They would initially be brought into the 'Funnel', where all new ideas were welcome. Those epics that made sense and aligned with the strategic direction of the business would move to 'Review' state. There they would be more thoroughly discussed and elaborated before moving to the 'Analysis', if we still believed that the epic was a good idea. In 'Analysis' we would perform thorough exploration with possible prototyping and so forth, and that's also where a lightweight business case would be developed for an epic. Based on that lightweight business case, the epic would receive a formal 'go' or 'no-go' decision from the portfolio team. In case of approval it would move to 'Backlog'. This would keep backlog much shorter, as many items would simply not make it through the thorough, multi-step selection process. After that, the top epics from the 'Backlog' would be pulled into the 'Implementing' step. And, once finished, they would be placed into 'Done'. Simple... At least so it seemed.

"We have captured all of the epics that both QCell and VeraComm brought into our infamous meeting," said Ed when we invited him and Zach to test-drive our 'state machine'.

He pulled out a thick pack of stickies, carelessly piled together into one big, messy heap. "There are a hundred and sixty of them," he said, pointing to the heap. "And there's a huge appetite for them all, make no mistake."

"We're gonna put them all in the 'Funnel'," said Sunil as he started the process. Soon we realized that to make it work we would need to substantially extend the 'Funnel' area of the board. Fifteen minutes later we had done it and the 'Funnel' was filled to the brim.

"Okay, now what?" asked Ed, giving Sunil and me a questioning look.

"Now we're gonna move the epics that align well with our business strategy to the 'Review' step," replied Sunil.

Ed looked at Zach, shrugged his shoulders and picked up the first item. "This one does align, I think," he said. He then picked up the next one, and then the next and the next. A minute later, after moving a dozen more stickies, he said: "Hey guys, this method makes it seem like everything is in alignment with the strategy. No wonder there are so many of them in the heap – we just don't have a good way of disambiguating what's actually good for the business and what's junk. Zach, we need your help, I think. Otherwise we'll spend all day here arguing about this, trying to understand how to narrow these down to something consumable," he said, pointing at the 'Funnel'. "I like clarity. We need a bullet list of the things that matter the most from the business perspective, and then we'll have a standard to validate these epics against."

"Well, I can give you the main themes, for sure," said Zach. "Who will be writing?"

"What you mean, 'who will be writing'?" asked Ed.

"I can't think and write at the same time," said Zach with a very serious expression.

"I'll write," said Sunil. "Go...!"

"Don't rush me, okay? It's a creative process," Zach said, staring at the flipchart where Sunil was prepared to capture the precious list.

"Integrate user identity and main workflows across VeraComm and QCell," he said, closing his eyes, clearly scanning for more. "Enhance flexibility and configurability of products with thorough API exposure," he said and soon added two more: 'Expand HD capabilities into different platforms and products' and 'Expand interactivity during the call'.

"Anything else?" asked Sunil, finishing the last bullet.

"Yeah..." said Zach, trying to spit out the words on the tip of his tongue. "Mobile... we need to provide equivalent mobile functionality and wherever possible – lead on the mobile side..."

"Zach, how about restating that one in a shorter and more usable form?" asked Sunil.

"How about this," said Zach: "Offer mobile experience that matches or extends desktop?"

"Better," said Sunil, writing it down.

"'Better', he says..." smiled Zach, looking at Ed.

"By the way, what was it you called these?" asked Ed.

"What? I didn't call them anything..."

"No, you did. You said a word that I liked. I just can't remember it."

"I think he said 'themes'," interjected Sunil.

"Oh yeah, themes!" said Ed. "Let's keep that name. I like it. These are our *strategic themes*."

Now that we had our strategic themes identified, the process went much easier. Some epics indeed did not align with any of the strategic themes and were left in the 'Funnel.' And despite that, we still ended up with a little over a hundred items to cross over to 'Review,' which offered no relief at all.

"Yeah, it helped, but not much," said Ed. "This load is gonna kills us, no matter what."

He was right. Even if we kept going, we wouldn't be able to cope with any reasonable analysis of the items that would move through the 'Review' state; much less implement them.

"We need to issue a company policy," said Zach, laughing.

"What policy?" asked Sunil, who still hadn't learned when Zach was serious and when he was just goofing around.

"A policy," Zach continued, cracking himself up, "that would prevent people from putting any more items into this..." he pointed at our state machine, "unless they have a written permit... from me."

Sunil finally realized that it was a setup and chuckled, too.

"Wait, wait, wait," I said, understanding that jokes can sometimes be helpful as well as funny.

"What? You like my idea?" said Zach, laughing even louder. "For protocol, Ethan, I *was* joking..."

"You know guys, I would like to invite someone who, I believe, did what you just said at VeraComm, only in a complete different domain." I pulled out my phone.

Less than five minutes later Raymond, director of IT and infrastructure support, was standing in front of us, probably wondering what was going on behind these closed doors.

"Raymond, when I was on the plane on my way to Adi's client eight or nine months ago, I remembered receiving an email from you where you told me that your guys used Kanban for... gosh... was it incident management?"

"Yes, that's correct. We used it for incident management and for infrastructure improvements. And we are still successfully using it," said Raymond.

"Tell us more about it, will you? What are the tricks?"

"Well, there are a couple of tricks, but the biggest one is establishing the WIP limits. It took a bit of time for us to fully internalize the notion, but soon afterwards it started producing amazing results. The flow improved by a factor of two, and in some cases even more - all due to good discipline around limiting the Work-In-Process."

"Can you give us an example of those WIP limits?"

"Sure," said Raymond. "Let's say, we pick the 'Evaluate' step for one of the teams in our incident management process. It has a WIP limit of 8. No more than eight items can be allowed at that step. And then they have four–if I remember correctly–as a WIP limit for the 'Fix' step. And then–"

"Wait," said Zach, giving Raymond a bit of a puzzled look. "You just tell them that there are no more items allowed? And what if you have more incidents than that?"

"Oh, we always have a lot more incidents than that," replied Raymond. "And the natural temptation is to start working on them all. But that's a big mistake, as we learned. The point is that if we are adamant about our WIP limits, the next thing you know, that long queue of incoming incidents is getting processed much faster. That's it. And all that comes from just sticking to your numbers."

"Well," said Zach, still looking surprised, "turns out that even when I'm joking, I'm actually offering invaluable guidance to my enterprise. Gosh, it's tough to be me..."

"Oh, and one more thing," added Raymond. "You may guess those WIP limits incorrectly initially, and that's totally fine. You actually need to start operating with your Kanban board for at least a little bit to know any better - Kanban is a highly empirical process. But make no mistake, even those less than perfectly accurate initial WIP limits are extremely helpful. The first order of business for us was to radically limit the overall bulk of WIP in the system, which we achieved from day one. Later though you will be fine-tuning the balance between the steps in your flow better, and that's where you're gonna keep playing with the numbers for a while longer..."

That discussion was extremely helpful. Not only because it was a great way of establishing the flow of value, but also because we now had a better name for the method. Everyone was very happy to get rid of the esoteric 'state machine' and talk about Portfolio Kanban from now on.

We defined reasonable WIP limits for both 'Review' and 'Analysis', and decided to keep 'Backlog' free of any WIP limits, until we knew better. The only remaining step was 'Implementing', and there we decided that defining a maximum number of epics in progress would be quite dangerous, as the actual variation in epic size can be very significant. Sometimes, five epics that you have in progress today may be twice as small as the next five in the backlog. So we decided to define the WIP limit naturally, as the cumulative capacity of all the value streams in the portfolio.

Our 'dry run' looked very promising and two days later we gathered all of the stakeholders to make a real pass over those epics. It was surprisingly simple to explain how our Portfolio Kanban system worked. As soon as we had agreed on the ground rules, we were able to advance quite far by moving a few epics from 'Funnel' to 'Review', using strategic themes as criteria. Then we defined those epics a little better, highlighting what they actually entailed, what was in scope and what wasn't, and what the success criteria for each epic would be (exit criteria, so to speak, formulated in business terms). But then we encountered a glitch that we had failed to envision during the dry run. Since 'Review' in our case had almost twice the WIP limit as 'Analysis', someone from QCell asked which epics from 'Review' should first move to 'Analysis', in order to occupy the few open slots in that step. It was a fair concern because epics were obviously supposed to require quite a bit of effort to be properly analyzed, so the choice of the 'candidates' really mattered.

"Why don't we apply Weighted Shortest Job First... WSJF?" asked Sunil. "We just take a very rough cut and see where it gets us. What do you guys think?"

Nobody seemed thrilled to hear that, clearly remembering the pain of applying WSJF to the endless list of epics that we had had last time. But this time around there were only fifteen epics to rank and we succeeded with the exercise surprisingly quickly, thanks to Sunil's facilitation.

"Now we just need to pull the top seven epics into 'Analysis'," he said, moving the items to the next step on the Kanban board.

"And now what do we do with them?" asked Marsha, pointing at the seven epics just moved into 'Analysis'. "How exactly do you suggest we go about the deeper analysis?" she continued. She was holding a simple, two-page lightweight business case template. The template included an entry for each of the most critical aspects of an epic, such as implementation strategy, actual size, potential child features or capabilities, value streams and solutions affected, capital investment involved, research and prototyping, hard dates, if any, and so forth. Finally there was a separate field–the most important one–'Go/no-go' decision from the key stakeholders. "Creating such a business case for each epic is a great idea, I really like it, but this is a significant amount of work that will involve people outside this group. Someone has to facilitate and coordinate all of that analysis effort."

And we realized that we had another big miss - we hadn't thought about anyone taking ownership over those items. The good news was that it was recoverable. We decided to assign an 'epic owner' to every epic in the 'Analysis' step. The idea being that they would drive the epic not only through the 'Analysis', but also through the rest of the steps in the Kanban system. And we realized that sometimes it would be someone from the portfolio team, but more often it would be people from specific value streams and trains, such as product managers, for example. Once all epic owners were assigned and the group was about to adjourn, Sunil pointed out that Kanban is a *continuous* flow system, rather than another form of Waterfall. He said that once we advance work a little further left-to-right, each time we meet in the future there we will be epics at all steps of the process. And that every such meeting will involve moving some epics from 'Funnel' to 'Review', others from 'Review' to 'Analysis', and yet others from 'Analysis' to 'Backlog', from 'Backlog' into implementation and, finally, some epics would be moved to 'Done'. He wished everyone good luck and ran off to his next meeting.

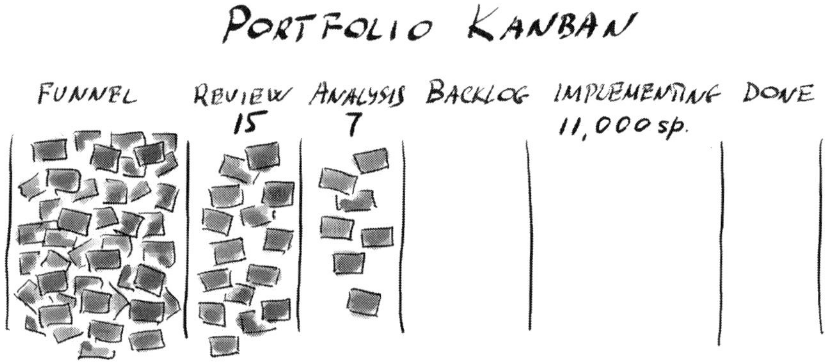

And that was how we survived the onslaught...

• • •

The rest of the PI passed incredibly quickly. For starters, we had too much work to do, now that multiple value streams were in play. But then the time came for Rachel and me to leave for London. Right before my departure Ed said that he wanted me to disappear from the radar for that week. That way I wouldn't have to work evenings and Rachel and I could enjoy the trip as much as possible. We walked, it seemed, every inch of the city and even travelled around the country a little bit, occasionally getting to the sea, enjoying the windy shores and the weather, which surprisingly enough stayed perfectly sunny for most of our visit. Living close to the Front Range neither Rachel nor I are spoiled in terms of weather, so although we were prepared for the worst case scenario, our precautions turned out to be superfluous.

Rachel's conference presentation went really well. She had quite a large audience for her talk, and she was happy that her field of study had attracted a significant number of people. It was a truly great trip for both of us. I'm so glad I didn't hesitate too much about whether to go with Rachel or not. Plus, there was something else... something amazing...

"Why are you looking so shiny?" asked Ed when I first showed up at the office after returning back to the States. "Had some good fun in London? I didn't know that museums, tea and scones, Marry Poppins and oversized snacks could make someone so insanely happy..."

I shook my head, unable to contain my wide smile.

"It must be something else then... You bought another bicycle? No? Then why the heck don't you just tell me what it is?"

"We are expecting..."

Ed stared at me for a while and then he realized what I was talking about.

"Oh! Congratulations, Ethan! Wow! I'm so happy for you guys. When did you find out?"

"Right in the middle of the trip," I said, realizing that I'm still smiling and nothing in the world could change that.

"So how does it feel?"

"I can't even tell you how great and yet how weird it feels. I don't know what to expect really, apart from the little bits and pieces I've picked up from the countless articles I read online. Not to mention all the calls from Rachel's mom that I now have to answer. She's calling every other day, bringing up various aspects of parenthood that I should be aware of."

"You know, it's funny..."

"What is?" I asked.

"Have you thought whether... well I'm sure you have... I mean, whether it's a boy or a girl? Or have you thought about your kid growing up and making different choices from those you would anticipate them making? Have you thought about how different your child's life may eventually unfold from how you think it should be?" he said, now smiling too.

"Well, as you can imagine, I have had thousands of thoughts of different sorts, Ed. And I can tell you that whether it's a girl or a boy... well, how can I even set preferences about something like that? It's most amazing, either way. But in terms of thinking about my kid's future... well, I'll tell you what. I don't think I'm able to think any more. Right now my head is just one big bowl of conflated thoughts, and that's all it is... Sometimes it feels like it's going to explode, like a pressure-cooker. But then I conveniently find myself tired enough and the next thing I know I'm smelling fresh coffee in the morning."

"That's good. What's also good is that we finally managed to stabilize the portfolio, at least for the time being. This PI showed us that what we thought about during that marvelous bike ride of ours–in terms of needing a bigger picture view of the entire organization–was exactly the right thing to do. This is the first PI that was successful, from the enterprise perspective."

"Agreed," I said, picking up my backpack and going towards the elevator.

"Hey Ethan!" Ed said, following me. "One last thing I wanted to tell you."

"Yes?"

"Regardless of whether it's a girl or a boy, I'm sure you'll be the happiest father in the world. But there's also one little prophecy I'd like to make..."

"Go ahead," I said, knowing that Ed can be really silly when he wants to be.

"Your child will be as smart as the mom and as courageous as the dad," he said with a smirk.

It took me a few moments to parse that. Lately things appeared to take longer to comprehend. I was fully consumed with thoughts and the anticipation of something absolutely new and exciting, waiting to break into my life and shed its light to every corner.

"Why not also as smart as the dad?" I asked, not realizing at first that I probably just stepped on a land mine.

And I surely had because I could see something detonate in Ed's eyes and he smiled widely, saying: "Because you agreed to take on the role of a change agent, Ethan. That wasn't smart at all. You disappointed me..." he said, cracking himself up. "I guess bad decisions make good stories," I heard him say in a pedantically-elaborate intonation as he disappeared around the corner of the lobby.

I entered the room where we had had our first meeting with all of the portfolio stakeholders. Our Kanban system looked really different now: there was a lot more going on there, including stickies at all steps and, most importantly, the first sticky that had made it to 'Done.' We reserved this meeting room for portfolio concerns only, and even in a little more than the PI's time had learned a lot about how a Lean-Agile enterprise should operate. When Adi visited us recently she was amazed by how far we had taken it. But we wouldn't have gotten anywhere if it wasn't for her in the first place.

Sunil eventually had to give up his RTE position on the train. He was just too valuable at the portfolio level. At first he refused entirely, saying that he would never abandon 'Arkenstone'–and the people he had become so attached to. But then Zach took him to dinner one night and there, I guess, Sunil had his 'road to Damascus' moment. Shortly after that he eagerly agreed to consider the opportunity and immediately started to work on transitioning his RTE responsibilities to a successor. I guess he was doomed from the moment he agreed to go to dinner with the Executive VP of Business Development. Now

Sunil is facilitating lots of interaction in the portfolio and you can really tell when Sunil is enjoying something. He's got this spark in his eyes...

Our restored ability to deliver value to the customer began to strengthen our market position. The user community had become hungry for more and that automatically restored the confidence of our investors, propelling our stock price back up. There's still a ways to go though: you can't restore your position from rock bottom in a short year's time, but the trend was extremely strong and the new flavor we started to acquire as a matter of our publicity, was very encouraging. It was especially gratifying to read an independent blogger–I imagine they still exist somewhere–writing about us and calling our products awesome, intuitive and reliable. It suddenly took me back in time, to the very infancy of this organization when I think I knew every person by name. I thought then we could be successful because small scale still allowed us to thrive. So maybe we really learned something along the way... It's not a trivial skill to be successful when you're big. But have we proved to ourselves that it's possible!

An even more promising development was the change that began to happen with engineering management. I think Ed performed a miracle in that regard. And I have a great appreciation for the fine balance between his extremely firm and at the same time, truly forgiving nature. Well, truth be told, some of the engineering managers left the company after it became apparent that they had started falling back into their old patterns of behavior. I guess I will never know whether 'they left' means that they really left, or that Ed fired them - you never know with the strange language of the HR people. They send out profoundly cryptic memos to all the affected persons when somebody ceases working for the company. Either way, it's all for the better. Those managers who stayed–and that was absolutely the majority–began to do some truly amazing things. Ed helped them as much as possible, primarily trying to create an environment where they could unleash their creative skills and think about how to help teams and the business establish ever faster and more reliable flow of customer value. He wanted them to think about that and not think about the KPIs and job security and all those other things that used to fully occupy their minds. Zach began calling Ed 'the liberator of middle management', always laughing, but deep inside knowing that he had the best CTO he could possibly imagine.

That's probably it in terms of the big news. And, yes, Ed may be right: we are a crazy bunch, those that agreed to lead the change in this organization. In hindsight I'm not sure I'd call that a smart decision either. At the beginning of this journey it looked too hopeless, frankly, and I have no idea where all that faith kept coming from. Oh yeah, we were definitely crazy... But maybe that's why we succeeded with this job. ...Best job I ever had.

ETHAN'S DIARY

- *I can't emphasize this enough: leadership must enable teams and protect them from overload, looking to remove the biggest impediments they have to becoming more successful. I've seen different examples of leadership at VeraComm, including bad ones. These cases must be addressed as soon as possible, because leaders that refuse to let go of the legacy mindset will be a huge impediment themselves. And for a change agent, resolving all such inconsistencies directly with these people is simply unfeasible, especially if multiple initial steps in that direction fail to change things for the better. In such cases, decisive action is required on the part of their bosses. If left unaddressed, it will continue to inhibit the jelling of the new culture within the enterprise.*

- *Apart from the right leadership mindset, there is another thing critical to enterprise success in establishing the flow of value. And that thing is: Lean-Agile portfolio process. It is not enough to identify value streams and launch trains within them. Somehow those large, cross-cutting initiatives—epics—must be managed as part of the flow. Otherwise, left to their own devices, individual value streams will produce increments of value inconsistent with the rest of the organization.*

- *Portfolio Kanban is the way to enhance visibility into the flow of epics. It also fosters collaboration among the stakeholders and, most importantly, allows the enterprise to dramatically limit WIP. You would be surprised how much we used to exaggerate our portfolio capacity.*

- *Our idea was very simple: align the entire portfolio on the PI cadence. This is important! That way we set the pace for the entire organization. It doesn't mean that solutions will be released on that cadence. The common cadence is used for planning and alignment, and closing the loop by reviewing the results. This cadence also sets the rhythm for all events associated with the portfolio Kanban: every time we approach the PI boundary, we know we need to make sure that there are epics in portfolio backlog, ready to be pulled into implementation.*

- *If it wasn't for our architects who knows if we would have solved the problem of coordinating portfolio work in a timely manner. Absolutely love those guys! But every time I remind myself of the 'state machine', I can't help but smile.*

- *I never told Ed that the reason why I was able to be a crazy change agent, ready to jump on every opportunity to make this company a better place (regardless of the consequences) was because, one way or the other, I always felt his support. And even when I had to go against the grain early on and show insubordination for the sake of 'Arkenstone's' successful first PI, I think deep inside I knew that he would eventually support me.*

- *My head is still overloaded with too many positive thoughts at the same time. Sometimes Rachel and I just stare at each other... in complete silence... unearthly happy.*

CHAPTER 14
Giving Back

"As a change agent, you will inevitably make mistakes..."

–SUNIL

THE ELEVATOR DELIVERED ME FROM my hotel room on the 27th floor to a lobby overcrowded with people wearing badges and carrying vivid bags. Inside the bags were the schedule and a huge number of various marketing materials: everything from simple flyers to magazines, estimation cards of all sorts, dice, mice and what have you. Even though the registration had officially started the day before, quite a few people–either those that had arrived today or that had arrived too late last night–were standing in line for their badges and conference-branded t-shirts.

I need to find the room where the presentation is going to happen. I have about twenty minutes to get there, but I'd rather hurry and be early. This time around I'm not here in search of a method that would provide a solution to allow us to survive turbulent times. Thinking back about last year's conference makes me smile... It's amazing how desperate I was... and how lucky, too. No, this time around it is my chance to repay the debt – I'm here as a speaker.

Alright, here it is – my room. It must be the right one because the flip-chart near the door has the correct title: 'The Rollout: A Fable about Leadership and Building a Lean-Agile Enterprise with SAFe.' That's our presentation. 'Our,' because I decided to do this presentation with Sunil. I thought that people might appreciate hearing not only from the head of the Transformation Team, but also from a facilitator who supported the execution once the basic structure had been established. Just a year ago, I was wondering what on earth it would take for a person like me to be accepted as a speaker at the industry's biggest conference. Now, just a short year later, I feel like I have a lot to present and everything feels completely different. And it's no wonder that it does, because we've been on a wild journey. It wasn't a year spent in the gym working the heavy bag and jumping the speed rope. It was a year spent in the ring, facing our own fears and defying our own limitations. We weren't wandering around acquiring theoretical knowledge, we were resuscitating an enterprise that many thought was certainly doomed.

Once we were sure that we had loaded the correct files on the presenter computer, that the clicker worked and that the computer audio was connected to the right output, I took the remaining couple of minutes to look out the window. The world outside was filled with an all-consuming sunlight and not a single cloud was visible. Directly across the street was an old church, the likes of which I'd probably only seen on my vacation trip to London. There was something that fascinated me about its mysterious architecture and the rough contrast with the clunky, boxy high-rises surrounding it on all sides. It was as if the church was being held hostage for an unknown ransom. It seemed for a moment that, squeezed between the tasteless structures, it would compromise a little and then, inch-by-inch, it would itself turn into something just as boxy and clunky as its surroundings. But the time-hardened stone of the church walls remained quiet, unwilling to engage. These walls seem to actually enjoy time; they are forced to converse with that element if they want to talk to an equal. The stained glass and pointed arches have witnessed a lot of change of scenery around them... The high-rise boxes will become outdated and replaced many times over, before these aged stone walls will even notice any change. The gravity of past generations, it seems, has warped the surroundings and stopped the normal flow of time. Everything stood still, waiting for a subtle cue from beyond the realm of this universe to bring it back into motion. I could see it all as if captured in an old sepia photograph: people on the sidewalk, seeking cover from the intense humidity and heat, birds sheltering from the thick sunlight in a maze of ornate church façades, and me trapped in the window, fascinated by the grandios view...

I was returned to the room from my brief journey across dimensions by the sharp voice of a volunteer. He briefly introduced Sunil and me to the audience. He assured us that he would give us the high sign so we wouldn't exceed our timebox.

The room was full!

We were so fully immersed in the action that I barely even noticed when Sunil and I started our presentation, describing to the audience the nature of the challenges we'd encountered. And of course we could tell only as much as we were allowed to, shading most of the detail of those challenges from plain view. We realized it simply looked too ugly and that it wasn't safe for a public company to disclose all of that detail. But it was obvious that we had a room full of people that were, just like ourselves, fluent in the cryptic language of organizational challenge. People were definitely identifying and connecting with us as we proceeded to the main points of the presentation.

We spent a lot of time on leadership. I told them about my big mistake at the beginning of the rollout, and how important it is to train the leadership in SAFe upfront, before undertaking any additional steps in the rollout. We related that such training only creates the *initial* awareness, but importantly, gets them started on a long learning journey with plenty of challenges as well as exciting turns. We talked about the challenges with management that we had encountered at VeraComm. Sunil had a good name for one such challenge: 'a semiconductor organization,' he called it.

"What is that?" asked someone from the front of the room.

"That's a strange physical phenomenon... It's when good news bubbles up the levels of management, but bad news stays down, where it is swept under the rug," said Sunil. Then he added: "It's a problem in two parts: the management and the system they operate as part of."

"We attacked this problem on both fronts," I said, picking up his thread. "On the one hand we worked directly with those development and program managers that needed to acquire newer, absolutely different instincts. But on the other hand, we quickly realized that sort of change alone wasn't going to get us anywhere really, unless the base rules of the system were to change. To solve the mindset problem of middle management, we needed to start working with their bosses to change the rules that drive unproductive behavior. We also leveraged upper-level support to coach middle management in newer and better ways of working... And yes, it takes time, but it must be done. Otherwise, no matter what Lean-Agile constructs and processes you try to adopt, they will all crash on the shoals of a gruesome reality, dictated by narrow-minded, myopic KPIs and false assumptions that continue to define traditional thinking. If you don't address the issue of leadership, you're gonna fail your rollout every time..."

And then we took some time to talk more about *mindset*—the most fundamental cause of all problems—and how to start changing it for the better.

"If you dig deep enough," I said, repeating almost word-for-word what Rachel had told me a year ago as she handed me a cup of

'Sleepytime', "you will eventually find that at its core, every mindset is a belief system. That's why it is so horrifically difficult to change. People don't like their core beliefs to be shaken up and gravely endangered. The harder you push, the harder they push back. What we learned was that mindset cannot be changed just by teaching people a new way to operate. They may honestly accept the new ideas, but as soon as the new ways of working cross one of their core beliefs - everything suddenly grinds to a halt."

"The best way to help transform the mindset is by moving those people directly into an environment where the real action is happening," picked up Sunil. "Lean has a term for that - 'Gemba', which translates to the 'real place'. And as part of the SAFe rollout, we found a way to pull them into Gemba which turned out to be very simple. SAFe offers many such opportunities as a matter of the standard cadence that includes such events as PI planning, System Demo, Inspect and Adapt..."

At that point we took the audience on a journey through the basics of SAFe, sticking strictly to what we had actually applied at VeraComm. We started with discussion around the Agile Release Train–the key building block of a SAFe enterprise. It's a self-organized team of Agile teams that plan together, execute synchronously and review the results together. We briefly touched on how to launch a train and keep it on the tracks afterward. I showed them multiple photos from our first train–'Arkenstone'–including its training sessions, planning events, demos, inspect and adapt sessions and so forth... Those pictures spoke better than words ever could.

But then we took a sharp turn as I told them the story of how we tried to adopt a systems view and solve the problem of disjointed teams, and how we ended up in just another form of local optimization, this time at the program level. Yes, we learned how to launch trains, but launching them within our traditional program boundaries suddenly appeared as a dangerous thing to us. That's where Sunil and I described the whole idea of value stream analysis and how to split those value streams into multiple ARTs if they get too big. We described how our value streams and ARTs ended up not only going orthogonal to our org structure at the time, but also cutting across the two organizations – VeraComm and our partner, QCell.

We moved on to the portfolio level and described how we built a Kanban system for epics and how those joint epic specification workshops are happening regularly at this point, in order to feed work to the value streams. We described how the entire organization began to operate on a common PI cadence. And how for the first time, it allowed us to exercise really effective governance for the enterprise as a whole, and how it is strictly based on the simple motto: 'no demo, no numbers.' We also talked about decentralized decision-making, and value streams and trains not only getting incoming work from the portfolio, but also having flexibility to define capabilities and features of their own, in order to best serve customer needs.

We went on to talk about engineering practices, the mystery of 'unchanging builds' and how a kitchen napkin helped us investigate the problem with branching. We talked about the fact that it's not only management whose mindset needs to change, but how developers and testers must also embrace the new reality to dramatically change their way of thinking. We talked about the huge importance of System Demos every two weeks to avoid 'waterfalling' the PI.

...And when the time came to cut off and switch to the Q&A, we were inundated with an enormous number of questions from all sides.

"Have you succeeded with the rollout across the entire organization or are there any areas left?" someone asked.

I took that question. "Here's where we are with our transformation: the part of the organization that works on software products is all operating in a new way. But we have another unit that still needs to be addressed - the group that develops our cyber-physical solutions, which involves a multitude of engineering disciplines: software, firmware and hardware development. It took us a little longer to get fully oriented in terms of the right approach in that case, for multiple reasons. But I have to tell you that even though practices vary, principles remain the same." I showed them the bottle with the nine SAFe Principles, the one that Adi had given me a year ago at a conference much like this... "This month we are launching our first Agile Release Train in the non-software part of the organization. We are excited about the learning opportunity and we strongly believe that we will see significant improvement, just like we did for software solutions. But that's a whole separate topic worthy of its own discussion. So, with your permission, I'll stop at that..."

Closer to the end of our Q&A, somebody asked if we could tell them what the key tenets are that every change agent should follow... a sort of core values, if you will.

"Such tenets do exist, indeed," replied Sunil. That was quite a surprise to me, as I had never heard of us ever formalizing anything like that. "And here they are," he continued, "the four core values of every change agent: One - courage..." he said and stopped for a second, giving them time to take notes.

"Okay, what's number two?" asked the same person.

Sunil gladly continued: "Two - courage..."

The people that were taking notes stopped for a quick second, a bit confused.

But Sunil quickly un-confused them by finishing his list: "three - courage and four - courage." I noticed how they had put away their notes and pencils and the whole audience had become curious about Sunil's impromptu statement. He continued: "You may wonder why am I glossing over some things and instead appear to be overemphasizing this one? Because this quality, while hard to acquire, is so important that without it you *will not* succeed. Plus, we're not talking about being perfect. As a change agent, you will inevitably make mistakes..."

I quickly slipped in, imagining how much Ed would appreciate this, should he hear me now: "...And the biggest mistake you can make is that of becoming a change agent in the first place."

The audience burst into laughter, as did Sunil.

But all joking aside, he was right, despite the fact that his list–whether he noticed it or not–contained some duplicates. And even more to the point, there are other things that matter, too. I nevertheless totally agree with him: what saved us so many times was our ability to move forward despite all the impediments threatening to smash us if we dared to continue pushing. But we were unwilling to give up or give in to the so-called 'conventional wisdom' that reigned in our organization and which had obviously failed us so gravely. We chose not to accept the grueling reality of a traditional process and mindset, and instead began to break the rules. Of course we took it on the chin a couple of times while doing that and there was nothing particularly pleasant about it. But there's simply no way to completely avoid the pain either, and the pay-off was just too compelling for us.

We could have chickened out many times, by the way. For instance, when our leadership rejected the initial idea of PI planning with all-hands-on-deck approach as too 'wasteful', we could have compromised and done it without the proper planning procedure. That would be an unforgivable mistake, because the result would be an ugly 'Frankenstein's monster' - a dangerous mix of Lean and Agile built on top of a legacy mindset. So yes, we chose to keep pushing until we succeeded. Similarly, we could have compromised when we got a direct order from the CEO to freeze scope commitments, despite objective evidence suggesting the opposite course. But once again, it would have just reinforced the old mindset - the most dangerous thing that can happen to a transformation. Yes, we picked a fight when we had no alternative left, like when we had to delay additional ART launches despite all the pressure from QCell, because we knew we had to perform value stream analysis first. And yes, it is important to compromise in some cases, some would say. And I totally agree with that: there are plenty of little, less relevant aspects that can be compromised. But compromise is typically not the problem. Unfortunately for us as an industry, we have become too comfortable with compromising virtually everywhere. And in so doing we have completely lost our ability to stand our ground, even in those rare cases when it is absolutely vital. That's why I think Sunil hit it right on the money. The most important things for a change agent are: courage, courage, courage and more courage...

And we are still gonna need this quality, because our journey is not over yet. In fact, all we have achieved so far is just a basic structure that allows us to iterate as a whole–a Lean-Agile portfolio–incrementing our solutions and relentlessly identifying and removing systemic impediments along the way. But there's a lot more on our agenda that we'd like to implement and frankly, there seems to be no visible end to this journey. And that's okay. The deeper we dive, the more exciting the jewels are that we pull to the surface, which is the exciting part of my job and the thing that keeps me up at night. And I know that what we do as change agents helps a lot. It helps our customers by enabling them to achieve more in their businesses. And it helps my company, all of those people that give everything they've got to deliver successful solutions. We've managed to stop the lay-offs and actually reverse the dynamic: VeraComm is now actively hiring to fill numerous open positions across our big portfolio.

I think this rollout may have taught us something else, too; something that may be the biggest paradox of my professional career. And I'm happy to accept this paradox the way it is: On the one hand, we learned as an organization that we can only be successful if we ultimately ground our existence in respect for the people that create value – on the other hand, the open and sincere demonstration of such respect, led to more selfless behavior by those people, thereby increasing their appetite for elevating organizational goals above other things. So, go figure...

Learn more about SAFe®

http://scaledagileframework.com

Become a trained professional

http://scaledagile.com

Index

Please note that in some cases a specific term may not appear in a particular entry, although the concept is discussed in the chapter.

Mindset

Initial discussion: Chapter 2
Management: Chapters 4, 10, 12
Engineering: Chapters 5, 9

Organizational Change Management (OCM)

Building coalition for change: Chapters 2, 4
Launching the first ART: Chapters 5, 6, 7, 8
Generating early results: Chapters 9, 10, 12
Designing the Lean-Agile enterprise: Chapter 12
Addressing management problems: Chapter 13
Addressing culture: Chapters 2, 4, 5, 6, 7, 8, 9, 10, 12, 13
Summary: Chapter 14

Organizational Structure

Chapter 12

PI Planning:

Simulation: Chapter 4
Actual planning: Chapters 6, 7, 8

Portfolio Kanban

Chapter 13

Scope adjustments

As part of Program Backlog refinement: Chapter 5
During PI planning: Chapters 6, 7, 8
During PI execution: Chapters 9, 10

Made in the USA
San Bernardino, CA
27 September 2018